INTERNATIONAL SERIES OF MONOGRAPHS ON
PURE AND APPLIED BIOLOGY

Division: **ZOOLOGY**

GENERAL EDITOR: G. A. KERKUT

VOLUME 5

THE BIOLOGY OF STENTOR

A

OTHER TITLES IN THE SERIES ON PURE AND
APPLIED BIOLOGY

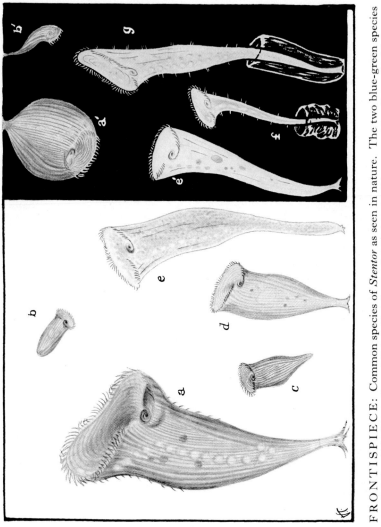

FRONTISPIECE: Common species of *Stentor* as seen in nature. The two blue-green species appear alizarin red by reflected light. *S. polymorphus* is shown with green chlorellae and without, as when grown in the dark. Drawn from life, to scale, the *coeruleus* being 1 mm long. The species are: *a, a'. coeruleus; b, b'. multiformis; c, igneus; d, niger; e, e'. polymorphus; f, roeseli; g, muelleri.*

THE BIOLOGY OF
STENTOR

BY

VANCE TARTAR

Department of Zoology
University of Washington

PERGAMON PRESS

NEW YORK · OXFORD · LONDON . PARIS

1961

PERGAMON PRESS INC.
122 East 55th Street, New York 22, N.Y.
Statler Center 640, 900 Wilshire Boulevard
Los Angeles 17, California

PERGAMON PRESS LTD.
Headington Hill Hall, Oxford
4 & 5 Fitzroy Square, London W.1

PERGAMON PRESS, S.A.R.L.
24 Rue des Écoles, Paris V^e

PERGAMON PRESS G.m.b.H.
Kaiserstrasse 75, Frankfurt am Main

Library of Congress Card No. 60–15714

Set in Imprint 11 on 12pt. and Printed in Great Britain at
THE BAY TREE PRESS, STEVENAGE, HERTS.

PREFACE

IN THIS monograph I have attempted to summarize all that has been learned about a certain group of ciliate protozoa pre-eminently suitable for class-room study and research. To this end I have tried conscientiously to review all the literature of *Stentor* so that the reader will need to turn to original sources only for minor details. A few publications were not available to me though I had reports of their contents, and these are so indicated in the bibliography. Many points I have been able to substantiate myself, and I have taken this opportunity to include previews of work in progress and miscellaneous observations from my own experience with these ciliates.

Naturally I am keenly aware of our indebtedness to all who have labored in this field and of my responsibility for reporting their studies accurately and commenting upon them fairly. When I use the words "seem" and "apparently" with their goading provisionality, this is not in derogation of a fine piece of work but simply means that confirmation of results assures a firm basis for further investigation. It is often surprising what differences may appear in both procedure and interpretation when different individuals undertake the same problem or even the same approach. On the other hand, there has been unnecessary duplication of effort for lack of a comprehensive review as here attempted, and I have myself been at fault in this regard. Studies in which *Stentor* appears as suitable material in a wider context — frequently biochemical — may also be led astray because investigators are not aware of relevant aspects of the biology of this animal which are crucial for proper interpretations. I hope to have provided the basis or background for extensive further researches.

The illustrations from my own studies do not represent general conceptions but specific cases drawn from laboratory records. Therefore they offer the basis for different interpretations, if these need be made, as well as suggesting many directions for further study.

v

I wish to thank Dr. Gerald Kerkut for proposing this book, and the publishers for their care in its realization. Emogean Saunders Tartar, my wife, prepared the manuscript. My own studies have been generously supported by the American Cancer Society and, currently, by our National Institutes of Health.

VANCE TARTAR

Aquaterre
Nahcotta, Washington
U.S.A.

CONTENTS

CHAPTER I

INTRODUCTION

WHAT are stentors good for ?

One would like to say that these exquisite little organisms are a sufficient wonder in themselves and that to study them as a part of nature is an expression of natural curiosity and that happy relationship between subject and object which carries its own self-justification. Doubtless this delight sustains the investigator throughout what would otherwise be the weary and protracted pursuit of other ends. Moreover, the experience of science has shown that pursuing a subject for its own sake is likely to turn up clues to which a more ulterior approach would be blind.

Yet this hobby-like vitality of interest is not sufficient. Our studies become truly exciting and fruitful to others only when they lead to general principles on the theoretical level. Of necessity we have to start with some specific organism, woefully unique in itself, out of the immense variety of existing forms of life, yet we want our study eventually to be relevant to general problems of biology.

To reword the question, we may ask what particular advantages *Stentor* may have with respect to these larger ends, that an entire book should be devoted to this one type of organism.

Most outstanding is that on stentors one can easily perform a wider range of micrurgical operations than on any other uni-cellular organism or tissue cell, remarkable though the experiments with *Amœba* and the single-celled alga *Acetabularia* have been. These operations are made possible by what for lack of a more subtle analysis we have to call the consistency of the endoplasm which permits grafting whole animals or cell parts in any number, combination, or arrangement desired. The relatively large size of these cells is a help, though the largest are no bigger than the period at the end of this sentence. Stentors, unlike amœbas, exhibit a high degree of visible cytoplasmic differentiation and in several species, including the commonest, the cortical pattern is conveniently outlined by a series of pigmented stripes so that the organization of individualities and the identification of local areas and grafted patches is quite evident in the living material. This offers many advantages. With cells and patches self-marked, operations can be guided and specified, and the whole range of classical grafting experiments and transplantations can be extended to the cell level of organization. Fixing and staining are not required to follow the performance of grafts so that experiments proceed rapidly and can be done in sufficient number for valid conclusions. Complex, specific, asymmetric elaborations of form increase the number of responses to alteration of the system which we can observe and measure, and render *Stentor* highly relevant to the great unsolved problem of organic form. A cytoarchitecture which has repeatedly been postulated as necessary to explain the orderly development of eggs is visibly displayed in stentors and does in fact play a cardinal role in their morphogenesis.

Different species of *Stentor* can be grafted together almost as readily as cells and cell parts of one species. The cytoplasms and nuclei of two or even more species can be combined in any desired proportions, and this is a new method of "transduction" by which not only different genetic material may be added to a cell but also alien cytoplasm. These chimeras persist and do not fall apart, cytoplasms mingle and nuclei are maintained at least for a considerable time in foreign cytoplasm on which they often exert a visible influence.

The macronucleus, which alone is significant in the vegetative life of stentors, is clearly visible in the living animal. Enucleations are not difficult. Stentors therefore provide additional examples in which the contribution of the nucleus may be assessed by determining the consequences of its absence. The more types of cell in which this operation is possible the more likely we are to come to general conclusions. Moreover, the extended form of the nucleus in *Stentor* allows us to remove all or only a desired portion of it. Such quantitative operations, when combined with additions of enucleated or highly nucleated cytoplasmic masses vary the ratio of nucleus to cytoplasm in extremes not heretofore possible. Interesting consequences of this imbalance are evident in stentors.

The same properties which permit grafting also make possible the transfer from one cell to another of nuclei retained within a thin envelope of endoplasm, allowing enucleated cells to be renucleated at any time or the nucleus of one species to be substituted for that of another with practically no admixture of cytoplasms.

When added to the simpler experiments on stentor fragments in which parts become wholes, the possibilities afforded by these operations and their permutations appear endless. The organic integration by which new individualities become one can be explored. Nucleo-cytoplasmic interactions and the nature of species differences are opened to inquiry with fresh material. Problems of polarity can be explored in heteropolar grafts of cells and cell parts. Cell differentiation under a variety of conditions occurs before our eyes. The intimate nature of aging, necrosis, and damage by various external agents can be investigated by testing the revival of "sick" animals after grafting them to healthy cells or cell parts in stentors as in the important work which Daniels (1958) is doing with giant amœbas. These are only a sampling of what can be done.

Stentors share, now or potentially, experimental advantages common to many protozoa. As free-living cells they are directly affected by alterations in the fluid medium; and it has been found that certain substances added to the medium may produce profound effects in the behaviour, reproduction, and morphogenesis of stentors. Since stentors undergo sexual conjugation at times, genetic experiments should eventually be possible. Irradiation or other treatments at the time when the nuclear complement is reduced to a simple anlage could produce mutations as genetic markers and indicators of cell activities. If mating types appear as in other ciliates we would have a differentiating characterization in the expression of which the roles of nucleus and cytoplasm could be investigated by direct operations. A fundamental need in the cancer problem as well as of general biological understanding is to learn precisely what incites the cell to division, whether it be an egg, a tissue cell, or a protozoan. The great amenability of stentors to manipulation encourages us to search for the answer in them.

Each of these experimental possibilities is important in itself but their unique combination within one organism makes *Stentor* one of the classical types in biology. These leads can more intelligently be pursued in all their modern implications, if one has a thorough background in the biology of *Stentor*. For this we can draw on all the many studies of stentors extending far back into the previous century as well as our own good observations. In what follows we shall therefore try to summarize all that is known about the ciliate protozoan, *Stentor*. Many of these details may seem tedious unless one keeps in mind the marvel that so much can be learned through the patient efforts of a long procession of able students about a single type of minute organism, and the wonder that so tiny and seemingly insignificant an animal reveals on close inspection so much integrated complexity of form and function.

CHAPTER II

FORM AND FUNCTION IN STENTOR

To BECOME acquainted with *Stentor* we begin with an account of those features of the organism which are open to simple observation, emphasizing *S. coeruleus* which, because of its commonness and revealing pigmentation, has been the favored type for study; but there is no reason to believe that even little-known species differ fundamentally in basic Bauplan or manner of living.

Several of the early investigators were impressed by what seemed to them to be the great variability in form of stentors, as the species name *polymorphus* and *multiformis* imply; but the form of *Stentor* is no more indefinite than that of an earthworm merely because it extends and contracts. The shape of *Stentor* is simply that of a cone capable of extension or of contraction into a sphere. Attachment is by the point of the cone, a small enough area to permit voluntary release; while the feeding organelles are at the broad end where they can most effectively produce a vortex bringing particulate food to the animal from a large region of the medium which lies beyond it like an imaginary extension of the cone. Set free and swimming, the shape of the cell under what seems to be minimum tension is, as Merton (1932) remarked, that of a gently rounded cone. Shortening of contractile elements pulls the cone into a sphere, and extension is the result of elasticity, pulling by the feeding membranelles, and possibly transverse contraction.

The surface is covered by alternating longitudinal stripes of two kinds: bands of granules, often colored, forming stripes which increase in width in an orderly way around the cell and, between these, clear stripes of relatively constant width which bear the rows of body cilia as well as a complex of fibers probably responsible for longitudinal contraction and ciliary coordination (Fig. 1). To accommodate for the decreasing cross-section of the cone the granular stripes taper near the apex and some of both kinds of striping stop short of the posterior pole. Cross-sections of contracted animals show a corrugated surface with the clear stripes lying in valleys between the raised granular stripes.

A thin pellicle forms the outermost surface of the cell. It could conceivably be the product of secretory activity, special elaboration of which may produce cyst walls and the cylindrical cases found in some species. The pellicle is not completely elastic and on contraction is thrown into transverse folds over the granular stripes, causing the surface of the rounded animal to appear like a scalloped theater curtain.

The graded variation in the width of the granular stripes provides a fundamental asymmetry to the pattern of the cell. In the oral meridian these bands are narrowest and they gradually increase in size around the cell from left to right so that the widest bands eventually come to lie next to the narrowest in a locus of stripe-width contrast on the oral or ventral side. Stripe multiplication occurs in this region, the widest granular stripes being split by the interpolation of new clear bands. Because this splitting generally proceeds from the anterior end and does not follow all the way through to the posterior, there results a triangle of shorter stripes which was called the ramifying zone by Schuberg (1890). This area is also the region in which the oral primordium appears.

All stentors attach by a temporary holdfast organelle at the posterior end. In undisturbed cultures only a few animals will be found freely swimming (Gelei, 1925), and this may be taken as the usual condition in nature.

Stentors sink to the bottom in agitated cultures, their specific gravity being greater than that of water. Attachment may serve the purpose of keeping them with minimum expenditure of energy in favorable locations toward the surface of the water where oxygen is abundant. It may also be assumed that the effectiveness of the feeding vortex created by the peristome is increased when the animal is attached.

Adherence is firm. Animals just detached remain sticky at the posterior end and Jennings (1902) saw them dragging trails of mucoid material behind. If water is pipetted out of a culture, the stentors remain fastened to the sides in a watery film. Rapid evaporation may even leave animals stuck to the rim of the vessel where they dry and die, seemingly unable to loose themselves.

In pipetting animals from the sides of a vessel the holdfasts are often torn off because of their firm adherence. Yet stentors can release their hold at will under favorable conditions in order to search for a better environment. Thus in unfed cultures many animals will be found on the move as if searching for food.

Some stentors form cases and are still more sedentary. Jennings (1902) described how *roeseli* seemed to explore the substratum with its anterior end and when a likely spot was found the tail bent over and attached. Then mucous was secreted over the posterior half of the body while the animal moved backward and forward on its side for about two minutes as it secreted an elongated cylinder. The tube was later compacted somewhat by subsequent contractions of the stentor.

In describing the feeding organelles at the anterior end we shall use the simplest and most unambiguous terms. Confusion and synonymy have arisen in the past largely from unjustified attempts to homologize these organelles with the upper parts of the human alimentary canal, with the result that stentor should have both a pharynx and an esophagus. There is said to be a buccal or cheek cavity, yet what is called the mouth or cytostome does not in fact open into this cavity but is homologous with the anterior pyloric sphincter. The membranellar band is usually called the peristome, but it does not encircle the cytostome, and the term "peristome" was originally used to designate a special fold generally running alongside this band (see Johnson, 1893). Regardless of more precise designations, however, it will be convenient at times to refer to the entire set of feeding organelles at the anterior end as the "head"; to the oral pouch, gullet, and cytostome as the "mouthparts"; and to the holdfast as the "foot".

The anterior end or frontal field is covered with alternating clear and granular stripes the same as the lateral body wall from which it is derived (Fig. 1). Being newly formed, the granular stripes there are narrow and the clear bands with their ciliary rows or kineties are close together. Bordering and almost completely enclosing the frontal field is a band of membranelles which normally spirals always in one direction as shown in the figure. Fully extended, the frontal field and bordering membranelles take the form of a broad funnel. At the left side, in most stentors the frontal field dips down sharply with its striping into an oral pouch which is often called the buccal cavity. The membranellar band runs along the outer edge of this pouch and then coils sharply inward into an invaginated tube which itself coils about one turn into the cell. This tube we shall call by the rather non-commital term of gullet. Food vacuoles are separated off the inner

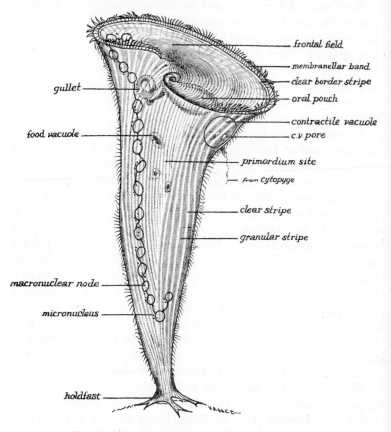

FIG. 1. Descriptive diagram of *Stentor coeruleus*.

end of the gullet, which therefore has a temporary film-like closure to prevent endoplasm from escaping into the gullet but capable of acting so as to allow passage of food into the cell. Probably the ectoplasmic lining of the gullet simply ends here in a thin membrane which can stretch and increase to form the wall of a new food vacuole and then close behind it as the vacuole is pinched off into the interior. But vacuolar walls can arise *de novo* as is seen when active rotifers are ingested and thrash around inside the cell but are later re-encapsulated and digested.

In feeding, the membranellar band by coordinated beating creates a powerful vortex which draws in particulate food organisms, large or small. Impinging on the frontal field, particles are moved by its cilia toward the oral pouch in which they are trapped and concentrated, whirling around within the cavity. In this region the food is apparently tested. If undesirable or in excess, particles are then ejected over the outer rim of the oral pouch and carried toward the base of the animal, away from the feeding vortex, by the backward-beating lateral body cilia. If to be ingested, the food is passed down the gullet by reason of its ciliated lining and is further concentrated while peristalsis of the gullet forces the material into the interior.

After digestion the residue in the food vacuole is cast out through the left anterior wall of the cell below the pulsating contractile vacuole. Especially when the stentor has been feeding on tiny flagellates, many exhausted vacuoles accumulate and fuse in this region, forming a very large bolas which requires about one minute to be voided. Whether there is a permanent anal opening or cytopyge may still be questioned.

On the other hand, the exit of the contractile vacuole is visibly persistent. Moxon (1869) observed openings in the broad granular stripes exterior to the contractile vacuole which is always located in the anterior left side of the cell. These openings are evident in pigmented *coeruleus* as clear spots. One, at least, of these openings expands noticeably when the contractile vacuole is voided, assuring their identification.

Larger species of *Stentor* have a moniliform macronucleus composed of many nodes lying within a common nuclear membrane. This nucleus lies underneath the ectoplasm and is deployed in a characteristic way as shown in the illustration. Adherent to the macronuclear nodes or nearby are many micronuclei. Smaller species show a single compact macronucleus; and micronuclei, which are very tiny in stentors, have not been seen in all species.

Endoplasm fills the interior of the cell and is in irregular cyclosis, possibly because extension and contraction itself produces sufficient mixing. The endoplasm has been described variously as alveolar or reticulate and contains reserve materials in the form of droplets and granules.

When maximally contracted, stentors become nearly perfect spheres. Most stentors are also capable of remarkable extension. When attached and feeding the body may stretch out to three to six times the diameter of the contracted animal while the feeding organelles expand widely to produce the stentorian or trumpet shape. All the complex structures of the cortical layer are therefore capable of wide displacements though maintaining their precise pattern and organization.

Next we shall consider what is known of the behavior of stentors and then we can deal with the fine points of structure in terms of which this behavior is to be explained and which demonstrate the highly complex and precise achievements of morphogenesis.

CHAPTER III

BEHAVIOR

IN BROAD perspective, multicellular animals enjoy periods of relaxation or inactivity, but their constituent cells are ever active as long as life maintains. Unicellular animals share with tissue cells this unresting activity, and stentors are no exception. In their reproduction, continual search for food, and avoidance if possible of unfavorable surroundings, the abiding impression is that stentors are always busy. Cessation of swimming and attachment by the holdfast is only the prelude to active feeding. If we define behavior as altered response to changing conditions, unresting stentors are continually behaving. Observing them even briefly, one is struck by the appearance that their activity is not mechanistically simple, though they may be high-grade automatons. If we place ourselves in the position of early investigators, the wonder is renewed that even in these minute and lowly forms of life we can undertake to analyze behaviour.

1. Food selection

Food selection in *Stentor* seems to have been clearly demonstrated in a nice series of experiments by Schaeffer (1910). He recorded the uptake by *coeruleus* placed for a time in a prescribed suspension of particles as well as observing what happened when single particles were introduced one at a time with a capillary pipette into the feeding vortex. In one of the "hand feeding" tests, for example, 12 *Phacus* were ingested and only three rejected, while 13 indigestible sulphur particles were rejected and only three taken in. In another test all 50 *Phacus* presented were ingested, while 18 starch grains were rejected and only one accepted. Size was not determinative because the starch grains were four to one-eighth times the size of *Phacus*. Again, 21 *Phacus* and 1 starch grain were eaten, while 7 *Phacus*, 12 grains, and 11 glass particles were rejected. *Euglena* was preferred to *Chilomonas*.

Phacus and *Euglena* recently killed by heat or alcohol were eaten as readily as live ones. Stentor even discriminated between two species of *Phacus*, predominately accepting *triqueter* and rejecting *longicaudus* but there were no observations on whether the latter was actually indigestible.

In mass feedings from mixtures of equal parts, a stentor took in 1,500 *Chlamydomonas*, 85 *Euglena*, and 10 carmine particles. In carmine alone 20 units were taken in. Hence generally less carmine was eaten when food was present than when not, and carmine was even rejected preferentially when much in excess over food particles in the mixture. In India ink alone only 3 granules were taken in, so the greater number of mistakes made with carmine as compared with the smaller ink particles was the reverse of that found with paramecia. These tests indicate that when fed, stentors become more selective but they also rejected more of the favored items as if no longer hungry.

Conversely, hungry stentors were found to be less selective. This may explain apparently contradictory observations, because an investigator testing the ingestion of a given type of material would be likely to use starved, clear stentors in which confusing food vacuoles were not already present. Thus on occasion stentors will ingest considerable numbers of fine carmine and ink particles (Schuberg, 1890; Jennings, 1902). Before Schaeffer's studies, Jennings had therefore concluded that there is no selection after the material reaches the oral pouch, "dissatisfaction" with the meal resulting only in cessation of feeding and turning in a new direction. Prowazek (1904) observed that *coeruleus* ate free-living *Chlorella* though it could only partially digest them; and I have found plentiful "food" vacuoles in samples of this stentor left unnutrified for nearly a month and apparently re-feeding on waste materials. Johnson (1893) remarked that *coeruleus* eats the alga *Scendesmus* in quantity but apparently does not digest it and quickly passes this material through the cell. Hence even when indigestible materials are eaten, the animal can short-circuit to the cytopyge food vacuoles with useless contents.

On the evidence, food selection does occur in *Stentor*, though by no means perfect and distinctly related in its acuity to the state of the organism.

The next consideration is the basis for this selection, and

Schaeffer's observations on this point are interesting though negative. As noted, live and dead food organisms were not discriminated nor were fragments versus whole organisms. When mixed in sugar, beef extract, and other solutions, ink and carmine particles were still predominantly rejected. Likewise, I have observed that the empty but well-formed hulls of long-dead rotifers were quickly rejected at the same time that their live fellows were being eaten. Therefore neither size, shape, taste nor activity of food particles seem to be the basis of selection, which remains a considerable mystery. Schaeffer's results are perhaps the more remarkable because his stock cultures were being fed on something entirely different, *viz.* "small paramecia", doubtless with bacteria; and materials like sulphur grains, carmine, and glass particles are probably never encountered by stentors in nature. His demonstration of food selection is rendered more credible by Lund's (1914) evidence of similar discrimination in the related *Bursaria truncatella*.

In a still more closely allied genus, *Parafolliculina*, Andrews (1947) found that an increase of 10 °C doubles the rate of feeding or the number of food vacuoles formed in a given period of time. Very likely it is the same in stentors, increased feeding being the consequence of thermal acceleration of the membranelles (Sleigh, 1956).

It remains, if possible, to locate the site of food selection as we follow the course of digestible material during the feeding act. Particles drawn in by the vortex produced by the membranellar band impinge on the aboral side of the funnel-shaped frontal field and are carried into the buccal pouch by the oralward beating of the rows of frontal cilia. In clouds of carmine, according to Schaeffer, the frontal field cilia may beat circularly, forming balls of this material which then fall over the edge of the disc. If so, this would constitute pre-oral selection, but Dierks (1926a) could not confirm this behaviour; and I found that the feeding vortex simply creates a locus of nearly zero water velocity at the non-oral end of the membranellar band where granules collect until a mass is built up and falls into the rejection current. Current velocity over the frontal field itself is too great to permit such accumulations as Schaeffer described.

When items of considerable size, like small rotifers or hypotrichs, fall into the oral pouch they are trapped by its partial
closure as already indicated by Johnson (1893) and Andrews (1946).
As I often observed, the rim of this cavity is independently contractile and closes a widely opened pouch until only a narrow
orifice is left while the rest of the frontal field remains completely
expanded. Cilia from extensions of the ciliary rows in the frontal
field into the pouch cause the particles to spin around inside.
Schaeffer stated that there was less of this looping if the animals
were either hungry or well-fed, as if in the first case they were in
a hurry to ingest the food while in the second they would not
bother to test it. He therefore thought that the oral pouch is the
organ of food selection; but Dierks maintained that selection
occurs principally at the opening into the gullet and I am inclined
to agree with him from observation that particles are not rejected
until after they have reached and spun around for a moment in
this region. As Schaeffer noted, particles may be rejected at the
same time that others are being ingested, so that selection is indeed
precise and implies a fine coordination. Even after particles enter
the gullet reversal of the cilia there may eject undesirable items,
but once they pass to the lower end the cilia invariably carry them
inward, according to Dierks.

Food is propelled in the gullet not only by specialized body
cilia but also by the spiral extension inward of the membranellar
band. The entire gullet seems to be formed by invagination and
extension of this band and of originally surface ectoplasm lying
adjacent, both spiralling inward. An orderly contraction of ectoplasmic myonemes thus carried into the gullet could therefore
produce the peristalsis observed by Dierks, which apparently
comes into play when large objects are swallowed. Dierks also
confirmed that *Stentor* is more selective of what it ingests as the
cell becomes replete.

The pouch and gullet, like the cell surface in general, are
capable of great extension and contraction. In cannibalization they
open wide enough to accommodate a fellow stentor nearly as large
as the predator. Gelei (1925) therefore thought that the fine meshwork surrounding the gullet which he observed in sectioned
animals is to prevent tearing of this organelle when greatly
stretched. He also found that the force of closure of the oral

pouch was such that pieces of stentor prey could be bitten off.

As in many other ciliates, the food vacuoles after they are pinched off from the inner end of the gullet may be guided into the interior by long fibrils dangling therefrom, first described in *Stentor* by Schuberg (1890). But these could also serve a different purpose. Andrews (1946) observed them in gullets everted by pressure. When released the gullet can reinvert in only 10 minutes and this may be accomplished by traction of the fibers in question.

Perhaps a nice point of morphology is that the rim of the oral pouch over which rejected particles are dumped is definitely below the level of the frontal field and membranelles so that rejects probably do not return to the oral stream.

Gullet cilia and membranelles can work independently, for Dierks noticed that ingestion may occur while the membranelles circling the anterior end have for some reason stopped.

Cannibalism has been observed in the three species of *Stentor* most commonly cultured and may also occur in others. Ingestion of its fellows by *coeruleus* was first reported by Johnson (1893) and was the subject of a special study by Gelei (1925) who also noticed cannibalism in *roeseli;* and Ivanić (1927) claimed that cannibalism occurs in *polymorphus*. I recorded indubitable evidence of cannibalism in all of the 9 stocks of *coeruleus* which I have growing in my laboratory. To paraphrase Gelei, at least three problems come to mind in regard to this peculiar food choice: Why stentors come to eat each other, how they are able to ingest such large objects, and what the consequences are for the cannibalizer, particularly whether it is able to digest its own species of protoplasm. These topics will be considered in that order.

Gelei noticed that hunger or the absence of other food organisms is not the cause of cannibalism, as may be inferred from the fact that stentors will ingest more of their fellows when they already have one or more of these huge " meals " in the process of digestion. I found one *coeruleus* with five others inside. I also noticed cannibalism to be most frequent in cultures only a day or two following their nutrification. But neither is satiety the cause; for cannibalism is found in starving samples, but not as frequently as one might expect. These observations disprove Ivanić's contention that cannibalizing stentors and other protozoa have a need and therefore a hunger for their own type of protoplasm because of some deficiency which has developed. Also it seems unreasonable to suppose they could correct this lack by ingesting animals in the same culture, therefore subject to the same deprivations. Likewise we have to question Johnson's plausible and attractive suggestion that cannibalism should help the species to survive a period of scarcity, although an "ecological" study and sampling of undisturbed cultures might demonstrate this to be the case. Gelei thought cannibalism a racial trait in *coeruleus* but its occurrence without exception in a wide selection of stocks is against this interpretation.

Stentors ingest only free-swimming stentors because the prey is taken in by the attenuated tail end. By agitating the culture jar to set animals loose, Gelei was able to increase the incidence of cannibalism from about 1.5% to 4.6%, but never more. The posterior point of the animal to be eaten is drawn deep into the gullet where it is held in spite of the prey's rotating and attempting to escape. In fact, the victims may usually manage to escape and I believe no one has actually observed the swallowing, but this may be due to disturbance by bright illumination under the microscope. As mentioned, the rim of the oral pouch shows contractions that may even bite off the posterior end of the prey. Ingested animals are usually smaller than the predator, yet Gelei stated that cannibals may swallow animals larger than themselves. Once inside, the victim is not surrounded by a food vacuole at first; therefore it remains alive and actively rotating for perhaps the better part of a day, during which it can be released and always, in my experience, will recover. If not released the prey is eventually surrounded by a membrane and enclosed as a food vacuole within which it stops moving, dies, and becomes wrinkled within an hour. Stentors will also eat individuals of a different species of the same genus. I have frequently found *polymorphus* ingested by larger *coeruleus*.

There is no doubt that stentors, like other cannibal ciliates, can digest their own kind. As Gelei described the process, coagulation is the first sign of digestion and the corpse becomes friable. Fat spherules then appear in "astonishing" numbers; this could be due to the coalescence of pre-existing lipoid droplets which are very tiny and not easily seen. The nucleus is digested, its nodes falling apart and becoming progressively smaller and more weakly staining. Pellicle and myonemes are digested slowly. Cilia are often the last to be digested and are first attacked at their distal ends, then gradually disintegrating and swelling towards the base. Gelei stated that pigment granules are not digested, and certainly the last stage of the food vacuole is a bright spot of concentrated pigment; yet the fading of stentors during regeneration and starvation may imply, as Weisz (1949a) maintained, that the animals are able to assimilate their own coloring matter. Cannibals doubtless receive advantages from their prey as food. However massive these meals may be and however easily most of the substance of their like may be assimilated, giant forms do not result, as in the case of *Blepharisma* (Giese, 1938) and *Stylonychia* (Giese and Alden, 1938). Regulation of size in *Stentor* is therefore such as to prevent gigantism or the production of forms two or more times the maximum normal size.

2. Swimming

That ciliates rotate when swimming and describe a spiral path through the water was first formulated by Jennings (1899) who pointed out that such movement serves the same purpose as in projectiles: by rotating, an asymmetrical body can maintain an over-all straightness in the direction of its course (Fig. 2A). Rotation is always predominately in one direction in a given species. Jennings (1899, 1902; Jennings and Jamieson, 1902) found that *S. roeseli* and *coeruleus*, like most ciliates, including *Paramecium*, rotate to the left, i.e., front end of the animal rotates clockwise. Slightly curved toward the oral side, stentors also tend to swerve in this direction so their course is a spiral. Bullington (1925), who has made the most extensive studies of swimming in ciliates, confirmed that three unnamed species of *Stentor* rotate and spiral to the left. On the basis of his surveys Bullington remarks that *Stentor* is with *Coleps* the only genus of more than one species in which all members spiral in the same direction. (*Paramecium calkinsi* for example rotates to the right.) This generalization may be valid, for I found that the new species *introversus* rotates to the left, as does *coeruleus*, *polymorphus* and *roeseli*. When backing up *coeruleus* continues to rotate to the left, as Jennings earlier noted for *polymorphus*.

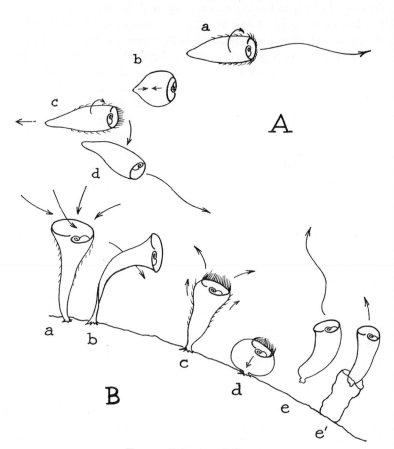

FIG. 2. Behavior of *Stentor*.

A. Avoiding response: (*a*) normal swimming with left rotation and slow spiraling; (*b*) contraction on adverse stimulation; (*c*) backward movement even if stimulated at the base; (*d*) turning to aboral side with resumed forward swimming in new direction.

B. Graded response of feeding animal to adverse stimuli: (*a*) undisturbed posture; (*b*) turning away; (*c*) feeding vortex stopped and beating of body cilia reversed; (*d*) sharp contraction; (*e*) holdfast released and animal swims away, abandoning lorica (*e'*) if present. With repeated stimuli the response decreases in the direction *e→a*. (After Jennings, 1902).

Like those of other ciliates, stentor fragments which are not of bizarre shape continue normal swimming behavior. Jennings and Jamieson (1902) observed that isolated heads, tails, and mid-body fragments of *coeruleus* rotate and spiral to the left. This indicates that the direction of beating of the membranellar band during swimming is not contradictory to the movement produced by the body cilia, as well as that it is not the asymmetric oral structures which produce the rotation. Rather, it is to be inferred that the body cilia do not beat directly backward but obliquely, as Párducz (1953) has elegantly demonstrated for *Paramecium*. Not only is the direction of beating of each cilium oblique, the whole ciliation is so coordinated that metachronal waves move slant-wise over the surface of the cell, giving the appearance of rows of grain moved in succession by the same gusts of wind. This apparently calls for a wave-like impulse passing over the cell surface or the successive "firing" of adjacent cilia down each ciliary row, as well as coordination between adjoining rows.

When a swimming stentor encounters a noxious stimulus it swims backward a little, reversing the beat of the body cilia and stopping the membranelles while pointing them forward, turns toward the aboral side and swims forward again, quite as with *Paramecium* (Fig. 2A). The membranelles then begin beating again as they are pointed backwards presumably to aid in the forward progression. Merton (1935) avers that the membranelles sometimes help in swimming backwards but I find them always held quiet then. He confirmed that posterior fragments can spiral forward and also noted that they, too, are able to swim backward "at will".

A common behaviour of stentors is to scoot over the bottom of the dish with the oral surface applied thereto, apparently to explore for and break loose food particles like a vacuum cleaner. This is the preferred method of feeding in the related genus *Condylostoma*.

The effect of various chemicals in narcotizing and reversing the ciliary beat, as well as cutting experiments concerning ciliary coordination, will be considered in Chapter XIV.

3. Avoiding reaction and learning

After feeding, the next commonest response of stentors is to manage to remove themselves from the reception of noxious stimuli. Jennings (1902) made a careful and interesting study of this avoiding reaction in *roeseli* and *coeruleus*, prodding them with a glass needle or, by gentle use of a pipette, injecting into the oral vortex substances of weak chemical stimulation, like carmine particles. As if to conserve their *status quo*, the animals performed a series of distinctly different responses of increasing intensity until the stimulus was avoided (Fig. 2B).

First, a light touch as from an impinging rotifer which could serve as food provoked no response in *coeruleus*, which merely went on feeding, and *roeseli* even made the positive response of bending toward the source of stimulation.

When the stimulus was a little stronger, as from a large, hard object or a cloud of carmine particles, the stentors "turned away." Remaining attached but twisting one or two turns on the axis, the animals then bent toward the aboral side always and therefore not necessarily away from the source of stimulation. This reaction is quite like the avoiding response of *Paramecium:* a fixed response without reference to the direction of stimulus, repeated if unsuccessful.

Third, the membranelles might stop and body cilia reverse for an instant, thereby propelling the carmine particles forward and away from the anterior end. Feeding currents then continued and the reaction was repeated several times if the particles were still encountered. This response sometimes occurred instead of turning away, but the variability may have been due to the difficulty of providing precisely graded stimuli.

If the noxious chemical stimulus still persisted, or if poked with the needle, the stentors instantly contracted, slowly extended again, and re-contracted if conditions were still undesirable. This reaction could continue for fifteen minutes if carmine particles were kept available or prodding repeated.

Fifth and finally, the holdfast was set free and the stentors swam away seeking a new environment. Sometimes *coeruleus* detached and swam away after the first stimulus but usually the other avoiding responses intervened. From my own observations it appears that stentors from cultures which have recently been fed are more likely to persist in the feeding response and to give the graded response, as if bothered by the interruption of a good thing, whereas unfed animals are more likely to detach and swim away at once, as if the negative stimulus finally prodded them to "decide" to go in search for food. However, the case-bearing *roeseli* would not abandon its home by mechanical shocks alone even though Jennings struck it with a glass needle for an hour.

Normal reactions of avoidance were also shown by stentors after their " heads " had been excised (Jennings and Jamieson, 1902). But stentors never became accustomed to truly injurious stimuli such as salt solutions (see also Merton, 1935) or sharp poking, though they learned to put up with a lot of minor disturbance. This may happen frequently in nature and stentors growing among *Tubifex* have been observed to continue feeding and not contract though constantly struck by the worms. Jennings provided a simple demonstration of this accommodation by attempted equal impacts with a glass needle repeated each time after re-extension of the stentor. After about a dozen strokes there was no contraction response unless the animal was poked several times. The longer this was continued the greater was the number of strikes which were necessary to elicit contraction, although there was some irregularity probably due to inequality of impacts. Eventually the animals detached and swam away. Sometimes there was a ready response only at first, repeated proddings then eliciting no response until the animals swam away. But in these cases he noted that the stentors did not remain oblivious to the blows but twisted continually and turned away as if to avoid them, finally detaching and swimming away. Hence in accommodation there was a reversal of the sequence of avoiding reactions, for example, contraction later replaced by merely turning away. Similar abolishment of major avoiding reactions occurred in other contractile ciliates (*Epistylis, Vorticella,* and *Carchesium*) and was noted by Holmes (1907) in *Loxophyllum*.

This orderly change in response was not due to reaction fatigue. About a minute was required for re-extension and this should have been sufficient for complete recovery. Also, stentors could be kept continuously contracting for an hour at a time, but they very soon ceased responding to weaker stimuli. Nor could the response have been due to sensory fatigue because the animals showed continued appreciation of the stimulus (by turning away) and because stentors subjected to strong mechanical blows or injurious salt solutions continued reacting indefinitely. Schaeffer (1910), for instance, said that *coeruleus* would swim backward, without spiralling, continuously for three hours in a dish of dense carmine particles. Therefore if learning be altered response due to previous experience, this did in fact occur.

The weaker the stimulus the more rapid the accommodation. To a jet of water from a capillary pipette *coeruleus* responded only once by contraction and thereafter merely bent in a new position.

If stimulated while swimming, Jennings (1899) reported that *polymorphus* contracts and backs up a short distance then turns to the right side always and swims off in another direction. This response was invariable, regardless of the point of stimulation. Though the posterior end was less sensitive than other parts, a sharp blow here elicited the same response, which therefore carried the animal toward rather than away from the point of stimulation. Unlocalized stimulation such as jarring the dish also evoked the same avoiding response, as did diffuse chemical stimuli.

Unlike *Paramecium* and *Chilomonas*, stentors were completely indifferent to bubbles of carbon dioxide or solutions of acids, not showing the spontaneous aggregations of the former (Jennings and Moore, 1901–02).

Even to relatively strong solutions of cane sugar *roeseli* showed no avoiding reaction and responded by sudden contraction only after the cell became obviously affected by osmotic pressure (Jennings, 1902).

4. Response to light

Jennings (1902) noted that *roeseli* does not respond to light of ordinary intensities. According to Schulze (1951) *polymorphus* shows contrasting reactions to light depending on whether symbiotic *Chlorella* are present: green animals appropriately went to the lighted side of the aquarium but white forms collected on the dark side. Hämmerling (1946) stated that *polymorphus* is sensitive to strong light and that cultures had to be screened, but in nature I have found these stentors fully exposed to brightest summer sunshine. In *coeruleus* the reaction seems to vary with the strain. Testing 8 races cultured in the same manner, fed on the same day each week, and producing animals of about the same intensity of green pigmentation, I found that two showed a strong negative response to daylight and quickly accumulated on the side of the dish away from the window; two showed no response; the remainder showed, fair, weak, or doubtful response.

That *Stentor coeruleus* moves to the dark side of an elongated aquarium was reported long ago by Holt and Lee (1901) and interpreted tropistically as due to an orientation in the field of light away from the source of illumination. An extensive study of this subject was made by Mast (1906) with different conclusions. Swimming animals placed in a dish lighted from one side simply showed repeated random avoiding responses of backing up and turning until they found themselves headed away from the light, and then they continued swimming forward to the dark side. This response kept animals confined to the darkened end of an aquarium, as if an invisible wall were present. That the confinement was not due to warming caused by the light was shown by the fact that paramecia which are quite sensitive to heat but not to light swam readily into the irradiated area. Attachment of course prevented the avoiding response of stentors, which did not even lean (tropistically) away from the light; but if the light was strong enough the animals detached and then gave the characteristic response. Mast concluded that the anterior end was most sensitive to light because, when the water was a thin film so that the stentors could not face the light source above and received stimulation only on their sides, collecting at the darker end was slower. This point is confirmed by my observation that decapitated stentors no longer avoid the light (unpublished).

Contrasting with *coeruleus*, the yellow *S. niger* shows a marked attraction to light, according to the studies of Tuffrau (1957). He states that all parts of the animal appear to be equally sensitive to the stimulus because there was no orientation in a field of light, yet the head end could be more sensitive if the response is not tropistic but one of trial and error. Although there was some individual variability, most of the animals accumulated rapidly at an illuminated opening in the side of a covered tube, and the response was so strong that a spot of light acted like a trap in preventing stentors from leaving it after they entered. The shorter the wave length of light, the stronger the attraction: red elicited almost no response and the aggregations increased as the spectrum shifted to blue, violet, and ultraviolet. Animals dark-adapted for fifteen hours recovered photoresponsiveness in an hour or two. The rapidity of

C

response varied directly with the temperature, and this may not be solely due to increased rate of ciliary beating but also to the enhancement of photoreactions in the cell.

Dabrowska (1956) was unable to get *coeruleus* to associate an electric current with its response to light, and hence learning by conditioned response was not demonstrated.

5. Response to heat and electric current

Alverdes (1922) found that *polymorphus* reacted to heat with a typical avoiding response. This response disappeared when the anterior end was cut off, for the cell body then swam indiscriminately towards the heated end of the slide and was killed. To a 1% solution of table salt the headless cell bodies gave the avoiding response just as whole animals. He concluded that warmth perception is limited to the anterior end while chemical sensation is over the entire body surface. This interpretation is open to question, first, because salt apparently compels ciliary reversal with continuous backward swimming by direct action on the coordinating mechanism, and second, because as Dierks (1926b) pointed out, the response of the isolated heads was not indicated. Anterior and posterior half fragments would better have been compared since both are capable of typical avoiding reactions, with use of a less noxious chemical stimulant like carmine particles.

With further regard to sensory localization, Roesle (1902) claimed that the mouth is the part of stentor most sensitive to electric currents but behavior of stentors with mouthparts excised was apparently not studied for comparison. Roesle also reported that an induction current stimulates *Stentor* to contraction only when the direction of the current was parallel to the axis of the animal, contrasting with muscle physiology in which stimulation is independent of the orientation. Yet Hausmann (1927) found that *polymorphus* contracted and backed up in an electric current but without correlation with its direction. *Stentor* was more sensitive than smaller ciliates of other genera so that at least the intensity of the response may be correlated with body size if the animals compared normally swim at the same speed. Dierks Roesle, neuroid (1926b), repeating the electrical stimulation studies of found that *Stentor* was more sensitive to the current than any of the other ciliates tested, which he credited to the presence of fibers.

6. The question of sensory cilia

Certain of the body cilia behave differently from most. According to Kahl (1935) the posterior cilia are strongly thigmotactic, coming to a stop when they touch something substantial. Along the ciliary rows it has been found that groups of cilia are stiff and pointed outward while the remainder of the ciliation is actively beating; and these have been called tactile spines, setæ, or Tastborsten (Fig. 3). They may disappear and reappear. Hence Stein, who seems to have first noticed them, thought they could be withdrawn into the body. Johnson, with more probability, said that

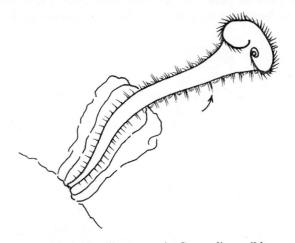

FIG. 3. Sessile body cilia as seen in *S. roeseli*, possibly sensory.
(After Kahl, 1935.)

they were only temporarily rigid cilia which could start again beating and only seemed longer than the others because they were stopped. He suggested a sensory function for the cilia in the rigid state because they are found mostly toward the anterior end where stimuli would presumably be most frequent. Since Johnson saw them both in *coeruleus*, which makes no case, and in *roeseli* which does, they are not uniquely correlated with case building. He found them most evident in the frontal view; and Kahl states that there is always one group of "bristles", five to twenty in number according to the species, in each kinety directly under the membranellar band.

7. Cystment

Hibernation in a cyst may be regarded as a response of *Stentor* to adverse conditions. Stein's is the only published account and characteristically he provided beautiful illustration of *coeruleus* and *polymorphus* cysts (1867, Tafeln V and VI). Although the final test of excystment was lacking, he can hardly have been mistaken because the *coeruleus* capsules retained the blue-green striping and the *polymorphus* were of similar form, with chlorellæ and colorless stripes. In both, the feeding organelles were dedifferentiated and the animal rested within a flask-shaped cyst with a gelatinous plug (Fig. 4). Only once have I seen *coeruleus* apparently beginning encystment within a membrane inside which

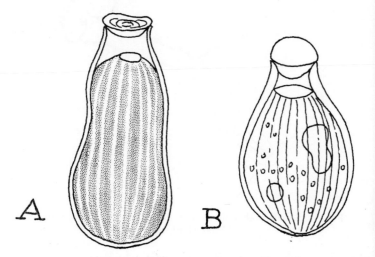

Fig. 4. Cysts of (A) *coeruleus* and (B) *polymorphus*. (After Stein, 1867.)

it rotated for a day but then died. In *niger*, however, cystment seems to occur readily, with small, spherical, brown cysts, though again, stentors have not yet been seen emerging therefrom (unpublished).

Altogether, stentors exhibit a considerable range of behavior in their orderly swimming movements, avoiding responses, food selection, and attachment or detachment of holdfast "at will".

To these frequent reactions may be added the "decision" to encyst or excyst, as well as the special response to each other which leads to the joining of pairs in a specific orientation for sexual conjugation. Of special interest is the accommodation to repeated adverse stimuli which Jennings demonstrated and which may be regarded as the best evidence of a primitive type of learning in unicellular organisms.

The ease with which stentors lend themselves to micrurgical operations should provide opportunities for analyzing the structural basis of coordination. After the immediate contraction response to cutting, stentors show no evidence of "pain" or lingering effects of injury as the fragments or cut animals swim away in a remarkably normal manner. Later they mend the cut or regenerate missing parts, but between the time of cutting and repair or reconstruction there is, it would seem, a sufficient period for observing effects on behavior of specific lesions and ablations. Are there circumferential cuts at certain levels of the cell axis which abolish coordination between adjacent rows of body cilia so that spiral swimming is prevented, or may such cuts prevent attachment or detachment of the holdfast? Are stentors from which the oral pouch has been removed or those—after a method which will be described later (p. 172)—developing without a pouch still capable of food selection? If not, could they be made to ingest unusual materials relevant to analysis of their metabolism? If decapitation abolishes the avoiding response to light in *coeruleus*, can selective ablations at the anterior pole demonstrate the sensitive area; and do similar operations also prevent the positive response to light in *niger*? Do stentors temporarily bereft of ingestive organelles still show the avidity of normal animals evidenced by quicker accommodation to mechanical stimuli when in the presence of food after a period of deprivation, or is the successful formation of food vacuoles the necessary prelude to this behavior?

These questions are but a sample of possible ways in which behavior on the cell level might be investigated in a form so amenable to operation as *Stentor*. Might the neurone itself, then be capable of considerably more "behavior" than mere "excitation", realizing as part of the nervous system something of the potentialities which have been evolved in a different manner but from the same cellular origins, in ciliates?

CHAPTER IV

FINE STRUCTURE

BEARING in mind our general survey of the morphology of *Stentor*, we can now probe the intimate construction of its parts as the structural basis of its living functions and behaviour. Every detail we learn only increases our wonder that stentors are capable of such remarkable feats of regeneration and reconstruction after the cutting needle comes crashing through these complex and highly organized cell differentiations.

1. Feeding organelles

The differentiations at the anterior end of stentor are formed in a few hours from an oral primordium in the most dramatic act of cytoplasmic elaboration shown by this animal. A band of membranelles develops on the side of the cell and carves out an area of the ventral striping to the right which it carries forward to the anterior end, as the posterior terminus of the band invaginates to form the gullet and the adjacent part of the isolated striping indents to produce the oral pouch. An important consideration is whether all growth and elaboration of oral parts occurs only through primordium development. If so, the size and number of membranelles should not increase thereafter, the gullet would not increase in resting diameter or length, and the number of stripes in the frontal field should remain the same after oral differentiation regardless of increase in cell volume through growth. Indications that this may be the case are found in the fact that adoral bands and gullets abbreviated by cutting do not grow out again *in situ* but initiate regeneration of a whole new set of feeding organelles. But in regard to decrease in these structures through dedifferentiation and resorption the situation is entirely different, for the membranellar band and gullet can shorten *in situ* (see p. 125).

(a) FRONTAL FIELD

The granular or pigmented stripes of this area are narrow and the ciliary rows correspondingly close together, not only because they are ventral fine stripes shifted forward, but also because there is usually an extensive formation of new stripes within the arc of the developing membranellar band. Some of the resulting pigment stripes in *coeruleus* may be so narrow as to consist of only a single row of granules. The disposition of the frontal striping follows roughly the curve of the membranellar band (Fig. 1). Some of the stripes end at the border, while those nearest the oral side continue as the lining of the oral pouch and proceed downward and spiraling into the depths of the gullet.

Like their lateral progenitors, clear stripes of the frontal field bear rows of small cilia, and contractile myonemes which are said to be finer than those of the lateral body wall and without branchings (Dierks, 1926a). Stevens (1903) thought that the frontal stripes can multiply *in situ* and not only alongside the developing primordium. This now seems unlikely because stripe splitting within the field is not observed. Likewise, when for some reason the stripes fail to increase adjacent to the anlage, the frontal field is then deficient and remains so until corrected by a later re-organization or re-regeneration.

The frontal stripe area is bordered by a wider clear stripe followed by a bordering pigment stripe and finally the membranellar band itself (see Fig. 1). According to Maier (1903), who studied *niger* but says that *coeruleus* is the same, there is a marginal ciliary row which neither Schuberg nor Johnson noticed on the clear border stripe, but no myoneme underlies it. Schröder (1907) seems to have been the first to mention the pigmented border stripe in *coeruleus* though Schuberg (1890) showed it in his drawings; I have found it along the right side of the developing oral primordium when presumably the clear border stripe is also laid down.

(b) ORAL POUCH

In some species (e.g., *introversus* and *roeseli*) the frontal field simply dips downwards like a ramp and forms a curved trough leading to the opening of the gullet. In *coeruleus* there is a definite in-pocketing such that the pouch curves back under the frontal field, forming what Johnson called the buccal fold. Oralward the wall of the pouch lies against the body ectoplasm, forming a thin wall which is apparently what Johnson called the " velum ". The membranellar margin of this wall bends inward, producing the groove which Schuberg emphasized, and is capable, by independent contraction, of increasing this over-hang or nearly closing off the cavity below. It was Schuberg who first pointed out that the oral or buccal pouch is not a part of the gullet but only a modification of the frontal field, which later experiments confirmed (see p. 172).

(c) MEMBRANELLAR BAND

On first inspection membranelles appear to be merely large cilia, and so they seemed to Stein (1867) and Simroth (1876); but Sterki (1878) first noted that they are flat plates. Each lamella is formed by many cilia clinging together in a sheet, presumably by the inter-locking, as in the barbules of a feather, of lateral spurs recently demonstrated through electron microscopy by Randall and Jackson (1958). The same occurs in the formation of cirri in hypo-trichs (Roth, 1956). All students had agreed that each membranelle in stentors was made up of 2 rows of cilia and I found the same in silver-stained *polymorphus*. It is therefore surprising that Randall and Jackson describe from clear photographs triple rows for the same species, except in the mouth region. This discrepancy will have to be resolved. It is possible that strains could differ in this respect and if so the number of rows could be an important genetic character. In the ciliate *Oxytricha* membranelles are composed of 3 rows of cilia (E. E. Lund, 1935).

The row of membranelles is held together by some sort of band or fibers at the level of the ciliary bases, and when shed in salt solutions the membranelles do not fall apart but come off as a continuous ribbon (Tartar, 1957a). Schuberg thought this union was accomplished by thickened pellicle; Schröder by a special meshwork or membrane. Dierks saw a fiber (of coordinating function he supposed) connecting the membranelles at this level, and such connectives are clear in the electronmicrographs of Randall and Jackson but afford no indication of whether the fibers are supportive, contractile, or coordinating. If isolated by crushing, Moxon (1869) saw in the membranellar band "tremulous waves passing along it after patches of cilia were detached ", but no one has confirmed this. That the oral lip is capable of independent contraction like a sphincter suggests some means of developing tension in the transverse direction. Whether actively or passively, the membranelles of the entire band do come closer together when the frontal field is contracted (Randall and Jackson).

Each membranelle has an extension into the endoplasm. Difficult to observe, the structure and function of these processes have occasioned conflicting interpretations, but recent studies with the electron microscope clarify the issues. Schuberg (1890, 1905) described a triangular sheet or lamella from the base of each membranelle, apparently bordered by two converging fibers and narrowing inward to an apex which continued as an end fiber, while the end fibers of all the membranelles were joined together by a deep-lying basal fiber. Most workers agreed with this picture (excepting Schröder, Neresheimer, and Dierks) and EM studies are confirmatory. Neresheimer (1903) interpreted the lamellæ as overlapping plates which were not joined by a continuous fiber and served for anchoring the membranelles. This view was expanded by Dierks (1926a) who described the lamellæ as anchoring rectangles with a twist which accounted for the other appearances including the basal fiber. In the light of the EM studies this view will be discarded, and also it may be added that in shed membranellar bands nothing like these plates is found, as would be expected if they had sufficient strength to serve for anchoring.

Fauré-Fremiet and Rouiller (1955) made an EM study of *polymorphus, niger* and *coeruleus*. They find that each membranelle is composed of *two* short, parallel rows of ciliary basal granules or kinetosomes which are connected to each other laterally and give off ciliary rootlets into the interior. Each bundle of rootlets combines with that from neighbouring cilia to form the triangle Schuberg described, which is now seen to be of a fibrous nature throughout. Randall and Jackson confirmed this picture and added new details (Fig. 5). The fibrils in the triangular bundle are fitted together in an orderly stacking. These fibrils do not appear to be striated, as is the case with some metazoan ciliary rootlets (Fawcett and Porter, 1954). Continuing inward, the fibrils form a long bundle, corresponding to Schuberg's end fiber, and these are in turn joined together at their ends by a composite basal fiber. The

connection is a smooth one, fibrils from the end fiber bending and
running into the basal fiber. Photographic evidence of these points
is very convincing. The whole basal structure of the membranelle
extends for about 20μ into the endoplasm.

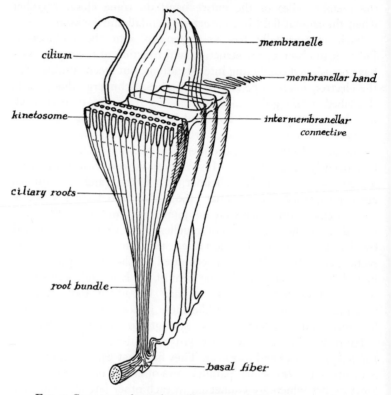

FIG. 5. Structure of membranelles as revealed by electron microscopy. (After Randall and Jackson, 1958.)

The function of this intracellular structure of the membranelles
has been variously interpreted as contractile, nutritive, supportive,
or coordinating, beginning with Brauer (1885) who thought the
basal fiber a muscle which contracted the whole frontal field.
Maier (1903) modified this view with a speculation that the basal
lamellæ retract or pull the membranelles inward while the basal
fiber draws them together; but the membranelles do not seem to
retract, and were the basal fiber contractile it would only pull the

tips of the end fibers together without necessarily compacting the membranelles.

Neresheimer (1903), Schröder (1907), and Dierks (1926a) all maintained that the basal lamellæ were to give solidity and support as anchors for the powerfully beating membranelles. It is difficult to see how much support could be given because the membranellar band is easily sloughed in salt solutions and when it comes off there is no sign of supporting structure below the membranelles.

Schuberg denied a muscular function for the basal fiber since it is thrown into convolutions when the animal is contracted and he thought that the basal lamellæ could achieve little anchoring in a fluid endoplasm. He suggested a nutritive function for the parts he described, though granting there was still no proof of this. The membranelles start and stop together and they beat in an orderly fashion, one firing after the other in regular series to produce a metachronal rhythm. It therefore seemed to Johnson that the basal fiber with its connections to the membranelles would be suited to a coordinating function. But even this reasonable interpretation is not without its difficulties. Neresheimer found that the usual nerve anæsthetics had no effect on ciliary action in *Stentor*; and also, if the membranellar band is severed deep into the interior, metachronal rhythm continues on both sides of the cut although the basal fiber must certainly have been sundered.

The wide, clear marginal stripe of the frontal field running along the inner margin of the membranellar band should not be overlooked as a possible site of fibers coordinating the membranellar beat. Clear stripes elsewhere carry fibers connecting the cilia, and in *Stylonychia* the membranelles of the oral region are apparently connected by a lateral fiber (Chen, 1944).

Although the electronmicrographs give no indication thereof, the membranellar band shows an intrinsic polarity. Bands or sections of bands similarly oriented will readily join and mend together without a break but not otherwise, and reversed mid-sections of a band are reincorporated only after they, invariably, rotate 180° in reorientation. This polarization appears during primordium development. The primordium can be cut through transversely in many places without effect, the severed parts merely healing together; but if a sector is cut out and replaced in reversed position it develops separately (see Fig. 41K).

From the complexity of its structure we appreciate that the formation of the membranellar band is indeed an astonishing achievement of differentiation, involving multiplication of ciliary basal bodies to 15,000 (judging from the data of Randall and Jackson), the precise alignment of these bodies in rows and the grouping of these rows by twos or threes, outgrowth of long cilia from these granules, ingrowth of ciliary rootlets and their precise association into triangular plates ending in a fiber, together with the elaboration of the basal fiber connecting the end fibers, not to mention the coiling and shifting of the entire structure to the anterior end. All this occurs within about 4 hours. The performance is the more remarkable in view of the fact that when the membranellar band is forming it can be slashed through many times with a glass needle without producing any apparent abnormality of construction (Tartar, 1957c).

(d) GULLET

The membranellar band continues in a sharply spiraled course down into the gullet, as does the ectoplasmic striping which lines the oral pouch and is itself continuous with the stripes of the frontal field. Opening into the right-hand side of the oral pouch, the gullet shows a double spiraling: as a pendant tube it takes about one complete turn as it penetrates into the endoplasm, while the wall of the gullet is itself under sharp torsion. Dierks claimed that the opening into the gullet is capable of closure, though no one else has observed this.

In everted gullets of *coeruleus* Andrews (1946) saw the membranellar band extending in a spiral to the lower end of the gullet, while decreasing to half its usual width (Fig. 6A). In *polymorphus*, Randall and Jackson describe the membranelles in this region as bi- instead of tri-lamellar. In pigmented species the appearance is often that only one side of the gullet is colored because the band of membranelles is itself unpigmented. However, Dierks maintained, apparently erroneously, that the membranellar band does not continue into the gullet. In any case, the gullet has its own specialized ciliation. Gelei (1925) found that the cilia here stained differently, and he likened them to the pharyngeal cilia of turbellarian worms which serve in swallowing. Dierks even denied that the kineties of the frontal field continue into the gullet, being

interrupted where new types of cilia begin. The latter investigator
made fine distinctions regarding the gullet tube. Its entrance he
called the cytostome which leads into a short passage called the
pharynx separated by a ridge from the extensive remaining portion

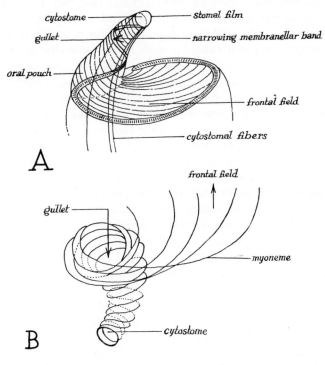

FIG. 6. Structure of the gullet of *S. coeruleus.*
A. Exposure of gullet everted by pressure. (After Andrews,
1946.).
B. Schematic course of myonemes in the gullet lining,
affording possiblity of peristalsis. (After Dierks, 1926a.)

or esophagus. Each of these parts was described as having its own
special ciliation: the "cytostomial" cilia look like the pharyngeals
but have the special function of selecting the food particles, and
the esophageal cilia were said to be different, the distance between
cilia increasing as they are followed down into the gullet. Andrews
agrees with Dierks that in the profundity of the gullet the

membranelles take the form of isolated cilia not joined in sheets.

Dierks granted, however, that the myonemes of the frontal field are continuous into the gullet, proceeding uninterrupted and in a sharply spiraled course to its terminus and also, as in the frontal field itself, showing no branchings (Fig. 6B). In the gullet the myonemes become much thicker and presumably stronger, according to Gelei, and their disposition more or less transverse to the length of the gullet could provide for the peristaltic movements in swallowing which have been observed. Gelei also described a fibrous net surrounding the gullet, which he thought might serve both to prevent the gullet from tearing when stretched and to coordinate cilia and myonemes in a swallowing action. Such an appearance may have been due to the system of vacuoles and interspersed fibers found near the gullet by Randall and Jackson. These numerous vacuoles have double or triple membranes and it was therefore suggested that they might be formed by invaginations from the gullet wall, as in the pinocytosis of *Amœba*. The adjacent fibers run rather deeply into the interior and may represent the pharyngeal fibers of Schuberg.

Following Schuberg we shall call the inner terminus of the gullet the cytostome. Again in everted gullets, Andrews (1946) saw the cytostome as a thin, clear membrane without visible structure which prevents the escape or regurgitation of endoplasm. Dangling inward from the periphery of this cytostome he found the long fibers described by Schuberg but not seen as such by others, and he thought that they formed part of a permanent canal which guides and might even propel ingested food into the endoplasm. By Andrews' account, ingestion may occur in one of three ways: small particles may collect at the bottom of the gullet and push out the stomal film until it breaks off as a membrane surrounding them; the film may be momentarily broken as objects like small rotifers pass directly into the endoplasm; or the film may be missing as the cytostome opens wide to admit larger organisms or clots of food. In the last two cases the ingested animals thrash around freely in the endoplasm but eventually are encased in a food vacuole and die. I once found a stentor that had ingested a cotton fiber with one end still protruding forward out of the gullet and the other end passing through the cell and emerging through the surface near the posterior end.

2. Holdfast

A history of our knowledge of stentor's anchoring organ is given in Andrews' (1945) most complete account of this organelle, which confirmed and extended the early observations of Gruber (1878). Stein (1876) thought that stentors fastened in part by means of a tiny suction cup. This idea was revived by Dierks (1926a) who described the myonemes as not continuing all the way to the posterior pole but leaving the ectoplasm near the tail end to turn inward toward the center of the cell where they took another bend as they joined together to make a bundle pointing forward. The result was a cone of contractile elements open toward the terminal pole. Assuming that the recurved ends of the myonemes are independently contractile while their anterior extensions remain wholly relaxed, and that the posterior end of the animal could somehow produce a tightly adhering cup, he conceived that this arrangement produces a suction which is the principal means of attachment. This scheme is highly dubitable. In the first place, the study was made on killed and contracted animals, unattached. Second, stentors can attach to the surface film where suction should not be effective. Finally, among the other assumptions mentioned, this conception was based on the questionable presupposition that amœboid processes with sticky substances could not account for the firmness of adhesion which is observed. Schröder (1907), however, also described myonemes as recurved at the posterior end, but he did not advance the suction idea. Instead, in the cone before-mentioned, he defined a special cytoplasm from which the attaching organ was presumed to be elaborated. I have sometimes observed the " hem " or sharp bend in the cell contour toward the posterior end which Dierks described as indicating where the myonemes turn inward but otherwise found no confirming indications of his description in living material. Whether Schröder's and Dierks' recurved myonemes are artifacts of fixation can only be decided by successful preservation of animals in the fully extended state.

Johnson (1893) figured the myonemes as running without deviation to the posterior pole and hence his conception of attachment was quite different. Body striping was described, however, as not continuing all the way to the pole itself but stopping short to leave a small terminal area which, because of its absence of structure, he designated questionably as endoplasm. This would correspond to the polar plasma later described by Schröder. Weisz, too, (1948a) emphasized that the posterior end is clear and structureless, but Dierks denied that there is any such " naked protoplasm ". Probably the pellucid polar endoplasm is responsible for this illusion. Rather it would seem that granular stripes, ciliary rows and myonemes cannot continue all the way to a fine point without an improbable anastamosis of unlike elements and that therefore at the posterior end the construction would not be strictly closed but allow an opening for extrusions.

The manner of attachment may vary with the nature of the substratum. To clean glass, according to Johnson, terminal protoplasm adheres as a smooth disc; against slime, pointed pseudopods are given out from this disc; and in attachment to the surface film pseudopods become broad and branching as Andrews later described more fully. Johnson also observed that stentors never attach until stretched out and that the terminal cilia seem to feel about for a place of attachment.

Enlarging much on these observations, Andrews (1945) described that in the outstretched stentor seeking attachment the posterior cilia on the stalk come to a stop projecting outward while the terminal cilia, somewhat like the scopula of a vorticellid, remain active, possibly seeking a favorable spot or effecting a preliminary attachment. By focusing downward on the foot of stentors attaching to glass wool or a cover slip he was able to give the most complete account of the holdfast, one which also has interesting implications concerning the relationship between cilia and pseudopodia. An amœboid disc of naked cytoplasm is first extruded from the posterior end to adhere by its stickiness, and some of the posterior cilia are apparently transformed into viscid, rigid, acicular pseudopods which he called " radiants". (If this does indeed occur it carries the surprising implication, contradictory to the hypothesis of the French school (see Lwoff, 1950) that formed cilia can transform into something else without new growth from a kinetosome specifically determined to produce such a structure.) Meanwhile some of the terminal cilia remain active ("undulants") but these gradually disappear with continued attachment. Then the adjacent ectoplasm with its pigmented stripes and ciliary rows is drawn out into extensive projections like pseudopodia which he called "radicules" (Fig. 7A). This would account for the observation that *coeruleus* even at low magnification shows a *green*, stellate foot. In side view after long attachment Andrews observed that the stentor is chiefly anchored by the

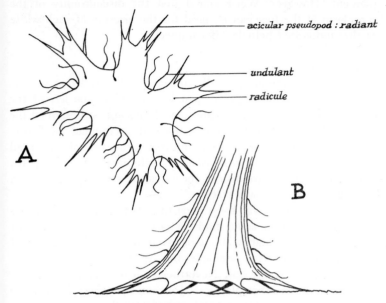

acicular pseudopod : *radiant*

undulant

radicule

A

B

FIG. 7. Holdfast of *S. coeruleus*.
A. Underside of attaching holdfast, showing ectoplasmic projections ("radicules") and active, undulating cilia said to convert into thicker, acicular, attaching pseudopods.
B. Side view. (After Andrews, 1945.)

acicular and lobose pseudopodial processes, like a balloon anchored by ropes (Fig. 7B), the openings between which would preclude any suction. If forcibly detached, the holdfast remains somewhat intact for a while and is so sticky that if touched with a needle adherence is firm and immediate. But later, or when the animal detaches itself at will, the holdfast is withdrawn. Then, according to Andrews, its structural parts resume their former forms and functions, which would imply that the striping of the pseudopods again takes the form of the posterior cell wall and the aciculars transform back into cilia. However this may be, it follows that structureless cytoplasm is not the *sine qua non* of attachment.

D

Johnson surmised that the pedal opening could be used for the extrusion of pigment granules but in this he could have been misled by appearances, as Weisz (1949a) noted, since the stickiness of the detached holdfast is likely to pick up debris, including cast-off pigment. However, Weisz stated that the discontinuity of the ectoplasm at the foot can be used for the ejection of such waste as the undigested pellicles of paramecia.

3. Cytopyge

Undigested material is usually collected and extruded at a single site on the anterior left side, just below and to the left of the opening of the contractile vacuole. As Johnson first described the process, the spent food vacuoles, if small, accumulate by fusion in this place. The pellicle then ruptures within one of the broad granular bands and the waste is slowly defecated as the slit opens, often so widely as to distort the adjacent striping; thereupon closing without leaving a trace.

Whether the cytopyge has a persisting structure is still in question. Moxon (1869) could find no pore but said the spot was marked by an irregularity in one or two of the granular stripes and Johnson found no fixed organelle, but Andrews (1946) made out a long slit with definite lips. Nevertheless, it is certain that defecation can occur in other places, as Johnson first observed. I twice observed *coeruleus* ejecting solid material in the normal manner simultaneously at two points far distant from the normal site (Fig. 8A). Defecation openings break or open through granular stripes, clear stripes carrying too much structure to permit exit.

4. Contractile vacuole

Stentors have but one contractile vacuole always located at the left anterior side of the cell. The structure of this excretory system seems to be less well-developed than in *Paramecium* in spite of the fact that Stentors are much larger, e.g., there are no star shaped canals and Haye (1930) found few lipoid granules associated with this system. Walls of the contractile vacuole were not blackened in osmic acid (Park, 1929). Schwalbe (1866) is said to have been the first to see the excretory pore, in *polymorphus*. With its pigmentation, *coeruleus* shows this part more clearly and Moxon described the presence of two or three unpigmented spots in the colored bands over the vacuole, one of which opens widely to void its content. Independently, Maupas (1883) discovered these spots which are evidence of persisting pores. Andrews (1948b) noted that rarely two pores may open at the same time as well as that the arrangement of the spots may vary in different individuals or in the same specimen at different times. The presence of these pores is easily confirmed (Fig. 8B).

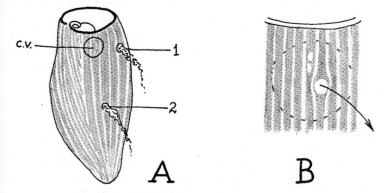

FIG. 8. Excretion in *S. coeruleus*.

A. Specimen showing location of contractile vacuole and normal site of cytopyge (1) but also excreting from a second opening (2).

B. Multiple pores in granular stripes, one of which is excreting contents of the underlying contractile vacuole. (After Andrews, 1948b.)

All students agree that the vacuole increases in size by the confluence of smaller vacuoles or at least by the draining of their fluid contents into the contractile vacuole. Although not as evident as in paramecia, a system of collecting channels has been described. In *coeruleus*, Maupas found variable canals formed by the alignment of adventitious vacuoles which presumably ran together and pushed their fluid toward the contractile vacuole. Johnson confirmed this picture and maintained that in divisions one of a pedally directed line of vacuoles becomes the contractile vacuole of the posterior daughter cell, even before separation beginning to contract regularly but not in synchrony with the old one and acquiring excretory pores in the pigment stripes above. Johnson also described a definite longitudinal canal in *roeseli*, recalling that in *Spirostomum*, in which also the new vacuole is produced at division simply by an enlargement of this canal. Anterior to the new vacuole a segment of the longitudinal canal separates both from this vacuole and from the posterior end of the anterior daughter, producing the circumoral " ring canal " discovered by Lachmann (Claparéde and Lachmann, 1858–1861) ; but this severed portion of the canal soon atrophies and hence is seen only in the young opisthe. Haye stated that *polymorphus* also has a longitudinal canal but he did not describe or illustrate it. In *coeruleus* Andrews saw many channels emanating from the contractile vacuole. One proceeded forward and led to a horizontal ring canal underlying the frontal field; others proceeded backward toward the foot and from such might come the new contractile vacuole during fission.

5. Cortical structure

The well-differentiated cortex or ectoplasm of *Stentor* is highly extensible, considerably elastic, sharply contractile, capable in part of being shed and regenerated, as well as bearing cilia with the means of their coordination. These properties and functions are to be related to the types of microscopic and submicroscopic structure present. Even today our knowledge of this correlation is still highly problematical; nor is it certain that all structural details have been revealed, though electron microscopy has made possible astonishing advances in this study.

From the standpoint of morphogenesis, the cell cortex with its enduring pattern is of greatest importance. For it is from this layer that other cytoplasmic organelles are elaborated, as when a midsection fragment regenerates a new head and foot. As will become evident later, both holdfast and oral primordium formation are intimately related to the polarity and pattern of the cortex, and we may hope that the causal basis of this relationship will in time be exposed.

(a) THE CELL SURFACE

Proceeding from the exterior, there is a pellicle, long ago demonstrated by Johnson who saw it lift off the cell on treatment with weak osmic acid while remaining firmly attached to the ciliary rows. Electronmicrographs of Randall and Jackson showed the pellicle to be a double or perhaps even a triple membrane, joined to the body cilia because continuous with their outer walls. When the pellicle is elevated the cytoplasm does not flow out into the spaces provided and hence there is another film, the plasma membrane, which was also shown to be double. One may regard the pellicle as being a somewhat dispensable secretion of the cell because salt treatments often produce the shedding of a layer which is presumably the outermost, but the stentor remains intact, appears not to be significantly affected, and probably re-secretes the layer. These remarks are demonstrably true for *Blepharisma* (Nadler, 1929).

In cross-sections of contracted stentors the surface is thrown into a series of ridges parallel to the longitudinal axis of the cell. Each ridge represents one of the granular or pigmented stripes ("Rippenstreifen" of Butschli) while the alternating valleys are the clear stripes (Zwischenstreifen). The bases of the rows of body cilia are implanted along the (animal's) left side of each valley or clear stripe.

It was early noticed that on contraction the stripes of pigmented or non-pigmented granules are thrown into folds, transverse ridges, or crenulations while the clear stripes are not. Schröder remarked that this pleating may cause the granules to be aligned in rows, which indicates that these particles have some freedom of displacement. Hence the original deception that these bands were striated muscles. The appearance described implies that the pellicle has a limited elasticity, at least over the granular stripes, and that it is more elastic or simply pinned down in the region of the clear stripes.

Presumably there is a break in the pellicle permitting extrusion at the holdfast and no pellicle over the cytostome.

(b) GRANULAR STRIPES: NATURE OF THE PIGMENT AND GRANULES

As already described in Chapter II, the ectoplasm is chiefly characterized by alternating clear and granular longitudinal stripes or bands. In colored stentors the granules are pigmented, giving the appearance of pigmented stripes. These stripes seem to be without specialized structures other than the granules located in them; but the clear bands mark the site of complex differentiations, including not only the ciliary rows but also a band which in living animals is often seen to be thrown into transverse waves or convo-lutions. Therefore, the granular stripes appear to be merely fill-ins where surface granules come to occupy spaces left between the structured clear bands and membranelles. Accordingly, it is the granular and not the clear stripes which should have been called mere "between-stripes" ("Zwischenstreifen") even though they are more obvious to the eye. Moxon, for instance, found that in crushed *coeruleus* the pigment stripes disperse while the clear bands persist as refractile structures, and Schröder remarked the same. The great change in width of the former speaks for the same conclusion, contrasting with the uniformity of the clear stripes. When the area of ectoplasm in *coeruleus* is greatly reduced, the patch remaining stretches to cover the whole and this stretching occurs mainly in the pigmented stripes which become very broad (Fig. 9A). Furthermore, where stripe increase occurs it can be seen that the pigmented bands adapt in width and contour to the exigencies of the situation (Fig. 9B), which would not be the case if they had to maintain a uniform and stable structure.

These stripes are characterized by uniform, spheroid inclusions about 1μ in diameter. They are not fixed in place but capable of a certain freedom of movement (Andrews, 1946) which Weisz (1949a) called Brownian motion. In all colored species the pigmentation is probably confined to these granules (though *S. Felici* was differently described), for there is not a second set of uncolored bodies. That cortical granules seem to be present in uncolored stentors indicates that they serve some purpose besides pigmentation. When pigmented, some granules can also be identi-fied in the interior of the cell; and Weisz indicated this to be the main site of a putative metabolic function, the granules being stored, as it were, in the ectoplasm and loosed into the interior to be utilized during starvation and regeneration. Within the interior of *coeruleus*, Andrews (1955) reported that the pigment granules move between the endoplasmic vesicles as if gliding along films, by a movement not yet explained.

Granules can also be cast off to the exterior by the action of mild irritants (see p. 250). This effect resembles the discharge of trichocysts, which are, however, always spindle-form. Hence the granules have been called protrichocysts by Prowazek (1904), Kahl (1935), and Fauré-Fremiet *et al.* (1956).

Extensive studies on pigment granules in *coeruleus* were made by Weisz (1949a, 1950a). He found them to have a basophilic core of protein pigment, surrounded by a phospholipid shell, and to give a negative test for RNA but positive for cytochrome oxidase.

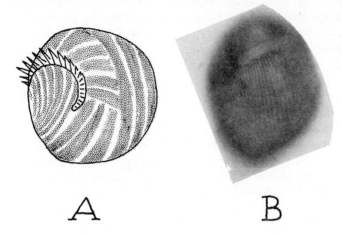

FIG. 9. Granular stripes adapting to space available.

A. Specimen from which most of ectoplasm was removed, granular stripes of the patch stretching to cover the endoplasm. The animal then regenerated.
B. Photograph showing granular striping of nonuniform width and contour according to the space provided.

The bright red appearance of these green particles in reflected light he attributed to phase interference by the outer shell. Andrews (1946) regarded the pigment granules of *coeruleus* as not mitochondrial; but Weisz concluded that they, as well as those of *Blepharisma*, are mitochondria, basing this on their enzymatic content, lipo-protein composition, apparent involvement in metabolism, and especially their selectivity for Janus green B stain (with no other bodies so staining). Admittedly it was difficult to make distinctions in staining a green body green.

A better test is the demonstration of villiform interior structure typical of the protozoan mitochondrion. The electronmicrographs of Fauré-Fremiet *et al.* (1956) and Randall and Jackson (1958) clearly reveal mitochondria in stentors, but these bodies appear too large and much too few in number to correspond to the ecto-plasmic granules. It is possible that the latter, if they do in fact contain an oxidase, may be a new type of oxidative center different from mitochondria, located next to the ciliary rows to assist in their energy metabolism. Such alternating rows of "mitochondria" and cilia have been described in other ciliates by Horning (1927) and Turner (1940). Clearly, the function of these granules calls for further investigation. However these questions may be resolved, Andrews was probably right in saying that the degree of pigmenta-tion is a delicate indicator of the physiological state in stentors (see p. 274). Healthy *coeruleus* capable of long survival on slides are invariably well colored.

Nothing is known concerning the origin of the bodies in the granular stripes. In the blue *Folliculina ampulla*, closely related to stentors, Fauré-Fremiet (1932) found many blue granules very close to the macronucleus yet he did not suggest that they were of nuclear origin. *Stentor coeruleus* also frequently shows pigmented granules surrounding the macronuclear nodes. Perhaps it is relevant to mention that when I grafted a nearly colorless *coeruleus* to another which was deeply pigmented the fusion mass became well pigmented throughout in the course of 4 hours, far more rapidly than in the usual regeneration of pigment in faded stentors left to themselves. A closer following of such cases as well as of the regeneration of pigment in animals which have been artificially depigmented through chemical treatments, or of similar studies on colorless stentors in which the granules have been artificially sloughed, would seem to offer considerable possibilities for obtaining clues regarding their origin.

The chemical nature of the pigments themselves is of interest. Of these there seem to be three, as Johnson remarked: the blue-green which gives the name to *coeruleus* and is probably also found in the similarly colored *introversus*, *multiformis* and *amethystinus*, if not in the related blue Folliculinids; the brown pigment in *niger* and possibly also in Johnson's *nigricans* variety of *S. igneus;* and a purplish-red in *igneus* which may be the same as the zoopurpurin of *Blepharisma*. Only the first two have so far been studied.

The pigment of *coeruleus* was given the name "stentorin" by Lankester (1873) in a pioneer work in which he remarked the extraordinary stability of this substance, not dissolved by fat solvents, acids, or alkalis. But Prowazek (1904) found that sulphuric acid turned it red, potassium hydroxide caused it to become grass-green and osmic salts changed it to black. Weisz (1950a) could bleach stentorin with chlorine gas or potassium permanganate followed by oxalic acid. Stentors of this species appear red by reflected light and blue-green by transmitted (see frontispiece), which is also the appearance of blue Folliculinids (Andrews, 1923). Correspondingly, Lankester demonstrated two strong absorption bands, one in the red and one in the green.

Prowazek grew *coeruleus* at higher than normal temperatures and one of the effects he reported was that the animals often became more reddish and showed fluorescence, warming in general producing deeper hues of color. He also found that most animals which feed on *coeruleus* do not digest the pigment, though the color may be altered somewhat in passage through the alimentary canal, as specifically confirmed by Gelei (1925) for the worm *Stenostomum*. Only certain species of a worm(?), *Nuclearian*, which grew in some of Prowazek's stentor cultures could assimilate their pigment and become colored throughout. Cannibalizing stentors do not assimilate the pigment of their own species but concentrate and eject it as a dark green excretion vacuole, according to Gelei (1925) and Andrews (1955), and this has also been my impression. So also in the resorption of oral parts in the transformation of Folliculinids the blue pigment granules are not metabolized (Fauré-Fremiet, 1932; Andrews, 1949).

In *niger*, Maier (1903) noted that the yellow pigment was of the granules and could be dissolved by chloroform to give a red solution. This unique pigment was later studied by Barbier, Fauré-Fremiet, and Lederer (1956), who found it to be soluble in alcohol and of two components. A minor component was brown in color and eluted by ether. The major portion, eluted by ether with 2% ethanol, was a substance of red-violet color which they called "stentorol". The latter could be dried to a dark powder, showing in ultraviolet a red fluorescence which was changed to yellow or blue after various treatments. Absorption spectra were obtained using different solvents, leading to the identification of the pigment as a polycyclic hydroxyquinone. They were impressed by the resemblance to hypericum, a photodynamic substance originally discovered in plants of that name.

The nature of the pigment in the cortical granules of *coeruleus* has been reinvestigated and much enlarged upon by K. M. Møller (1960). Instead of Lankester's (1873) spectrometric absorption maxima of 662 mμ and 562 mμ he found with living or extracted stentors, only, a strong band at 618, a weaker one at 568, and a third and very weak band at 527 mμ. This difference can be explained on the basis that Lankester used stentors concentrated in the gut of an aquatic worm, which may have ingested photosynthetic organisms as well or even *S. polymorphus* with its algal symbionts. Stentorin itself does not resemble chlorophyll; and tests by Møller and C. Chapman-Andresen demonstrated that it has no photosynthetic action: *coeruleus* grown in the light do not incorporate C^{14} bicarbonate solution.

The predominant blue-green pigment is indeed resistant to solubilization but is dissolved in acetone–water and completely extracted by ethylenediamine. Solutions, like the living stentors, are dichromatic and appear green by transmitted and red by reflected light, but this is no proof of fluorescence. However, Møller discovered that some races of *coeruleus* have an additional, ethanol-extractable pigment in the cortical granules which renders them red fluorescent in ultraviolet light of wave lengths from 366 to 590 mμ. Because the fluorescence appears only after these stentors are dead or dying — as when dried on filter paper or killed with boiling water — he inferred that the pigment is probably bound to some protein (or carbohydrate) carrier which uniquely quenches the fluorescence in living animals. The production of this fluorescence is a nuclear-dependent character (see p. 322). Møller and A. H. Whiteley (unpublished) found the alcohol-extracted pigment or aqueous homogenates only of fluorescent stentors to be photolethal (killing action of pigment plus strong light) to *Paramecium caudatum*, *Colpidium*, and to the stentors themselves but not to non-fluorescent *coeruleus*. Yet living fluorescent stentors seemed to affect non-fluorescent animals, but not the reverse, in the same medium (separated by a screen) causing the latter to become colorless, smaller in size, and even fluorescent.

Both the fluorescent and the major pigment not extractable by ethanol are in their spectrometric and chemical properties different from yet quite similar to hypericin, a photolethal substance previously found only in certain plants, which is phototoxic to herbivores. These tests by Møller showed that the pigments which may comprise stentorin apparently belong to the mesonaphthodianthrone group of compounds also including the photodynamic pigments hypericin and phagopyrin. The function of pigments in *coeruleus* is still unknown. Like the apparently related chromatic substances of *niger* they may render these stentors sensitive to light. Alternatively or in addition, if the pigment in *igneus* is the same as that in *Blepharisma* which Giese (1949) found to be toxic to certain other protozoa, and if that of at least certain if not all races of *coeruleus* and *niger* be phototoxic to some predators as eaten, then stentor pigments might have some protective value for their bearers.

(c) CLEAR STRIPES AND THEIR FIBER SYSTEMS

In the living animal the highly differentiated clear stripes show a row of cilia on their left margin and in the center a wide, subpellicular band best revealed by polarized light or phase microscopy. This band doubtless represents the original "Muskelfaser" described by Lieberkuhn in 1857. Later students of this minute structure (notably Schuberg, 1890; Johnson, 1893; Nerescheimer, 1903; Schröder, 1907; Dierks, 1926a; and Gelei, 1926) published varying accounts of its precise nature which are now rendered obsolete by recent studies with electron microscopy. Earlier accounts agree, however, that these bands run the length of the animal, branch and rebranch in correspondence with the clear stripes, are tapered toward the anterior end but much thickened posteriorly, in cross-section appearing pendent from the pellicle adjacent to the ciliary rows as shown in Fig. 10C, being contractile in function and hence deserving the name myoneme. The possibility of fiber connectives between the basal granules of the cilia, presumably required for their coordinated movement and universally found in ciliates through subsequent study of silver–line and infraciliature systems, was completely neglected.

After the strained efforts with light microscopy, the EM studies come as a revelation, though partially anticipated by Gelei (1926). To date, we have the reports of Fauré-Fremiet and Rouiller (1955), Randall (1956), Fauré-Fremiet, Rouiller and Gauchery (1956) and Randall and Jackson (1958). Fig. 10A attempts to combine in one diagram the accounts of these two groups insofar as they concern fibers lying under the clear stripes.

It is now seen that the bands immediately underlying the clear stripes are of lamellæ, stacked edgewise and attached to each other as well as to the pellicle by their outer margins, their inner edges lying free. Each lamella is composed of a stack or layer of very fine fibrils, regularly spaced, adjacent lamellæ being connected by even finer processes.

According to the French workers the main body of this lamellation, which we shall refer to empirically as the ribbon bundle, constitutes the "ectomyoneme", a contractile organ of unique structure. Number of lamellæ varies with the level of the body. The ribbon nearest the ciliary row, somewhat different in shape and often separated from the other lamellæ, was identified as the kinetodesma which they supposed to connect the kinetosomes or basal bodies of the cilia, and the whole was referred to as the myociliary complex. This connection was demonstrated by the British workers whose photographs indicate that all lamellæ in the pile achieve connection with cilia. They therefore called the ribbon bundle the "km band", suggesting that all parts are possibly involved both in ciliary coordination and in contraction. Fibers leave the bundle and bifurcate as they attach to opposite sides of a kinetosome, corresponding to the peduncles observed by Villeneuve-Brachon (1940) in light microscopy. It was further suggested that a given fiber may terminate forward on one kinetosome and posteriorly on another, presumably facilitating coordination of ciliary beating.

Either the restricted kinetodesma of Fauré-Fremiet et al. or the entire km band of Randall and Jackson follows the rule of desmodexy (Chatton and Lwoff, 1935b) in that the fibrous connectives between the kinetosomes lie to their right; but otherwise the system is entirely different from the infraciliature of other ciliates, with the exception of Spirostomum (Randall, 1956). In other forms the interciliary fiber or kinetodesma appears simple and single, and transverse connectives between the kinetodesmata are often found. According to the pioneer work of Worley (1933, 1934) on coordination of body cilia in Stentor and two other ciliates, stentors do have these connectives and a metachronal wave down a line of cilia can escape around a small surface

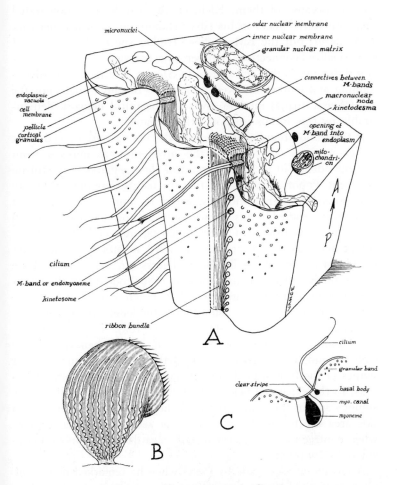

FIG. 10. Fine structure in *Stentor*.

A. Stereo-diagram showing structure revealed by electron-microscopy. (After Fauré-Fremiet *et al.*, 1956 and Randall, Jackson, 1958.)

B. Drawing of stentor beginning to re-extend, showing convolutions in the fibers of the clear stripes. (After Johnson, 1893.)

C. Section through ectoplasm showing parts distinguished by early microscopists. (After Schröder, 1907.)

incision because of them. Klein (1932) may have demonstrated such transverse fibers in his silver staining of a cortical network in *S. igneus*; but the EM studies of other species have revealed no specialized connections between adjacent rows. Another important difference is that the system in *Stentor* is refractive to silver–staining and neither the wet (Villeneuve-Brachon, 1940) nor the dry (Weisz, 1949a) method gives the beautiful network demonstrable by this means in most other ciliates.

If the ribbon bundles we are now discussing were indeed what earlier workers described as the myonemes, as appears from correspondence in location, certain of their remarks may still be pertinent. Popoff (1909) stated that the bands were not only more numerous but correspondingly wider in larger stentors, 57 of which were studied in this connection. Anteriorly, Schröder (1907) found fine extensions of their much-tapered ends leaving the cortex and passing inward and forward to attach to the outer margin of the membranellar band. Dierks (1926a) seems to have seen something like this too. Johnson (1893) noted that the bands are straight during contraction but much convoluted at the moment of beginning extension before the lengthening of the cell has again stretched them straight (Fig. 10B). This observation was confirmed by Fauré-Fremiet *et al.* as the behavior of the ribbon band. Gelei (1926) reported that the bands in the clear stripes of the frontal field are not tapering but of uniform thickness. In the expanded field he found the bands to be still slightly sinuous and in the contracted field they were strongly coiled. In this area the bands therefore did not seem to become straight when contraction occurs, yet he still regarded their function elsewhere as contractile.

A nice point was made by Gelei when he remarked that if the fibers responsible for sharp contraction were fastened only at their anterior and posterior ends they would, on developing a tension, pull to the center of the cell and not form an arc following the contour of the surface as is in fact observed. Contraction would then draw the cell into the shape of a much-flattened sphere. (Incidentally this very shape, with corresponding retraction of the frontal disc, actually occurs in *introversus*, in which the disposition of the contractile fibers may therefore be quite different from that in all other known species of *Stentor*.) Therefore Gelei postulated that the contractile bands were attached at successive points to the "epimuscular band", by which I think he meant the pellicular clear stripe. The ectomyonemes or *km* bands fulfill this requirement in their connection with the pellicle. And this connection not only allows the bands to draw the whole cell into a compact sphere rather than merely pulling the head and foot together, but also makes possible the continued contraction of isolated fragments because the bands need no end anchors. It might even make possible the independent contraction of different sections of the band, thus accounting for Dierks observation that in simple contraction the anterior part of the band shortens while the posterior part remains unthickened and thrown into curves, itself straightening and thickening if super-contraction follows. If indeed contractile, the ribbon bundles as muscles should have their antagonists (Ishikawa, 1912), which would be whatever is responsible for drawing out the cell. Elasticity of the pellicle may be one factor here and the accessory bands shortly to be mentioned another, but this matter is quite uncertain.

Lying interior to the ribbon bundles, Fauré-Fremiet *et al.* made out a layer of trabecular cytoplasm which in the study of Randall and Jackson seemed to be another set of bands under the clear stripes, tapered forward, wider posteriorly, and having transverse connectives (Fig. 10A). In their composition, these bands and their connectives showed only short fibrils more or less randomly arranged but tending to align with the axis and not orderly stacking of long fibers. This is the type of structure Fauré-Fremiet and his associates find in the "endomyonemes" of stalked ciliates like *Vorticella*. Therefore these bands may be contractile. Accordingly, Randall and Jackson referred to them as "M bands". The transverse connections may be what Prowazek (1913) observed *in vivo:* delicate transverse connections between the substance of the clear stripes in the expanded ectoplasm of stentors "exploding" or deliquescing on the surface film. Randall and Jackson found that these transverse connections between the M bands were prominent posteriorly but fewer at the forward end of the animal. Their demonstration that the matrix of the bands is continuous with that of the connectives would seem to imply that action of the latter could not be independent, say, in causing extension of the animal.

Extension of stentors to over six times their length when maximally contracted calls for an adequate explanation but is still a mystery. Randall and Jackson's report states that the volume is quadrupled on extension but I think they must have meant the surface area.

Walls of the M bands as described by the British workers are surprisingly indefinite, becoming confluent with endoplasmic vesicles so that the bands are very intimately related to the endoplasm, and this could account for the trabecular appearance observed by the French investigators. These bands seemed to have no connection with the pellicle, which of course poses the problem of how they could produce the movement of anything but themselves. One also wonders why stentors should have two parallel contractile bands when one would seem to be sufficient. These and other problems of structure and function we hope will be resolved by further studies in this actively developing field. Apropos of this, Causin's (1931) surprising statement may be repeated: that although a cut into the side of a stentor is followed by prompt healing and does not initiate the formation of a regeneration primordium, there results nevertheless a cryptic resorption and replacement of the myonemes. This observation should certainly be checked.

In addition to understanding the static structure and short-time activities of the cortex, we need to learn how its elements grow and dedifferentiate, develop and increase in number, as well as how they manage surprising performances in mending and realignment after cutting and other gross disturbances. These capabilities seem contradictory to the fineness and complexity of the structures present and tax the imagination to conceive how they are possible.

(d) FIBER SYSTEMS OF DOUBTFUL STATUS

Still other types of fibers have been reported in the clear stripes. They were located adjacent to the myonemes and described as unvarying in thickness and convoluted in the contracted animal, therefore presumably nervous in function and not contractile. We have to call them doubtful because these reports did not present at the same time a clear description or, indeed, indicate any awareness of possible kinetodesmata. Neresheimer (1903) seems to have had a bias for completing the roster of "tissues" in *Stentor* by identifying nerve structures. Following him closely and yet insisting on the uniqueness of what he had found, Dierks (1926a) also sought a nervous system because he thought that the coordinated behavior of *Stentor* implied its existence.

Neresheimer called his fibers "neurophanes" to contrast them with "myophanes", the term used by Haeckel for the myonemes. In retrospect Neresheimer seems to have stained and been examining the ribbon bundles, which may indeed have a nervous function if they serve to coordinate the body cilia. But in whole mounts he could follow these bands only from the posterior end to the middle of the cell. Along this course the fibers branched and some of them ended in minute bulbs or boutons which he regarded as sensory but which Dierks and Gelei (1926) thought to be mere optical artifacts. Most of the study was on pieces of ectoplasm loosed from the animal by treatment with methylene blue, and Schröder (1907) criticized the results as artifacts from injury and distortion. In reply, Neresheimer (1907) admitted that he could not find his neurophanes in all preparations but insisted that they were evident in some. Apparently he saw something of the ribbon bundles but could not divine their intimate structure and actual extent. To demonstrate that his fibers were nervous in function he treated stentors with drugs which act as nervous excitants and depressants in metazoa and found they had a similar effect on stentors but not on other ciliates in which "neurophanes" are lacking.

The fibers described by Dierks were called "neuroids". He pictured them as running close to but above the myonemes (ribbon bundles) and present throughout their entire extent, either ending in these bands or sending side branches to them. The "neuroids" may very well have been kinetodesmata or strips torn loose from the ribbon bundles, as Villeneuve-Brachon suggested. In any event, nothing like them has so far been found with the superior resolution of the electron microscope.

Although Dierks (1926a) himself questioned why stentors should need "nerves" when the myonemes are so intimately in contact with other parts of the cell, he nevertheless considered the "neuroids" nervous in function. This assumption was based on the response of stentors to the potassium ion which causes them to relax in the extended state as if the "neuroids" were anæsthetized;

E

but on fixing the animals always contracted, as if the myonemes were then being stimulated directly by the fixing agent.

Simultaneously, Gelei (1926) found the ribbon bundle exterior to the "endomyonemes" and described it quite accurately within the limits of light microscopy. Identical in location to the so-called neurophane or neuroid, he regarded this fibrous band as giving support and attachment to the myonemes, therefore "skeletal" in function.

(e) THE CILIA

Cilia comprising the oral membranelles are evidently not only longer but also of larger diameter than the body cilia, according to Randall and Jackson. They found that the body cilia of *poly-morphus* measured 20 μ in length, while in light microscopy they appear to be 10 μ (Andrews, 1945, found them to be 13 μ in *coeruleus*). This discrepancy may be due in large part to the fact that the cilia have very fine tips, not easily visible. Thus, in a pioneer work of Schuberg (1905) on *coeruleus* cilia stained by the Golgi method it was shown that the proximal two-thirds of the cilium stains darker and is of uniform diameter, the distal third being much narrower and pointed at the end. Because the freed cilia were curved, he foretold the view now generally held, that the contraction of the cilium is intrinsic. He also noted that fixation seems to preserve the cilia in phases of their rhythmic beating, thus anticipating the interesting work of Párducz (1953). This general picture was confirmed with the electron microscope by Randall and Jackson whose figures also show that the fine tip is prolonged into the length of the wider portion as its axis.

Randall and Jackson unmistakably show that at the posterior end of the cell the body cilia are paired and no longer form a single row, raising the question of how in division the proter, acquiring a new posterior end out of the middle parts of the cell, could develop a double row. Possibly there is new growth there, as Johnson first suggested.

Electron microscopy reveals in stentors the universal fine structure of the cilium. The outer layer is continuous with the pellicle and the axis shows the typical 9+2 fibers (Fauré-Fremiet and Rouiller, 1955; Randall and Jackson, 1958). A characteristic septum or basal plaque was found at the level of the cell surface where the two central fibers end, and there also is to be seen a "kinetosome" or ampule terminating the central fibers. According to the latter report, the base of the cilium, with its prolongation of the peripheral fibers, continues inward as a cylinder without rootlets extending into the endoplasm but sometimes showing minute granules in longitudinal rows along its cylindrical wall.*

6. Fine structure of the nuclei

Light microscopists describe the matrix of the macronucleus as of homogeneous granules in a sort of meshwork with one clear spherule, the nucleolus, usually found in each node of a chain nucleus. The nuclear membrane swells loose in distilled water as a highly birefringent and therefore well-organized layer; significantly like the shell of the pigment granules, its composition was indicated to be phospholipid (Weisz, 1949a). Resting on the macronuclear membrane, Park (1929) described osmiophilic, bleb-like bodies, 1 to 22 for each node. He suggested that they might be secretory droplets, reminiscent of the parabasal body associated with the nucleus in flagellates.

Electronmicrographs reveal further details (Fauré-Fremiet and Rouiller, 1955; Randall and Jackson, 1958). The granules within the macronucleus turn out to be clusters of filaments, possibly beaded, these masses being more or less equidistantly spaced within a clear nuclear sap. The outer layer of the macronucleus is porous, showing curious tubular processes extending and branching into the endoplasm, while the inner membrane appears to be a system of tubular vesicles joined by sheets, resembling spaghetti laminated in plastic.

In his cytochemical studies, Weisz (1949a, 1950b) made Feulgen and Millon tests which indicate that protein and nucleotide or potential nucleotides are homogeneous in concentration in the macronucleus at all times, except of course during conjugation when the old macronucleus is resorbed. His methyl green tests suggested however that the nucleotide—desoxyribonucleic acid—

---

*From observations on stentor membranelles, Sleigh (1960) ingeniously integrated motor and recovery strokes of cilia as resulting from one wave of localized contractions passing up and around the cilium, the propulsive phase occurring when bending starts on one side at the base and the rest of the cilium is straight.

varies in degree of polymerization along the nuclear chain. Fauré-Fremiet and Rouiller speak of this DNA as in the form of microsomes. In dark-field illumination I have found that the exposed macronuclear nodes are often a glowing light blue, which may indicate something of their composition or state as affecting the scattering of light.

The micronuclei of stentors were first described by Maupas (1879) and later by Johnson (1893). These very small nuclei reside on or near the macronuclear chain. Multiplying mitotically, they are typically chromosomal, as further substantiated by their behavior during conjugation (see p. 329).

7. The endoplasm

The interior cytoplasm was examined by Weisz (1949a) who found that it did not stain with basic dyes and only diffusely with acidic. Neutral red was taken up by the living *coeruleus* and stained various inclusions so that stentor may be said to have a "vacuome"; this dye was segregated by the contractile vacuole. Chromidial nets and metachromatic volutin granules were not present.

By introducing minute electrodes into the cell, Gelfan (1927) went to much trouble to prove that the electrolyte concentration in *Stentor* is higher than that in the surrounding fresh water medium, a conclusion which could have been inferred from the pulsation of the contractile vacuole in voiding water imbibed through osmosis. The specific conductance was lower in stentors than in three other ciliates tested. Internal conductivity decreased with injury, presumably due to the leakage of electrolytes from the cell.

The endoplasm of stentors presents a foamy appearance which was first emphasized by Butschli in keeping with his theory of the alveolar nature of protoplasm. Correspondingly, Randall and Jackson found by electron microscopy that the endoplasm consists of numerous vacuoles within a matrix which shows many small particles and vesicles. An endoplasmic reticulum was not revealed. The vacuoles have a definite membrane and seem to be especially numerous in the sub-cortical regions. Within the endoplasm are also found typical protozoan mitochondria. Randall and Jackson (1958) found them to be Janus green B positive and having triple membranes of equal width, if one counts the material between outer and inner layers as the third. The enclosed tubular vesicles terminate on the inner membrane. Both membrane and vesicle walls showed small opaque particles and the interstices gave the appearance of a finely particulate matrix. Empty mitochondria were found, as well as others without bounding membranes amongst the normal forms of these bodies, reminding one of Weisz's (1949a) suggestion that the mitochondria are utilized in starvation and regeneration.

Food reserves are also present in the form of fat droplets and glycogenoid granules. In addition, *multiformis* and *introversus* have yellow, brightly refringent bodies or crystals in the endoplasm, the nature of which has not yet been determined.

Altogether, this detail of fine structure represents about as extensive and intensive a cytodifferentiation as we are likely to find, comparing favorably with that of the most complex hypermastigont flagellates in arthropods and ruminant commensal ciliates. The number of definable parts which have been "compacted" into the minute volume of a stentor is quite amazing and attests the extremely fine-grain structure possible to organisms. For instance, there are about 32,500 fibers in the complement of ribbon bundles or *km*-bands alone, not to mention the countless cortical granules, etc. Not only in number but in their greater diversity the minute parts of an organism like *Stentor* stand in contrast to the cytodifferentiation of most tissue cells. This difference in manifest complexity is one of the reasons why some biologists have hesitated if not refused to call protozoa cells or unicellular forms. Yet a stentor represents no more or less a separate nucleocytoplasmic system than a neurone. And a bridge between protozoan and tissue cell may perhaps be found in the egg; for if one refuses to call a fertilized egg a cell, all seem to agree that its cleavage products are cells and from either of the first two cells, let us say, the whole complex multicellular organism can be derived by embryogenesis. It may therefore not be too much to infer that such a cell is intrinsically as complex as *Stentor*, if not more so, but manifesting this complexity in development through multicellularity instead of more directly in itself.

What, then, shall we "do" with all the complex cytodifferentiation we find in *Stentor*? One approach is to study, if possible, certain types of parts in themselves. For example, the *km*-bands may represent a unique contractile structure the elucidation of which might define a specific parameter of muscle physiology. This is the orientation of Randall and his co-workers. Or by emphasizing differences in the parts of descendant individuals one might explore new aspects of genetics such as the importance of cytoplasmic inheritance, as in the work of Sonneborn; and potentially this approach could be most fruitful in *Stentor* in which micrurgical exchange of cytoplasms and nuclei is not difficult.

One may also consider all the fine structure from the standpoint of epigenetics or morphogenesis. Obviously the criterion of regeneration and other types of epigenetic performance, is the fine structure also what "does" the morphogenesis? Is the fine structure the cause or the result of morphogenesis? For instance, in the simple healing of an incision in *Stentor* the ribbon bundles and their many fibers in the clear stripes apparently rejoin; therefore in addition to their function of conduction and contraction have these fibers also the capacity for guiding their reintegration? In some way of which we have yet no understanding all the fine structure is integrated, an obvious inference from the integrity of the organism and its normative tendencies which will receive specific documentation as we proceed into the experimental studies. It is as if, in addition to its specific physiological functions, every meridional unit of a stentor "knows" when one of the mouthparts is missing or the oral structures are misplaced, for all seem to cooperate in correcting the deviation from the norm, some parts, often quite distant from each other yet somehow in effective communication, taking the leading roles.

For example, if the head is rotated 180° on the body, the mouthparts disconnect from the membranellar band, migrate into the frontal field and are resorbed—this specific disjunction and taking down of structures being in its way a compounding of the marvel of their original construction. Then, in a far distant part of the cell a new oral primordium begins on some signal, and experiment indicates that all parts of the cortex support anlage formation and are involved in the timing of its development.

But this is to anticipate a part of our story, yet such phenomena pose the further problem of the integration of all the parts of *Stentor* in terms of the fine structure we have described if not some further principle.

CHAPTER V

GROWTH AND DIVISION

1. Growth

Division in *Stentor* is of course usually preceded by growth to the definitive size. Authentic structural growth and de-growth occur, as well as stretching of parts. The first is seen, for example, as increase in the number of lateral clear stripes with their fibrous elaborations; the second, in resorption of striping or macronuclear nodes under various conditions; and the potentialities for stretching are shown when small patches of ectoplasm come to cover the surface (see Fig. 25A) or when isolated nodes change from round to spindle form (see Fig. 82A). We still have no comprehensive understanding of growth in the individual stentor cell and no investigator has yet addressed himself directly to this problem, but the pigmented stentors, especially, offer many advantages for such a study. In the first place, most stentors contract into a sphere and a fair estimate of their volume can be obtained by measuring one diameter. Grafted pairs can be identified by their pigmented stripes, which are often seen to increase both in number and in length (Fig. 11A). Natural markers sometimes are found in the cortex of the cell and indicate growth by their apparent displacement (B,C). Similar markers for following the growth of the ectoplasm could be made by small disturbances of the pigment striping, for the smaller these disarrangements are the longer they persist before correction (Schwartz, 1935).

Differential growth of major cell constituents is to be seen in the recovery of endoplasm in stentor "skins" (see Fig. 25B), as well as in the rapid recovery of the macronuclear mass when all but a single node has been removed from the cell (see Fig. 86c). In normal stentor cultures I have occasionally found specimens which were much longer than usual, with half the normal number of lateral stripes, as if growth in length had occurred at the expense of growth in width. On isolation this disparity was later corrected.

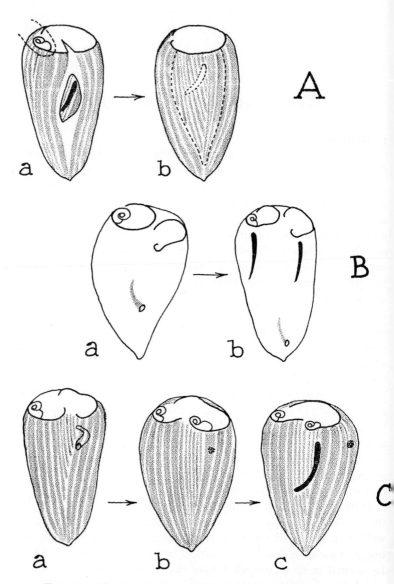

FIG. 11. Observations suggesting ways of studying growth in
stentors.

The lateral striping undoubtedly increases in length, though we do not know when or how this occurs. Johnson said that during division the striping at the posterior end of the future anterior daughter cell lengthens as a new tail pole is formed for it. But we do not know, for instance, how new body cilia in a growing longitudinal row could be interpolated between those already present, or whether cilia are added only at the end of a row, or increased in number only during fission.

Increase in the number of lateral stripes is much more obvious. Brauer (1885) first suggested that the shorter stripes which do not run from pole to pole are new ones resulting from multiplication, and that pigment stripes multiply by the interpolation of a new clear stripe was proposed by Johnson (1893). The number of granular and clear stripes increases with the size of the animal. Largest specimens of *coeruleus* have about 100 stripes of either kind. Tiny individuals from starving samples which were about one-sixteenth the maximum cell volume had approximately 66 stripes of either type. When a cell divides transversely, the division products have about 80 stripes of each kind at their circumference because about 20 are carried into the frontal field of the opisthe or posterior daughter cell. Presumably, interfissional increase is from 80 to 100 as the volume is doubled. The number of stripes thus increases with the volume but less rapidly, some of the surface increase probably being accommodated by widening of the granular stripes. These remarks agree well with earlier conclusions of Popoff (1909).

A. A case of differential increase in length and breadth of a grafted patch. *a:* Patch bearing primordium grafted into back of a host from which mouthparts were then excised. *b:* Primordium resorbed but length and number of stripes of the graft also promptly increased.

B. Shift in relative location of a tube formation. *a:* Grafted pair developed an adventitious, gullet-like tube. *a:* In process of reorganization-regeneration next day, with tube now displaced far posteriorly, possibly indicative of differential growth and resorption in the ectoplasm.

C. Problems of growth indicated by another marker. *a:* Grafted pair developed a tube which was resorbed (*b*) leaving patch of dense pigment granules at the surface. *c:* Specimen reorganizing two days later with pigment clot now far to left of primordium site.

Very small species of *Stentor*, like *multiformis*, are not miniatures of the larger since they contain fewer stripes which are therefore relatively much wider in proportion to the cell volume.

The lateral stripes tend toward a certain maximum number. When stentors were cut in two longitudinally, slender fragments were produced which had half the normal complement of stripes. The aboral halves not bearing the mouthparts were followed because stripe increase in them is more easily seen than in oral halves with their finer stripes, as Stevens (1903) noted. Stripe multiplication occurred at the line of heal (Tartar, 1956c), and in 5 days the specimens regained the normal width and number of

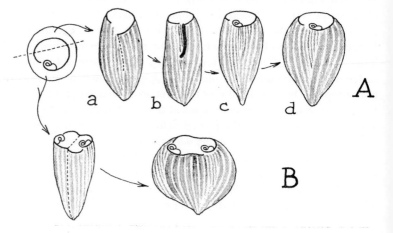

FIG. 12. Increase in lateral striping.

A. Non-oral longitudinal half has less than half the normal number of stripes (*a*). *b:* New fine granular-stripes appear as regeneration primordium forms at suture. Continued splitting of granular bands with interpolated clear stripes (*c*) increases stripes to the normal number (*d*).

B. Parabiotic graft of two oral halves has somewhat more than the normal number of lateral stripes yet increases the complement to near 2*N*, in correlation with the double individuality.

stripes (Fig. 12A). When two of the oral longitudinal halves were grafted together in homopolar parabiosis producing artificially a more than normal sum of stripes, stripe increase still occurred and very wide doublets with about twice the normal number of stripes were produced (Fig. 12B). From such experiments we may eventually learn how the number of lateral stripes and fibrous bands is controlled.

Stripe multiplication apparently can occur in any meridian of the cell. When it occurs on the dorsal side where the pigment stripes are wide, the pigmented stripes seem very quickly to attain the width normal for that area after they have been split in two by the interpolation of new clear stripes. Figure 13 thus shows

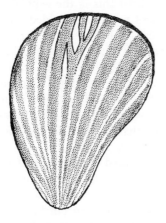

Fig. 13. Specimen suggesting that splitting of granular stripes in wide-stripe area quickly leads to broadening of these stripes in harmony with those adjacent.

branches of the pigment stripes as wide as the "stem". This illustration also demonstrates that the splitting of the granular stripes can occur in either direction. But the greatest stripe increase occurs at a specific region in the side of the cell where the mouthparts are located. This area has become a key to stentor morphogenesis.

Brauer (1885) had early described in *coeruleus* that posterior to the mouth there is a "fiber which may give up to 10 secondary members lying against each other". Essentially this triangular area is a place where about 25 clear stripes and an equal number of alternating pigmented bands do not run all the way to the posterior pole but are bounded on each side by stripes which do (see Fig. 1). Since the stripes become shorter as they approach the left boundary stripe and because that stripe takes something of a diagonal course, the appearance is that the left boundary stripe is branching. Schuberg (1890) therefore called this area the "ramifying zone", evidently the area of stripe multiplication and also the site of the oral primordium. In the left anterior corner of this triangle the widest pigment stripes begin splitting into narrow stripes. As the split proceeds posteriorly the next wide stripe to the left begins splitting, with the result that a series of stripes of ever increasing length is formed to the right and the characteristic ramifying zone is thus achieved. At least this is the general impression, though other details doubtless need to be added. If so, growth takes a spiral course, as it were, with the zone of increase gradually moving to the animal's left as new short stripes are added and older stripes to the right increase in length until they reach the posterior pole. Correspondingly, the oral primordium which appears in this zone would continually shift leftward, with the result that new mouth parts appear always somewhat to the left of those preceding. Such spiral growth recalls that of the fruiting body in certain fungi (Delbrück and Reichardt, 1956).

We have already remarked that pigment stripes are mere fill-ins and their splitting is doubtless due to the emergence within them of new clear stripes with their ciliary rows and fibrous structures. Each new clear stripe would then not be connected with others, corresponding to the description of Villeneuve-Brachon (1940). Later the clear stripes do join together and cut off the split branches of a pigment band. Older figures thus show fibrous structures of the clear stripes as branching and re-branching in the ramifying zone. From what we now know about kineties and myonemes it is evident that anastomosis would entail great structural difficulties and we have to leave this problem until appropriate EM studies are available. Because the number of stripes tends toward a fixed upper limit, the need for stripe multiplication may therefore vary, possibly being minimal in stentors that have lived for a long time without dividing. This would account for the observations of Johnson, and much later of Dierks, that the ramifying zone is variable in its aspect, sometimes even unidentifiable as such.

Multiplication of clear stripes could not occur by simple splitting since this would leave one branch with cilia and one without. One branch would have to migrate sub-cortically and then push up through the adjacent pigmented stripe somehow. Apparently the new clear stripes with all their attendant complex differentiations arise *in situ*, but of their origin we know nothing. If we accept the genetic continuity of the kinetosomes and regard them as fibrogenic granules which produce not only the cilia but also the fibrils of the ribbon bundles in the clear stripes (see Lwoff, 1950), the new kinetosomes will have to be traced to their progenitors.

Growth of other parts of the stentor cell present their own special problems. The young daughter cell has a membranellar band proportionate in length to its size. When full-grown the length has increased and is still proportionate. Morgan (1901a) therefore thought that this organelle grows in length and implied that the number of membranelles increases. But if this were so, *Stentor* would need two ways of producing membranelles: through primordium formation and *in situ*. If the length of the membranellar band is abbreviated by cutting, compensating growth does not occur, contrary to a dubious observation of Stevens (1903). Therefore it seems more likely that increase in length is accomplished by the spreading apart of membranelles, already present, as obviously occurs during the development of the oral primordium. This point could be settled by counting the membranelles. Both the total mass and the surface area of the macronucleus increase, together or separately. Growth of the nucleus will be discussed in a chapter devoted to that organelle. For the present, we may merely remark that the trophic macronucleus, perhaps like the giant salivary gland chromosomes of insects, represents a form of nuclear material which adapts to the size of the cell and not vice versa (cf. Goldschmidt, 1940).

2. The course of normal division

From regeneration studies we may say that a stentor could multiply by simply cutting itself in two, the resulting daughters then regenerating those structures which they lack. This would be cell fission in the strict sense of the term and does occur under unusual conditions of experiment. A stentor might even cut itself into several fragments each of which would be viable, for neither the whole nor the half represents a minimum unit of potential organization. But in nature division is accomplished by trans-

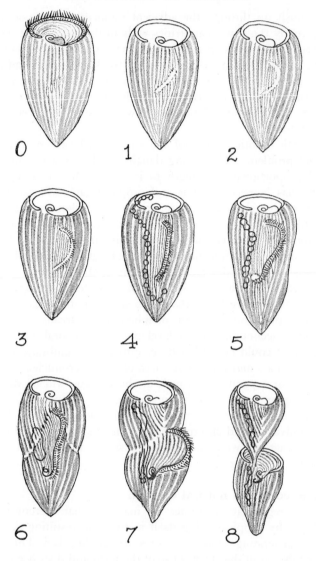

FIG. 14. Stages in division as seen in living *S. coeruleus*.
Stage 0. First indication of fission: a splitting of granular
bands at the bulk-center of the cell on the oral side. (Fine striping
of frontal field and ciliary membranelles shown here but omitted
in remaining sketches.)

forming the parent organism into two individualities the morphologies of which come to exclude each other and are finally separated by fission. To paraphrase one of the ablest students of *Stentor:* the situation in ciliates is the reverse of that in metazoa since all

---

Stage 1. Initial appearance of oral primordium for the posterior daughter cell, as a transverse rift in the lateral ectoplasm.

Stage 2. Primordium enlarges by extending anteriorly with a new curvature to the right. Anlage has a faint glisten in reflected light but no cilia are apparent yet.

Stage 3. Primordium increases in length and membranellar cilia are visible but not yet grown to their final length. Continued multiplication of striping within curvature of the anlage.

Stage 4. Primordium grown to nearly its full length and oral cilia are organized into closely-packed membranelles which beat in slow metachronal rhythm. Moniliform macronucleus still shows no change.

Stage 5. An enlargement or etched space appears at posterior end of the primordium, site of the future mouthparts. Anlage now embraces many fine stripes. Macronuclear nodes begin fusing.

Stage 6. Posterior end of membranellar band coils inward sharply to form gullet and cytostome. During this stage severing of stripes begins at each side of anterior end of the primordium and progresses on both sides around the cell to form the fission furrow. Macronucleus fused to a compact mass. Fading or partial dedifferentiation of oral pouch and gullet, begun at stage 5, is now at its maximum.

Stage 7. Primordium migrates posteriorly, its anterior end being cut out of the anterior daughter cell whose stripes heal together at once in a herringbone pattern which will for a long time distinguish proter from opisthe. Gullet and cytostome are now nearly complete and fine striping enclosed by the anlage is being carried forward as the new frontal field. Compact macronucleus elongates to rod shape and begins renodulation from the ends.

Stage 8. Oral pouch is now formed as an inpocketing of the frontal field adjacent to the cytostome. Primordium migrates to its definitive position at anterior end of opisthe and body striping becomes parallel to the membranellar band. Rod-shaped macronucleus is divided by constriction of the furrow which has nearly separated the daughter cells and formed the new posterior pole of the proter. Mouthparts of proter redefined, membranellar band probably proportionately reduced from length in original cell. Fission products then twist apart. (After Tartar, 1958c.)

the "embryology" occurs before instead of after reproduction (Johnson, 1893). (An exception is found in budding, such as chain formation in lower worms in which new individualities are completely formed before separation, an analogy with protozoan reproduction first suggested by Gruber (1885a).) A self-cutting or fission line is indeed formed in *Stentor*, but it is neither the cause nor the necessary result of the conversion of one individuality into two.

Multiplication by fission in *Stentor* was first observed by Trembley (1744). With continued refinement of the microscope, further details of division were given by Stein (1867), Moxon (1869), and Cox (1876); yet it remained for Schuberg (1890) to provide the first really comprehensive account of what takes place. *Stentor* division as a developmental process was beautifully and accurately drawn in the illustrations of Johnson (1893) and Schwartz (1935). Visible changes during division have been designated as a numbered series of stages (Tartar, 1958c) and are shown in Fig. 14.

Restricting the story to the best-known species, *coeruleus*, the first sign of the formation of a new individuality is a splitting of the pigment stripes on a diagonal in the mid-ventral region (Fig. 14-o), first noted by Stevens (1903) and very probably representing the insertion of new clear bands. In this area of stripe multiplication a rift soon appears as the very beginnings of the new set of feeding organelles for the future posterior daughter cell. This primordium lengthens at both ends according to Johnson and broadens quickly to its definitive width while the long oral cilia develop within it. At this time the anlage is usually in the form of a crescent and this appearance is generally diagnostic of an early divider. (Occasionally the anterior end of the primordium may extend straight forward towards the old oral region, as it does in reorganizing animals, so one cannot always be sure.) There is increasing multiplication of stripes as pigment bands at the anterior border of the primordium split into 2, 4, and 8 rows (Fig. 15A) (Schwartz, 1935). It is these new, fine stripes embraced by the presumptive membranellar band which will form the new frontal field of the opisthe. Such additions may increase the circumference of the cell according to Stevens and Schwartz, though this is certainly not obvious.

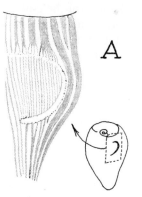

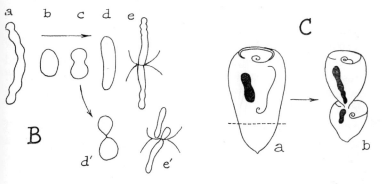

FIG. 15. Details of division in *S. coeruleus*.

A. Eight, four and two-fold splitting of granular bands to produce the fine bands of the new frontal field enclosed by a stage–2 primordium. The number of interpolated kineties (clear stripes) is correspondingly increased.

B. Macronuclear division according to Johnson, showing clumping of nodes, followed by rod formation, pinching in two of the nucleus by the dividing cell and beginning renodulation. A preliminary constriction of the massed nucleus (*c*) may go to completion (*d′*) with larger portion extending into and contributing to the nucleus of the proter. (After Johnson, 1893.)

C. Persisting fission in late divider after posterior excision; rod-form macronucleus distributes itself accordingly and is unequally — but proportionately — divided. (After de Terra, 1959.)

F

Continuing its development, the posterior end of the primordium begins to coil inward to form the gullet (stage 6). At this time the cell usually shows a central contraction tending slightly toward a dumbbell shape, but this constriction is not coincident with the future furrow (Johnson) and makes its appearance earlier, as our figure shows.

A fission line then appears at both sides of the anterior end of the primordium. To the right it cuts off the presumptive frontal-field striping and runs approximately perpendicular to these stripes which have been somewhat distorted by the movements of the anlage. To the left, the furrow runs sharply posteriorly while cutting obliquely across the wide granular stripes in this area, the two ends of the fission line moving more and more transversely as they proceed around the cell to meet on the lower dorsal side. By being oblique, the furrow can cut the primordium, which runs far anteriorly, into the posterior cell and yet divide the parent into approximately equal daughters. The fission line is made evident by a change in the pigmented stripes which leaves a colorless band across each one. Possibly this may be caused by the formation of new transverse contractile structures, pushing the granules aside and later responsible for constriction at the furrow.

Only when the membranellar band is fully formed and the gullet begins to develop (stage 5–6) does the macronucleus undergo a relatively rapid series of changes. At this time the nodes of the nucleus begin to coalesce within the common nuclear membrane. According to Johnson, this fusion occurs at separate loci because it sometimes may result in a premature breaking of the chain. Eventually the nucleus is compacted into one more or less spherical mass in the center of the cell, though unsuccessful enucleation experiments performed at this time indicate that occasionally one or more nodes may remain isolated. Johnson described the clumped nucleus as then showing a preliminary constriction which lasts for about half an hour, then disappearing as the nucleus elongates into a rod (Fig. 15B). But sometimes this constriction was completed, the nucleus then and there separating into two parts, not always equal. When unequal, the larger part showed a secondary division later, resulting in a more equal allocation of the nuclear material. These observations of exceptional behavior, as well as the fact that division usually occurs later in the rod stage, indicate that clumping is not for the purpose of dividing the nucleus equally. Hence Johnson suggested that both the clumping and the preliminary constriction are a recapitulation of phylogeny, harking back to the form in fission of the nucleus in less specialized protozoa. Nor is there any evidence of macronuclear reorganization occurring during clumping; for Johnson found that the character of the macronuclear matrix remained unchanged and he stated explicitly that there was no indication of linear arrangement of threads or the formation of something like chromosomes.

At the earliest, a new contractile vacuole for the opisthe makes its appearance in the proper location at stage 4. Its formation is therefore probably not initiated by the division furrow, which is not yet visible, though Weisz (1951b) found that cutting the stripes of non-dividing stentors transversely would induce the temporary formation of a posterior vacuole and I have confirmed this.

As the division line cuts around its upper end, the primordium can bend more sharply and move backwards into the future opisthe. Schwartz described how the anlage shifts with reference to the striping on the left side so that these lines, at first parallel, come to lie at right angles to the new membranellar band. The cut ectoplasm of the future proter, or anterior daughter, closes together immediately as the primordium migrates posteriorly, with the result that a herringbone-pattern of stripes is formed which is somewhat asymmetrical because the furrow ran more sharply posteriorly on the left side. Anterior can be distinguished from posterior daughters long after separation because this pattern may persist for three days afterward in starved animals. Gradually the abbreviated stripes grow posteriorly to reproduce the typical ramifying zone.

In the meantime the anterior portion of the opisthe bearing the primordium has been bulging outward while gullet and oral pouch have been forming and shifting forward. The clumped macronucleus then elongates parallel to the main axis to form a long rod, which begins to nodulate simultaneously at both ends. As constriction continues the stripes of the proter are drawn together to form its tail and possibly extend in length as they narrow to a point. The half-nodulated macronucleus now divides in two; Johnson thought that its division is autonomous and the same is implied in Causin's (1931) report that even in regeneration the macronucleus can divide within the single cell, the separated parts then rejoining. Yet it has been found (Popoff, 1909; de Terra, 1959) that if cell division is unequal the macronucleus is likewise, quite as if this nucleus were passively pinched in two at the rod stage by the constricting furrow (Fig. 15c). The proter is now connected with the opisthe only by the tail pole, still attached at the aboral end of the latter's membranellar band; and up to this time the daughters have continued to coordinate their backward and forward swimming together (Gruber, 1886). Final separation seems to be due to a twisting apart which sunders the fine connection between the two cells.

According to Johnson's account the micronuclei swell and undergo mitosis after macronuclear division is completed, i.e., within the essentially separate daughters. Each daughter thus achieves about the same number of micronuclei as the parent cell. After completing nodulation there are about the same number of macronuclear beads in each product as there were in the original animal. Therefore these nodes are half the size of the original ones and nuclear growth consists largely of increase in the size of the new nodes, though occasionally one segment may later divide in two. This doubling of the nodes of the macronucleus was first noted by Balbiani (1882) and later confirmed by Johnson; Stolte; and Tartar (1959c). It is therefore plausible that the macronucleus clumps together to make possible its renodulation at once into twice the original number of nodes.

De Terra's (1959) studies on *coeruleus* have shown that the uptake and incorporation of radiophosphorus is very rapid before division but drops to one-twentieth of this rate when the macronucleus is compacted and fission is in process, indicating that nuclear increase does indeed occur by growth of the nodes and not when the nucleus is in the coalesced stage immediately preceding fission.

The time required to complete the act of division is probably quite variable but about 6 hours would be a reasonable average. The first stages having to do with primordium formation proceed more slowly. Fusion of the nodes of the macronucleus can occur in one hour according to Johnson and the nuclei renodulate as rapidly. Timing of the complex events in division presents special problems in the integrated action of the cell, and one possibility is that any specific event triggers the next following (see p. 295).

From the general description of division we see how the daughter cells are composed of parts both old and new. Endoplasm and nuclear material are halved, but the macronuclear beads are reconstituted and new micronuclei appear as division products of the old. The original feeding organelles go to the proter. They may undergo a slight dedifferentiation during fission, with the oral pouch temporarily disappearing as such, but there is no comprehensive regression and redifferentiation as in *Bursaria* (Schmähl, 1926) or *Condylostoma* (Villeneuve-Brachon, 1940). Nevertheless, the original oral structures which are at first too large are gradually reduced to proportionate measure in some manner which is not yet understood (Weisz, 1951b). The proter also retains the original contractile vacuole but it has to form a new tail-pole and holdfast. The original tail goes to the opisthe and is also at first too large, but the posterior daughter has a new set of oral structures formed entirely independently of the old. It also develops a new contractile vacuole, though this may be but an enlargement of contributory channels of the old. The striped ectoplasm is divided largely unchanged between the two daughters, although there may be a growing out of stripes and fibers in the formation of the new tail as there is also a post-fissional stripe multiplication in the opisthe to form a new ramifying zone (Schwartz, 1935). There is, however, a marked decrease in the number of lateral stripes because those in the ramifying zone are shifted to the frontal field. Presumably the old body cilia are passed on unchanged, for there is never a time when ciliation is lacking. One should keep in mind, however, the amazing possibility described by Schmähl for *Bursaria truncatella*, in which a ciliary molting seems to occur, resorption of old cilia and formation of new ones occurring simultaneously and therefore easily overlooked.

3. Nature and location of the fission line

We still know practically nothing of what happens at the division furrow. It seems highly improbable, as Johnson remarked, that the line represents the edge of a plane passing through the interior of the cell though Weisz (1956) conceived that there might be some sort of separation or pre-division of the endoplasm which later comes to expression on the surface. There is no obvious rupture in the surface of the cell as Schuberg (1890) first thought, for even with the most drastic manipulation of dividers no gaping or separation occurs along the fission lines. Yet it is reasonable to suppose that there is a severing of the granular stripes and fibrous structures in the clear stripes, because we know that the striping also has a strong tendency to heal together when cut and this proclivity would have to be overcome. The severance is, however, not necessarily irreversible. Popoff (1909) described one case and I have seen another in which division was aborted and the fission line disappeared without a trace, showing the pigment stripes again running continuously from pole to pole.

All that we can be certain of at present is that the pigment granules are moved away at the levels where the colored stripes cross the future furrow. Something of how this occurs may be shown in the aboral longitudinal half of a stage–4 divider which still continued on its course and attempted division. As shown in Fig. 16A, the granules at mid-level in each stripe were seen in one place to have shifted from the center of the stripe posteriorly and this may have been the prelude to the complete depigmentation of the stripes in the adjacent region. This appearance resembles that of stripe multiplication, and it is possible that new, short, posterior kineties were being introduced which pushed the pigment granules aside as they formed double rows of cilia demonstrated by Randall and Jackson for the new tail pole. The half-cell did not complete division, but it did form a secondary tail-pole, very likely because the body striping remained severed. This case is also significant in showing that although the furrow normally begins at the anterior end of the oral primordium this is not essential to furrow formation.

The fact that the fission line does not form all at once but progresses in two directions around the cell suggested to Weisz (1951b) that there are two waves of dissolution, each beginning at one point on a given stripe and spreading radially until it touches and sets off a new center of dissolution in the next adjacent intact stripe, like the firing of a fuse. This would not explain, however, why the fission line moves sharply posteriorly on one side of the primordium; nor why, in Stevens' (1903) observation of longitudinal halves of dividing stentors, the furrow stopped short by two pigment stripes on each side of the line of heal; nor why the line stops at "indifferent" striping (Fig. 16B). The latter blockage is probably not because the indifferent component is not in a "state of division" since Weisz (1951b) had shown that, although removal of patches of ectoplasm in the path of the presumptive furrow still

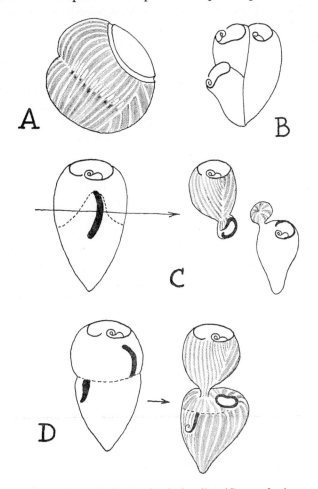

Fig. 16. Pertaining to the fission line (*S. coeruleus*).

A. Continuation of furrow formation in the non-oral half of divider cut longitudinally at stage 4. Note how pigment granules withdraw from the middle of granular stripes and accumulate posteriorly.

permits normal fission as the division line crosses the suture, if other ectoplasm from the same dividing animal is shifted to fill the gap the furrow then does not cross over. Evidently, as Weisz remarked, the path of the fission line is strongly and uniquely determined and cannot be initiated by local point-to-point processes alone.

Fixity of the presumptive furrow is shown by the observation, first reported by Johnson, that if the anterior or posterior end of a divider is cut off just before the furrow is to appear, unequal daughters are formed because the fission line appears in its normal place. If at the same stage a cell is prematurely divided by cutting, fission still occurs along the predetermined oblique path half of which lies in each fragment with the result that small blebs are separated (Fig. 16C). An artificial cutting of the body stripes is thus not used as a substitute for the normal fission line. Also, if pre-furrow dividers are cut through transversely, first on one side and then on the other so that the two halves remain fused together, division still occurs but it is oblique and not in the line of heal. Still more convincing is the experiment in which these cut halves are rotated 180° upon each other so that the body striping does not match or heal together, as evidenced by obvious discontinuities in the granular stripes; for even in this case relatively normal and equal division occurs with both parts of the severed primordium going to the opisthe and division was obviously not in the line of created discontinuities (Fig. 16D).

These cutting experiments not only attest the fixity of the fission line, even before it is visible as such; they also strongly indicate that division in stentor is not due to ingrowth of separating membranes, surface tension changes, or other mechanisms which have

---

B. Stage–5 divider grafted to a non-divider. Fission continues on the divider side but furrow stops when it meets indifferent striping. Daughter cells do not separate because held together by the partner of the graft.

C. Stage–4 divider cut in two continues fission along the pre-determined fission line resulting in separation of small blebs.

D. Stage–4 divider with anterior rotated on posterior half, separating the primordium into 2 sections. Both parts of the anlage still go to the opisthe. Fission line does not follow the discontinuity of striping at the suture.

been invoked to explain cleavage in eggs. And the old notion of a constriction band which must remain a complete ring in order to exert a pull is of course precluded. There is no doubt that constriction occurs, which is probably from point to point on the furrow. Localized contraction together with the cutting of the lateral stripes and bands are probably the two agents directly involved in fission.

We now consider observations and experiments relating to the question of how the division line is determined so that it should be at a certain level on the cell, normally such as to produce daughter cells of equal volume. This line appears to be precisely laid out as a perfectly smooth curve without indefinite zig-zagging.

Suggestively, there is a cell constituent which comes to follow this contour during division. This is the complement of glycogenoid granules which comprises the carbohydrate reserves of *Stentor*. Weisz (1949a) had previously noted that these reserves are about equally distributed between the two daughter cells though initially lying at the posterior end, and later I supplied an exact account of their distribution (Tartar, 1959a). In a well-fed pre-divisional stentor the granules lie in a broad sub-cortical band at the posterior end, exclusive of the pole itself and interrupted or missing in the post-oral meridian (Fig. 17). About stage 5, considerably before the first visible indication of a furrow, half of the granules migrate forward. Those left behind become somewhat more diffuse than they were before. The anterior border of the migrated complement is also irregular, but its posterior boundary forms a sharp line precisely defining the path of the fission line which soon appears. When furrowing occurs, therefore, it merely segregates the reserves which were previously divided. These events do occur at just the time when the fission line is being determined with respect to its location. But if immediately preceding this stage the carbohydrate reserves are excised from the cell by cutting off the posterior end where they still reside, division can still occur in their absence. Therefore the peculiar behavior described is not the cause but rather seems to be the sign of other factors which locate the fission line.

Whatever it is that determines the path of the division furrow, there is further evidence of the pervasive nature of this agent from unpublished experiments in which excision of parts far distant from the circumference of the cell produce grossly unequal daughters, not accounted for by the relatively small loss of cytoplasm. Enlarging upon an experiment by Weisz (1951b), I found that if the mouthparts or the membranellar band or both are minimally excised or caused to be shed by salt treatments from early dividers, proters are later produced which are only about half the volume of the opisthes (Fig. 18A). That this difference is too great to be due to the ablations alone is obvious, and confirmed

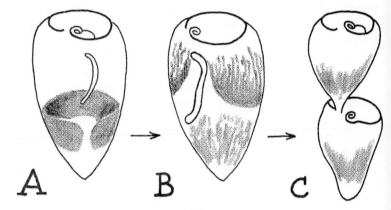

Fig. 17. Predivision of carbohydrate reserves (*S. coeruleus*).

A. Normal distribution of glycogenoid granules in a subcortical band at the posterior end, open in the primordium meridian.

B. Separation of granules into two groups at stage 5, the posterior border of the anterior aggregation precisely coinciding with the future fission line and the posterior granules somewhat diffuse.

C. Division leaves about half the carbohydrate reserves in each cell. (After Tartar, 1959a.)

by the fact that such operations on dividing animals at stages 5 and 6, when the division line is already determined, do yield products which are approximately equal. It therefore appears that such interferences have a marked effect on whatever determines the level of the fission line, shifting it far forward from its usual position. A rare case of division in a fusion complex of parts of two stentors suggests that the fission line may also be laid down far posterior of its normal location (Fig. 18B).

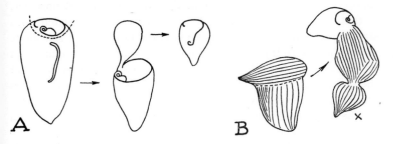

FIG. 18. Experimental conditions affecting location of the division furrow.

A. Head only of stage–4 divider excised; furrow is shifted forward with result that proter is only half the volume of the opisthe. Proter begins regeneration only after fission is completed.

B. Oral side of a *coeruleus* grafted transversely to animal from which anterior end was excised. Unusual subsequent dividing off of an anucleate product without an oral primordium (*x*) indicates how extensively process of division may be upset by misarrangements.

By centrifugation, Popoff (1909) was able to produce unequal fissions in *coeruleus*. The macronucleus was also unequally divided, yielding, for example, a small cell with 3 nodes and a larger one with 16. Presumably the level of the fission line was located other than normally, though no details were given. Prowazek (1904) likewise reported unusual cases of shift in the fission level leading to unequal daughter cells, as did Packard (1937), without being clearly aware of what he was observing. Altogether, these studies show that the fission line becomes fixed beyond altering only late in division, and can be shifted in its location by earlier influences.

4. Incitement to division

No one yet knows what causes a cell to divide and *Stentor* is no exception. In all the experiments on stentors by myself and others no operation has been established as promptly and invariably leading to cell division. Yet the search for the inciting cause is so important that it is appropriate to discuss the few efforts that have been made in this direction with stentors. Generally, stentors attain a certain maximum size before dividing, i.e., dividers are found only among the largest animals. All we can assert, however, is that whatever precipitates division is usually correlated with size increase, for many circumstances demonstrate that size alone is not the determining factor. Stentors of smaller than maximum volume can divide, and yet when many stentors are grafted together the combined "cell", of extraordinary mass, generally shows no tendency whatever toward fission.

The idea that division is caused by a progressive deviation from some normal ratio of macronuclear volume to cytoplasmic volume (Popoff, 1909; Causin, 1931) does not seem to be confirmed in *Stentor*. It is sufficient to say that in a variety of experiments in which nucleus or cytoplasm is at once added or subtracted there is no clear evidence of division occurring promptly as a consequence. Nor does micronuclear mitosis trigger division (Weisz, 1951b) because (a) mitosis occurs near the end of fission (Johnson), (b) reorganizers and regenerators also show mitoses though not dividing, (c) emicronucleate stentors divide (Schwartz), (d) and many other amicronucleate ciliates reproduce normally.

In certain unpublished experiments I have found that when the membranellar band or the mouthparts alone are removed from rather large specimens the stentors almost always promptly divided and the resulting anterior daughters with the abbreviated feeding organelles then regenerated a new set (see Fig. 39B). The same operation performed on the smallest stentors in the culture, however, yielded no divisions at all. Hence the combination of size with this specific operation seems to have done the trick, but further study is needed.

Weisz (1956) conceived that the problem of division in *Stentor* could be approached by determining the effect on smallest, post-fissional *coeruleus* of large pre-divisional and dividing cells grafted to them. First he fused largest animals which were soon to divide but which had not yet produced a division primordium with smallest cells or products of recent division which therefore would not be expected to divide until they doubled their size. Division of the larger partner was then greatly delayed but this could be attributed to injuries of operation since ungrafted controls also postponed fission if they were sliced into. After this delay a division primordium finally appeared in the larger partner, followed by an induced primordium in the smaller, promptly if the connection between the two components was quite intimate; and the complex then divided as a unit, often separating into two proters and a doublet opisthe.

When the larger partner had already entered division and carried an early division primordium, its division was still delayed and the anlage was resorbed after grafting. Again, this response could be attributed to the operation, because control animals also resorbed the primordium with cutting injuries and did not recommence division until 6 hours later. In the graft combination, primordia then appeared in both large and small components which divided simultaneously about 6 to 7 hours later.

If the dividing partner was in mid-stage division with a well formed membranellar band, grafting then resulted only in arrest of the anlage and not in its resorption. An induced primordium then appeared in the small component which divided along with the larger. But if the divider had already advanced to the stage at which mouthparts were beginning to form at the posterior end of the primordium, then no secondary anlage was induced and fission was largely confined to the side of the original divider. Yet there still could be some effect on the smaller component. If the macronuclear nodes of the divider had not yet clumped, then those of the small partner coalesced also. Weisz further stated that a division furrow sometimes extended around the smaller component, but I suspect from what has already been said concerning blockage of the division line that in these cases the furrow passed above or below the smaller graft.

These results were interpreted by Weisz as demonstrating that pre-divisional animals or stentors in early stages of fission can induce fission in graft partners which otherwise would not have divided, and that this induction is produced by some influence emanating from the dividing cell and passing to its partner. I am obliged to say, however, that these demonstrations are in need of further clarification and control before such conclusions can be asserted with certainty. If dividers are grafted to regenerators one might expect that division would be the more easily induced because the non-dividing partner already carries a primordium; instead, I found that fission occurred only on the side of the divider and did not include the partner, which merely regenerated. Furthermore, combinations like Weisz's did not always yield the same result and frequently when dividers were grafted to non-dividing animals the complex then simply reorganized doubly, the single division primordium first resorbing, to be followed by two anlagen which served only to replace the original feeding organelles and no furrow formation occurred (see Figs. 38D and C). In only one case did I obtain what appeared like a prompt and indubitable induction: a stage–2 divider was grafted to a small non-divider, the division primordium was not resorbed and another was induced in the smaller component, whereupon simultaneous division occurred; and yet the same result was obtained in one case when a stage–1 regenerator was used in place of the divider, though fission then proceeded more slowly. Further studies, however, may firmly establish a phenomenon of induced division, and if so, this would afford great potentialities for causal analysis of division in *Stentor*.

5. Persistence of division

Clues to the nature of the fission process may be sought in its persistence in spite of often drastic operations. Long ago, Balbiani (1891c) reported a case in which a longitudinal half of a stage–6 divider completed fission without either a nucleus or the division primordium. In other instances, whether of aboral or adoral halves, the division products did not separate though it was clear that the cortical striping had been divided into two systems because double cell shapes resulted. This was also the experience of Stevens (1903) who obtained division without separation in aboral halves and even in one enucleated oral half, which correlated with her studies of the year preceding showing that enucleated halves of sea urchin eggs are still capable of division. Much later Schwartz (1935) described one instance of complete division into two daughter cells after removal of the macronucleus from what was, to judge from his drawings, a stage–6 divider. This has been confirmed by de Terra (1959) and myself. Yagiu (1951) found the same in *Condylostoma*, and Suzuki (1957) in *Blepharisma*. These cases show that there is some "momentum" in the processes of division, or that after the primordium is well formed the final shifts in the disposition of the anlage as well as the cutting of the cortical striping into two systems and even their total separation can be effected.

In de Terra's study on *coeruleus* it was demonstrated that during fission the uptake of radiophosphorus (P^{32}) dropped to one-twentieth its rapid predivisional rate and was in fact the same as that of enucleated dividers from which the compacted macronucleus had been removed. This indicates that the large nucleus is not very active biochemically at the time of fission and thus helps to explain why division can continue to completion in its absence.

Extension of studies on persisting division called for operations on still earlier stages of dividers. In recent tests yet unpublished I found that division in *Stentor coeruleus* can go ahead after some rather drastic operations and often when the division process is by no means nearing completion. Dividers in stages 2 to 5 were cut in two transversely but the two halves allowed to heal in place. The primordium also rejoined its parts and division could be consummated in a perfectly normal manner. Stage 4 dividers were cut longitudinally and the oral half rotated 180° on the other in heteropolar orientation; furrow formation still occurred and division was nearly complete although the division products did not separate (Fig. 19A). The mouthparts of dividers in stages 2, 3 and 4 were excised and the cells either split down the back and opened out flat or cut and spread out in three parts like a clover leaf, and still division often followed, yielding proters which regenerated the missing mouthparts later. Isolated longitudinal halves of dividers cut before there is any visible sign of a furrow (stage 5) could cut the striping and form furrows. Usually the fragment did not actually separate into two pieces, as others have also found; yet in two cases at the preceding stage 4, longitudinal oral halves did complete division. These tests clearly indicate that the division process is not so delicate and precisely adjusted that disturbances cause its undoing.

The oral primordium was excised from dividers as early as stage 3 and the animals continued division. Because the headless opisthes later formed oral structures through a regeneration primordium we can infer that the macronucleus was also divided. Well-formed primordia at stage 4 were also circumscribed and rotated 180° *in situ* and subsequent fission was still successful. These experiments, as well as certain of the aforementioned, show that although the fission line begins at the anterior end of the primordium this site is by no means the necessary initiator of furrow formation. The same is also indicated by a case in which the primordium of a stage–3 divider was shifted to the posterior end; the cell still divided in two (Fig. 19B). Nevertheless if for any reason the dividing stentor resorbs the oral primordium itself, division is then not continued (Weisz, 1956; Tartar, 1958c).

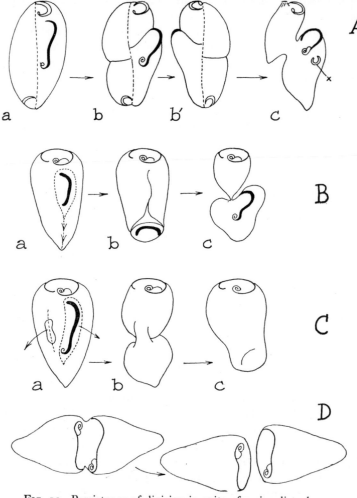

FIG. 19. Persistence of division in spite of major disturbances; separation of a heteropolar pair.

Division, but without separation of the products, can even occur though both nucleus and primordium are excised before there is any visible beginnings of the fission line (Fig. 19c).

Total removal of the macronucleus as early as stage 4 does not always preclude division even though complete development of the primordium cannot occur without nuclear support. However necessary for the original stimulus to divide, the macronucleus, as Yagiu (1951) also found in *Condylostoma*, does not seem to be the immediate trigger for the actual process of fission. (Micronuclei are of course not concerned, because Schwartz (1935) showed that growth and division occur in stentors from which these nuclei have been removed.) At stage 5, when the division line is presumably being determined, the cell can be cut through with a glass needle following exactly the path which the furrow will take, or in stage 6, when the furrow is visible, it can be slashed through with the needle around its entire course, and still division is completed. Together, these operations indicate that the division furrow is not a structural elaboration; for if it were, the nucleus would presumably be indispensable for the synthesis of new parts, and because any specialized " organelle of division " would be destroyed by the

---

A. *a:* Left half of stage–6 divider rotated in polarity reverse of that of right half, with no fission line yet begun. *b, b′:* Furrows develop along predetermined course in both halves, as seen in ventral and dorsal views, but not joining. *c:* Hence daughter cells held together by cytoplasmic connections, only later pulling apart.

B. *S. coeruleus* continues division and anlage develops completely though stage–3 primordium shifted to the posterior end. *a:* The operation; *b:* resulting arrangement; *c:* fission consummated.

C. Continued fission of stage–6 divider after both nucleus and primordium removed before any sign of cutting of stripes to form the fission line. *a:* The operation, excision of the anlage patch and clumped macronucleus. *b:* Division nearly completed but products held together by a cytoplasmic bridge probably due to cortical pattern disturbances from cutting. *c:* Substance of opisthe now largely absorbed into the proter.

D. Tail-to-tail heteropolar grafts easily pull apart; but even head-to-head pairs like this, in which the heteropolar striping does not join, also can separate or "divide" neatly by a course which was not observed.

operations just described. Instead, it appears again that furrow formation involves only the severing of longitudinal structural elements of the ectoplasm, which was merely hastened or abetted by the needle. Constriction is probably due to the action of contractile elements largely already formed.

Cutting of stripes alone does not result in fission however. The ectoplasm of non-dividing cells can be completely cut through around the equator and division never follows, the cortical structures merely healing together, often without leaving any indication of the operation. Conversely, in abnormal situations one sometimes finds stentors in which complete furrowing seems to have occurred but division does not follow. These cases indicate the importance of constriction in division, for it is almost certain that had constriction occurred, this type of specimen would have been divided in two.

Division is not the only means by which two separate stentor individualities can become separated. Fusion masses of two or more stentors show a strong tendency for the components to pull apart. This is especially the case in the heteropolar pairs, whether joined by the heads (Fig. 19D) or the tails; for when stripes of opposite polarity meet it is quite evident that they do not join and at this locus of discontinuity a separation may occur. Weisz (1951a) remarked that separations of tail-to-tail telobiotics are "strikingly reminiscent of vegetative division"; yet they are different in that pulling apart requires a long time for completion, as if sharply localized constriction could not occur at all.

By growing *coeruleus* in what were probably rather putrid cultures of beef extract, Stolte (1922) produced animals with highly vacuolated endoplasm which showed many anomalies of division. Animals could divide into three parts instead of two, producing posterior daughter cells without primordia or nuclei, or showed very unequal divisions yielding abnormally small opisthes. A case of partial vertical fission was even described which resulted in an animal with two holdfasts. Since the conditions were obviously abnormal, the interpretations offered seem dubious; yet these observations suggest, as Weisz (1956) proposed, that the endoplasm is important in division, vacuolization greatly disturbing whatever its function may be.

Postponed fission, in which division is much delayed but eventually realized, may be regarded as another manifestation of the persistence of division. I have observed (see Fig. 64A) repeatedly that dividing stentors do eventually undergo fission even though the original process may be cancelled by causing the primordium to be resorbed, or by intervening reorganization or regeneration even with loss of cytoplasm (Tartar, 1958b). The response is as if, once stimulated to divide, a stentor is bound to do so eventually, in spite of intervening catastrophies. This recalls the interesting hypothesis of Swann (1954), originating from studies of egg cleavage. He conceived that, as a separate mechanism, the cell builds up a reservoir of something which is essential to or stimulative of division alone, so that this store is depleted only by division. Adapting this idea to *Stentor*, greatly postponed division could be the consequence of presence and persistence of a reservoir of this factor which is not exhausted by other intervening acts of morphogenesis.

Reproduction by division in a form like *Stentor* normally involves first the transformation of one individuality into two, followed by the physical separation of the two individualities produced. The integrative tendency of the organism toward unitary wholeness, which theoretical biologists have generally emphasized, is therefore suspended or violated during reproduction in ciliates. From this observation, together with numerous phenomena in the regeneration of multicellular forms, we are led to suppose that the organism is in an important aspect beyond individuality, though tending to individuate as one or more than one, depending on circumstances. Of this we shall have more to say in the concluding chapter. For the present it is sufficient to say that "wholeness" is no metaphysical principle which organisms are compelled to maintain and is in fact transgressed every time a stentor divides.

Stentor also bears on another issue which in the past at least has been prominent in biology: namely, whether a fully differentiated cell is capable of division. If not, then regeneration of metazoa would imply either dedifferentiation of cells or the presence of "embryonic cells" still capable of rapid fission and pluripotential differentiation (see Brønsted, 1955). Basing his argument largely upon the fact that apostomatous ciliates undergo detorsion of the lateral striping (kineties) preceding fission, and thus apparently return to a more primitive state of differentiation, Lwoff (1950) maintained that division does require a more embryonic state and that "The ciliates have solved the problem of perpetuating complex adult structure by cyclical dedifferentiation". Although this statement may apply to apostomes and to forms like *Euplotes* which form new feeding organelles for both proter and opisthe, it is not apropos of *Stentor* in which preexisting cytoplasmic differentiations are obviously passed on to the daughter cells, and therefore cannot be generalized. I think that the important point is that most ciliates do not dedifferentiate before or during fission until they are quite formless and then divide. For it is apparent enough in the example of *Stentor* that maintenance of the complex structures of lateral striping which continue their ciliary and contractile functions throughout this process and are simply cut in two is not incompatible with division, and that therefore cell division does not necessarily require that a cell regress below a high state of differentiation.

Persistence of cortical differentiations in dividing stentors also precludes surface tension changes as a means of cell division in these forms and their allies, and the separation of asters in a mitotic figure is also ruled out. Studies on cleaving eggs in which these and other forces seem to be operating hence cannot be taken as characteristic of all cell divisions. Perhaps we can learn from *Stentor* of other factors equally important or effective, especially with regard to multiplication of tissue cells. It has been amply demonstrated above that stentors can be operated upon during fission in many ways which afford a promising approach to problems of cell division, as it has also been shown that the questions of differential growth even within the confines of a single cell are in this organism amenable to experimental analysis.

CHAPTER VI

REORGANIZATION

AT SEEMINGLY irregular intervals stentors form an oral primordium which serves neither for division nor regeneration but merely replaces oral structures already present. This has been called reorganization or physiological regeneration. As these terms imply, it has been supposed that this act is a necessary renewal of worn-out organelles, but this is by no means certain and the real meaning of the act is still to be ascertained. The problem of this peculiar redifferentiation of the cell is not unique to *Stentor*. Reorganization also occurs in the related *Condylostoma* (Tartar, 1957b) and *Bursaria* (Lund, 1917), as well as in many other ciliates.

The course of reorganization in *coeruleus* was well described by its discoverer, Balbiani (1891a). To this description Schwartz (1935) added many significant details in the most complete and best illustrated account in the literature, and additional points were contributed by others, as will be noted.

1. The course of reorganization

The first indication of reorganization is the beginning of an oral primordium. Approximately at mid-body level below the mouth-parts a splitting of pigmented stripes occurs as in division, but multiplication of clear and granular stripes is not so extensive (Fig. 20). The good reason for this is that a complete new adoral field is not to be formed but only an addition to the old one. As the primordium lengthens and develops, its anterior end meets the old membranellar band at the point where the latter begins to form the margin of the oral pouch. At stage 5 the original mouthparts begin to dedifferentiate. Macronuclear beads start to fuse and form a compact mass by stage 6, beginning renodulation at stage 7. According to Weisz (1949a), some of the terminal nodes may not fuse and if this occurs they break free. He also reported that endoplasmic streaming carries the clumped nucleus as well as any free nodes forward to a position directly under the developing primordium and he claimed that this is a precise and invariant event in reorganization, though neither Schwartz nor I confirm this. Essentially, the macronucleus clumps and renodulates without dividing.

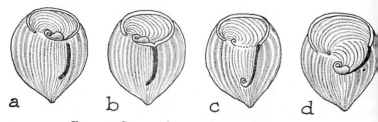

FIG. 20. Course of reorganization (*S. coeruleus*).

a: Morphologically complete animal shown with stage–3 primordium. *b:* Stage–4 anlage intimately joining with original membranellar band. *c:* During stage–6 of primordium development the old band between joining point and mouthparts, together with those parts, is resorbed. *d:* New mouthparts and addition to membranellar band moving into place and carrying new fine stripes into the frontal field which now shows a double pattern, 2 swirls.

Since the granular carbohydrate reserves in the posterior end of the cell undergo remarkable shifts in division, their behavior during reorganization should be noted. Weisz reported that the granules remained in place without change, but I observed that generally they diffuse forward under the ectoplasm though not separating into two groups (Tartar, 1959a). The chief resemblance between reorganizers and dividers is that in both cases a primordium is formed although feeding organelles are already present. In the tendency of the carbohydrate reserves to migrate there is also a slight similarity, but points of distinct difference are that no second contractile vacuole is formed during reorganization (Johnson, 1893) and of course no fission line.

The anterior end of the anlage now fuses with the original membranellar band, often causing a slight deflection where it joins; and the section of the old band between this juncture and the mouthparts then dedifferentiates and is resorbed along with the last traces of the gullet. The original oral pouch apparently is not resorbed but simply rises and flattens out to the level of the adoral field with whose stripes its own are continuous. As the primordium migrates forward and carries with it some ecto-plasmic striping to the right, new and old frontal-field stripes are brought together, but though homopolar they do not join. Instead, the anterior ends of the new stripes are pulled over to the point where the old mouthparts dissolved and the resulting frontal field therefore shows two swirls of striping (Fig. 21). This doubleness is an enduring character which identifies stentors that have under-gone reorganization, a sign which is often useful in following the performance of experimental animals. Sometimes one finds stentors with three disjunctive systems of striping in the frontal field, indicating that these animals have twice reorganized, though they may be proters from an ensuing division.

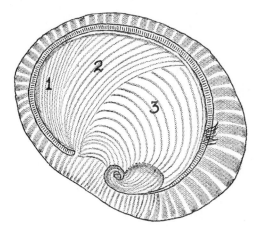

Fig. 21. Anterior end view of a *coeruleus* which had reorganized twice, showing multiple pattern of frontal field.

After the reorganization primordium is nearing completion, a secondary stripe multiplication occurs just below the newly-forming oral region quite as in the opisthe of dividers, as pointed out by Schwartz. This stripe increase will form a new ramifying zone and completes the reorganization process. It now remains to report what has been done toward analyzing the sequential events in reorganization and above all to inquire into its possible signifi-cance for the life of the organism.

2. Analysis of the reorganization process

There have been few experiments on reorganizing stentors and this area of study is prickly with paradoxes, but I have some unpublished data which is suggestive. These relate to the central question whether resorption of mouthparts is uniquely character-istic of animals in process of reorgnization.

When the aboral half of the membranellar band is removed, an oral primordium is formed and as it moves into place the original mouthparts remaining are resorbed (Fig. 22A). Is this regeneration or reorganization? Such cases are like regeneration in compensating

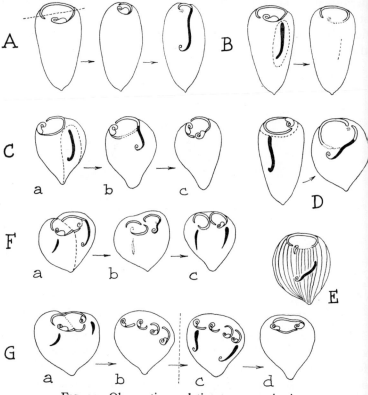

FIG. 22. Observations relating to reorganization.
A. When one half or more of the membranellar band is excised delayed formation of a regeneration primordium follows and original mouthparts are resorbed as in reorganization.
Regenerant then gains a peristome of normal length.

for an excised part, but they resemble reorganization because the mouthparts are replaced. Both Schwartz (1935) and Weisz (1951b, 1954) called this reorganization, and this may be permissible; for if, in such cases, the well-formed primordium at stage 4 is removed by a minimal excision or caused to be resorbed, the mouthparts are still completely resorbed, the animals then regenerating later (unpublished). The same occurs with true reorganizers, bearing complete feeding organelles (B). It would appear that in reorganizers and regenerators with mouthparts, these structures are predetermined to be resorbed. In contrast, an adaptive resorption of

---

B. Primordium of reorganizer excised at stage 4, before visible resorption of mouthparts has begun. Oral structures nevertheless subsequently resorbed though there are no new ones to take their place. Regeneration follows.

C. *a:* Stage–5 primordium grafted to a non-differentiating host. *b:* Developing anlage breaks into the oral zone, joining with the original membranellar band, a section of which is resorbed to permit incorporation of the new mouthparts. This imitates band resorption in reorganization, but the host mouthparts are not resorbed and a doublet stentor results (*c*).

D. Stage–5 reorganizer with head circumscribed and rotated 180°. Original mouthparts are resorbed, although now on side opposite to primordium. Anlage breaks into the peristome, free ends of same join on far side and a normal stentor results.

E. Specimen reorganizing after anterior was rotated on the posterior half. The primordium formed far down on the side of the cell yet the old mouthparts and adjacent section of membranellar band were resorbed as if the anlage were normally located. Later the new organelles moved forward, joined with the original membranellar band and produced a normal stentor.

F. Stage–4 reorganizer grafted to non-differentiating stentor. *a:* By stage 6, the reorganizer (right) had induced a transient reorganization primordium in its partner. Both original sets of mouthparts were resorbed, as also the out-of-phase accessory anlage. *c:* Partner left without oral structures now regenerating, with induced re-reorganization in the other animal. Oral resorption may therefore extend to other mouthparts present in the graft system.

G. *a:* Parabiotic graft of two stage–2 dividers. *b:* No division occurred, and the anlagen moved forward instead but the original mouthparts were not resorbed as in reorganization. *c:* Specimen then produced two reorganization primordia and all four pre-existing sets of mouthparts were resorbed as the usual doublet was formed (*d*).

sections of the membranellar band is shown by the observation that late regeneration primordia grafted into the backs of non-differentiating cells can and frequently do break into the oral ring through a localized resorption of the membranellar band (c). This interpolation also occurs in reorganizing stentors in which the head has been rotated 180° in place, but now the mouthparts are also resorbed though on the far side of the cell (D).

There are other evidences that oral resorption is a separate and predetermined part of the reorganization process. In one interesting case the stentor was transected and the anterior half rotated 180° on the posterior. This specimen then reorganized. Because of the disarrangement of the striping, the anlage remained for a long time in a diagonal position across the center of the cell yet the mouthparts and adjacent membranellar band were resorbed long before the primordium moved forward (E). It is also pertinent that mid-stage reorganizers can induce transient primordium formation in non-differentiating cells to which they are grafted; reorganization goes to completion on the reorganizer side and the mouthparts of the other component are also resorbed although there is not a new set to take their place (F).

On the contrary, it appears that in the state of division or regeneration there is little predisposition for the feeding organelles to be resorbed. When two stage-2 dividers were grafted together in homopolar parabiosis division did not continue, the two primordia moved forward but the original mouthparts remained intact (G). True reorganization then followed, in which all four of the existent oral parts were resorbed.

These experiments suggest that in reorganization the mouthparts are somehow invisibly dissociated, or cut off morphologically, and therefore usually predestined to dedifferentiation. This interpretation seems to be supported by the fact that if regeneration is induced by excising the head and a new head is then grafted back into place later, then, if the primordium continues developing, reorganization ensues and the old mouthparts are resorbed (see Fig. 37B). Also if the heads of non-differentiating stentors are circumscribed and rotated 180° in place, reorganization follows in the majority of cases. So in both types of experiment it would seem that isolating the whole set of feeding organelles has the same effect as the hypothetical disjunction of the oral region only. It should also be mentioned that although injury to the cell usually causes resorption of early primordia in dividers, this occurs very rarely in reorganizers. In every case when early, stage-2 reorganizers were split into a clover-leaf shape the primordium was not resorbed and the animals completed reorganization after the parts of the cell fused together. Such persistence of the anlage almost always did not occur in dividers unless the mouthparts were also excised at the time the cell was split. Therefore the reorganizers behaved as if their mouthparts were not present, i.e., as if these parts were effectively, if cryptically, isolated somehow from the rest of the cell. This hypothetical, morphological disjunction of parts would be of a subtle nature, however—possibly at the level of fine fiber structures—for when I tried to duplicate it by sectioning the membranellar band with a needle at the point where it meets the oral pouch, the band merely mended together and there was no reorganization. Obvious isolation of mouthparts

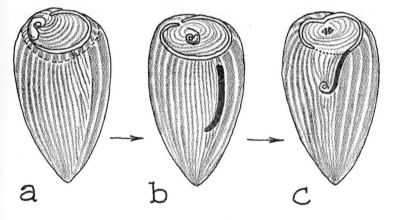

FIG. 23. "Autotomy" of mouthparts.
 a: Head of stentor rotated 180° with mouth now opposite the primordium site. *b:* Several days later the mouthparts — such as are resorbed in reorganization — separate from the membranellar band and move into the frontal field, with ends of the band rejoining behind them. Then a "reorganization" primordium appears. *c:* Old mouthparts cut into the frontal field are then resorbed, together with part of the membranellar band which permits integration of the anlage to produce a stentor of normal orientation.

by cutting and shifting does act as a stimulus to primordium formation although no portion of the feeding organelles is excised.

Even when heads were rotated 180° in place and primordium formation did not occur at once, a remarkable readjustment of the cell pattern took place (Tartar, 1959b) as shown in Fig. 23. The mouthparts, including the oral pouch and its membranellar margin were autonomously severed and thrust in towards the center of the frontal field while the membranellar band closed together. In the primodium site there appeared a "reorganization" anlage which eventually broke into the oral ring and provided a new set of mouthparts, now in the correct location. In this performance we see that the very structures which are resorbed in the normal course of reorganization can in fact be "autotomized".

3. Stimulus to reorganization and the significance of this process

The seemingly adventitious occurrence of reorganization in stentors, which appear to be the same as their non-reorganizing fellows, gives the impression of a quite unnecessary act which leaves the animal just as it was before. Hence the enigmatic character of reorganization. Yet we naturally assume that ciliates would not go through this complicated process without good reason, and several hypotheses have been advanced in the case of *Stentor*, though there is none which has not left its residue of paradoxes.

(a) To REPLACE DEFECTIVE MOUTHPARTS?

On discovering reorganization, Balbiani (1891a) suggested that the process is for replacement of worn-out ingestive organelles. The act would therefore be essentially the same as regeneration which is evoked by removal of these parts. Having well observed that the entire membranellar band is not replaced, Balbiani (1891a) assumed that the mouthparts are the most "used" and therefore the most subject to deterioration; but there was also a hint in his initial report that aging alone might result in these parts eventually becoming defective. Among modern students of *Stentor*, Weisz (1954) accepted this interpretation of the *raison d'être* of reorganization and emphasized (1951b) that injury or defect might be either structural or functional, justifying the term physiological regeneration. In either case there should be less successful feeding and one would expect that reorganizers would appear under-fed, transparent, and with few if any food vacuoles. But as I recently pointed out (Tartar, 1958c) reorganizers are quite as replete as their fellows. In fact, Weisz (1949a, 1954) almost implied this himself in explaining that pigment granules and carbohydrate reserves are not decreased and utilized in reorganization as they are in regeneration because reorganizers can continue feeding.

There are other strong objections to the defect hypothesis. Johnson (1893) independently discovered reorganization in *Stentor* and he seems to have followed Balbiani's interpretation, yet he described a case of two successive reorganizations in *coeruleus* which cannot be explained on the improbable assumption that the mouthparts just formed by the first primordium had become defective through use or aging. Then Morgan (1901a) noted that in most instances the old feeding organelles of reorganizers are still active and appear entirely normal, though this, he said, was not always the case. In my own studies, I tallied 36 cases in which newly-formed feeding organelles, wholly normal in appearance, were promptly subjected to reorganizational replacement, quite apart from the fact that in graft stentor complexes repeated reorganization is the rule (Tartar, 1954). These cases cannot be explained on the defect hypothesis unless one supposes, against all appearances to the contrary, that the preceding differentiation was inadequate.

If the mouthparts wear out, this should occur sooner in proters which retain the old ones; yet Hetherington (1932b) did not find reorganization in the continued isolation of proters for five generations, i.e., of feeding organelles five generations old. Finally, and most conclusively, one can specifically injure the mouthparts by thrusting a needle down the gullet and cutting laterally, whereupon the injury is simply repaired and no reorganization follows (Tartar, 1957c) (see Fig. 33B).

(b) Response to change in the medium?

Hetherington (1932b) was strongly of the opinion that reorganization does not occur in stentors under constant conditions of culture, and that reorganization if it occurs at all, is brought about by changes in the medium, not necessarily unfavorable, such as transfer from old to fresh culture fluid. It may be that reorganization is a response to disproportionality of cell parts (see below) and that under the most uniform conditions growth in all parts proceeds so harmoniously that no disproportion arises. But Hetherington's argument is vitiated by several contradictions. First, he says that no physiological regeneration occurs in stentors. Then he admits that he did find "reorganizers" in unchanged stock cultures of *coeruleus*. To explain this, he asserted that such animals were regenerating from cryptic injuries; and he stated that renewal of mouthparts is not the same as reorganization though he did not offer a different definition. He said that his animals were invaded by bacilli from which they were freed by repeated transfers into new medium, during which reorganizations were frequent; but then it might be held that the infection was really the cause of reorganization. Hetherington's contribution, then, was to direct attention to changes in the culture medium as a possible cause of reorganization; and to raise, if not resolve, the question whether replacement of worn out or injured mouthparts should not properly be called regeneration, as reasonably as when excisions are the inducement.

That "depression" conditions in the culture may be the cause of reorganization, though not the only or principal one, was also suggested by Balbiani (1891a), and Weisz (1949a) assumed the same; but Causin (1931) found that unfavorable conditions never seemed to cause reorganization. Merely adding new water to the cultures was said to bring about reorganization (Weisz, 1949a). Yet it is difficult to see how such a mild stimulation as change in the medium could elicit reorganization when the most severe cutting injuries involved in many stentor experiments do not. I therefore also question Causin's (1931) remark that if the tailpole is cut off a stentor the cell then undergoes a partial reorganization as if in response to a mild injury. He did not describe what happened beyond saying that the nucleus did not clump together completely.

Stentors in small drops under cover slips are incited to divide as well as to reorganize, according to Balbiani (1891a), but this certainly does not occur with regularity in depression slides. I reported (Tartar, 1958c) that a dilute solution of methyl cellulose brought about extensive reorganizations in a stentor sample, but this procedure was not easily reproducible.

(c) Need for nuclear reorganization?

In one of his cytochemical studies, Weisz (1950b) reported that in the chain macronucleus of *coeruleus* a gradient in affinity for methyl green seems to develop in anticipating reorganizers and pre-fissional animals, the posterior nodes staining less intensely. In both cases, after clumping and renodulation the nuclear beads stained uniformly. In this there is the implication that reorganization might be to reinstate uniformity of composition of the nucleus in animals which for some reason are not yet able to divide. But Weisz did not say so explicitly, perhaps because he found reorganizers in "all cycle stages", i.e., at any time during the interfissional period.

(d) For growth of the adoral band?

It will be recalled from the account of the reorganization process that important new additions to the membranellar band and the frontal field take place, while only the gullet and the border of the oral pouch are obviously resorbed. Therefore a considerable enlargement of the head should result. Schwartz (1935) carefully counted the membranelles and found that approximately twice as many are added as are resorbed. This suggested to him that reorganization may be a periodic growth process serving in part for the increase in the length of the membranellar band as well as perhaps the enlargement of the mouthparts. Favoring this conception is the finding that if for any reason the primordium produces too small a head, with a short membranellar band and limited frontal field, reorganization soon occurs with resulting enlargement of these parts (Tartar, 1958b).

In at least one case, however, I found that when an extra head was grafted to a stentor and this fused with the original to form a supernormal number of membranelles, reorganization nevertheless occurred. There are other arguments against the growth hypothesis. When there are repeated reorganizations the membranellar band does not become of exaggerated length. We are obliged to assume that the immediate increase results in a compensatory resorption of membranelles in some part of the band. Only in grafted doublet and triplet stentors does the frontal field and membranellar band become much enlarged over the normal, as if the excessive girth of these complexes could support a larger structure. It seems clear that reorganization is not an essential growth process, for otherwise it should occur with great regularity. Considering only the opisthe, a daughter cell starts with a set of feeding organelles which appears to be proportionate to the cell volume and therefore about half the size of those of the parent cell. If the membranellar band can increase only by adding new membranelles through primordium formation, reorganization should occur always before the next division and probably at a certain time when disproportion sets up a tension. But reorganization does not occur with regularity and, ever since Balbiani, it has been observed that stentors of any size can be found reorganizing. This includes even very tiny individuals, which I can vouch for, as well as animals in which the oral structures do not appear in any way disproportionate to the cell size.

(e) NEED FOR ADJUSTMENT OF NUCLEAR DIMENSIONS?

Although Balbiani did not find an increase in the number of macronuclear nodes following reorganization, Johnson reported that this was usually the case. Of 18 reorganizers, he found that 14 increased the number of macronuclear nodes, 2 remained unchanged in this respect, and 2 even decreased the number of nodes. The increase was sometimes to twice the original number of nuclear beads, but the new ones seemed to be smaller. Therefore he suggested that reorganization is for the purpose of increasing the active surface but not the size of the macronucleus, or that the surface–volume relation is adjusted as required, even in the direction of decrease. I may mention here that I have also observed cases of decrease in nodal number following reorganization of regenerated stentor fragments that contained too much nuclear material.

A striking demonstration of this correlation between nuclear size and reorganization was given by Schwartz when he showed that reorganization could be induced at will by cutting out most of the nuclear beads. Weisz (1951a) and I have confirmed this. When only one or two nodes were left, they at first enlarged the surface by becoming spindle shaped, just as Prowazek (1904) had previously observed. This earlier investigator also noted that without primordium formation and nuclear clumping there are at most only one or two nodes which may divide. Schwartz completely cinched the point by showing that regeneration of the depleted macronucleus occurs only after primordium formation, when there is also a mitotic division of the micronuclei leading to their increase in number. Moreover, such an increase in the nuclear complement seemed definitely to be called for, because he found that the "entire metabolism" of stentors with reduced nucleus is upset. After great reduction of the macronuclear volume there may follow a series of reorganizations, according to Schwartz, with the implication that in each only a limited increase in the macronucleus is possible. This I have also observed.

That mitotic multiplication of the micronuclei occurs during reorganization when there is the increase in the number of macronuclear nodes, Schwartz deduced as follows. If one assumes that in division there is but a single mitosis of each micronucleus so that the total number is only doubled, then the demonstrated presence of about the usual number of these nuclei in both daughter cells of a stentor which had previously been induced to reorganize by removing most of the macronucleus (and therefore most of the adhering micronuclei) implies that the micronuclei as well as the macronuclear nodes must have increased during the reorganization. Furthermore, it has been demonstrated directly in *Blepharisma* that micronuclear mitosis accompanies reorganization (Suzuki, 1957).

It may well be that anything which may lead to a macronucleus becoming too small for the cell volume results in reorganization. The essence of reorganization would then not lie in the fact that the mouthparts are replaced, for this also occurs after excision of substantial lengths of the membranellar band. Nor would it be a response to injured or worn-out mouthparts, since this is essentially regeneration and the evidence for this condition's being the necessary cause of reorganization is overwhelmingly in the negative. Changing the medium does not in my experience act as a stimulus to epidemics of reorganization, and reorganizers are found in cultures that have not been altered. Hence it would seem proper to regard reorganization as a wholly spontaneous and intrinsic response to certain disproportionalities or disarrangements of parts

H

CHAPTER VII

REGENERATION

Stentors have long been the preferred subject for studies on regeneration in the protozoa because of the large size of common species, their amenability to cutting operations, and the elaborate system of cortical differentiations which calls for a substantial performance in morphogenesis and provides a definite end-point for experiments. It must have been a dramatic moment when Nussbaum (1884) extended to the ciliates the earlier experiments of Greeff, 1867, and Brandt, 1877, on heliozoa in demonstrating the general "divisibility of living matter" at the cell level. Of course cells divide, but now it was shown that man could do the dividing himself with similar results. A year later Gruber (1885a, 1885b) published his finding that, in contrast to division, stentors can be cut into three pieces, each of which could produce a new individuality, and his drawing of the regeneration of a trisected stentor was reproduced in dozens of textbooks. He proved that regeneration was in fact complete, for the fragments not only regained the normal form but could then subsequently grow and divide. These studies were carried forward by Balbiani in a series of notable early investigations. Following these pioneers, investigators have turned repeatedly to *Stentor* as a form in which regeneration and reconstitution can be studied within the confines of a cell, the "structural unit of life".

1. The course of regeneration

(a) ORAL REGENERATION AND ITS REQUIREMENTS

Excision of the head or any appreciable portion of the feeding organelles leads to oral regeneration. A primordium appears on the side of the cell and then moves forward to the anterior end as it develops a new set of ingestive structures. If any part of the original membranellar band and frontal field remain, they persist and are integrated into the new head (Stevens, 1903). But if only

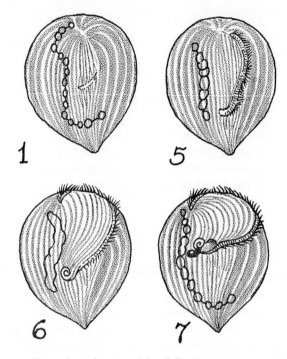

FIG. 24. Stages in oral regeneration following excision of feeding
organelles (*S. coeruleus.*)

Stage 1. Anterior end healed over and primordium appears
as a rift across fine striping near area of widest stripes. (Omitted
stages correspond to those in the development of the oral anlage
in division — see Fig. 14.)

Stage 5. Primordium with expansion at posterior end where
mouthparts will form. Multiplication of fine stripes within the
arc of the anlage which will form the new frontal field.
Macronuclear nodes coalescing.

Stage 6. Invagination of the end of the primordium to form
cytostome and gullet. Nucleus compacted, but usually not as
much as in division. Stripe multiplication below anlage will
form a new fine-line zone and recover approximately the normal
number of lateral stripes.

Stage 7. Gullet and cytostome now well formed and oral
pouch invaginating as primordium moves to anterior end.
Macronucleus renodulating. (After Tartar, 1957c.)

the membranellar band suffers ablation, the old mouthparts are resorbed as the new ones take their place. Regeneration has been staged according to visible changes in the primordium (Tartar, 1957c) as in Fig. 24.

Just as regeneration can occur in starving metazoa, so in *Stentor* the process imposes no nutritive demand. Weisz (1949a) remarked that in regeneration of *coeruleus* there is an extensive loss of pigment granules which he presumed to be utilized in supporting primordium formation, since this occurred in posterior and middle fragments but not in anterior pieces which do not have to produce a new set of feeding organelles. I too have often noticed a fading in the animals, which seems to be correlated in degree with the number of times they undergo primordium formation, though this is not always apparent. Carbohydrate reserve granules may be utilized in regeneration, if this can be dissociated with their employment in mere survival; and Weisz (1948b) claimed that oral regeneration could not occur in the absence of these reserves or their potential equivalent in the form of food vacuoles, but this could not be confirmed (Tartar, 1959a). Regeneration or further development of a regeneration primordium already begun can, however, be greatly delayed by cold (Morgan, 1901a).

Apart from the necessity for the presence of a segment of the macronucleus, the character of cutting injuries and ablations imposes few limitations on regeneration potentialities. Central–disc fragments with widely exposed endoplasm folded upon themselves to cover the wound surfaces and neatly regenerated (Fig. 25A). Collapsed stentor "skins" from which almost all the endoplasm has been squeezed out easily regenerated and recovered the normal plump form (B), quite as in similar tests with *Condylostoma* (Tartar, 1941b). When almost all the ectoplasm was sliced off, the patch remaining greatly stretched to cover the exposed endoplasm and regeneration was consummated (C). But endoplasmic spheres completely bereft of ectoplasm never regenerated, though they remained intact and alive (insofar as they resisted bacterial attack) for two days (Tartar, 1956c).

These tests effectively dispose of the notion (Prowazek, 1913; Sokoloff, 1924; Weisz, 1948a) that the ratio of ectoplasm to endoplasm (how measured?) cannot be altered far from an optimum if regeneration is to be possible, as well as the opinion that wound healing is an important factor in regeneration (Causin, 1931; Weisz, 1948a). Weisz's (1951b) statement that any portion of the endoplasm is capable of supporting regeneration is subsumed in the fact that no significant amount of endoplasm is needed at all.

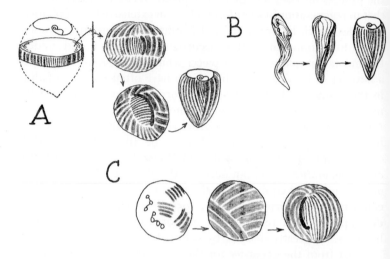

FIG. 25. Regeneration of *coeruleus* under severe conditions.

A. Mid-ring fragments regenerate in spite of extensive wound surface and exposure of endoplasm, because the piece folds to cover surface with ectoplasm and anlage promptly appears in short section of original primordium site. A normal stentor can be formed within a day.

B. Specimens with collapsed ectoplasm after removal of practically all the endoplasm by vigorous pipetting can regenerate and fill out the cell shape within a day.

C. In nucleated endoplasmic spheres with almost all the cortical layer excised the remaining ectoplasm stretches to cover, with granular bands becoming excessively broad and pale. Here the reconstitution was abnormal and the primordium, appearing on the "wrong" side, produced a stentor of reversed asymmetry. Usually such specimens, with greatly reduced ectoplasm do not live or regenerate, possibly because even maximum stretching cannot achieve a cortical continuum with no "edges". (After Tartar, 1956c.)

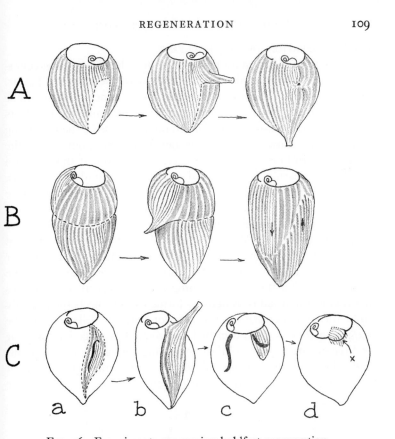

Fɪɢ. 26. Experiments concerning holdfast regeneration.

A. Removal of posterior portion of primordium-site sector is followed by temporary tail formation from cut ends of the lateral striping; but the anteriorly located extension is later resorbed in favor of holdfast reconstitution at original posterior pole. (After Weisz, 1951b.)

B. Temporary tail-pole formation at suture may occur when anterior is rotated on posterior half. Misaligned stripes do not rejoin and projection occurs in oral meridian of anterior half, but is soon resorbed as stripe patterns interpenetrate.

C. *a:* Sector with stage–3 regeneration primordium grafted heteropolar into a non-differentiating host. *b:* Anlage is resorbed and temporary pedal pole formation occurs from posterior end of graft. *c:* Extra tail resorbed, graft patch diminished, and specimen reorganizing doubly. *d:* Short, anterior primordium contributes only a sector (*x*) of membranellar band, forming no mouthparts.

(b) REGENERATION OF THE HOLDFAST

This occurs much more readily and quickly than oral regeneration. It can even take place in the absence of the nucleus (Tartar, 1956c). Within 2 hours after excision a new attachment organelle is formed (Morgan, 1901a; Weisz, 1951b). By removing holdfasts and posterior portions of the left boundary stripe of the ramifying zone, Weisz showed that a new tail was then produced at the posterior terminus of the stripes remaining, even if this led to a holdfast appearing forward and projecting laterally (Fig. 26A). (Actually a substantial portion of the ramifying zone must have been removed.) The regenerated holdfast then moved toward the posterior pole, possibly through an accelerated growth of the striping anterior to it. When the original holdfast was not removed the new one was soon resorbed. I have found that when a stentor is cut in two transversely and the anterior half rotated 180° on the posterior so that the lateral striping is out of alignment and does not rejoin, a new tail is sometimes formed and projects temporarily from the oral meridian of the anterior part (B). Likewise, if the ramifying zone is circumscribed and rotated in place its posterior end regenerates a new holdfast projecting forward (C). Consonant with these results, Weisz offered two important principles of holdfast regeneration: first, the presence of one good organelle

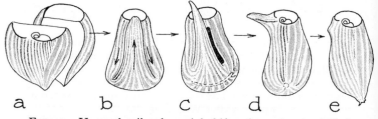

a   b   c   d   e

FIG. 27. Unusual tail-pole and holdfast formation in folded non-oral halves. *a:* Longitudinal cut through the axis to yield aboral half lacking widest and narrowest pigment stripes. *b:* Wound healed by folding which brings head and tail-poles together, polarities indicated. *c:* Lateral striping is self-severed across the sharp bend of the fold, giving same appearance as a fission line. Oral primordium develops where widest granular stripes lie adjacent to their attenuated extensions. *d:* Cut ends of striping drawn together to form a new pole. Original half-tail extends temporarily but is later resorbed as the new holdfast becomes functional (*e*). (After Tartar, 1956b.)

tends to inhibit the formation or persistence of an extra holdfast, and second, that free posterior ends of one or more stripes in the ramifying zone are inductive of tail formation.

Surprisingly, a new posterior pole and holdfast can be formed in a way which one would never expect to occur in the usual life of stentors (Tartar, 1956b). As Balbiani had noticed, longitudinal aboral halves tend to fold on themselves to close the wound, and if this situation persists, a new pole is formed at the point of bending. There one observes that the pigment stripes are severed just as in the formation of a division furrow, the cut ends of these, and doubtless of the fibrous alternating clear bands as well, are then brought together at a point from which a holdfast emerges (Fig. 27). Sometimes when the original half-holdfast persisted and moved posteriorly to a more normal location, it was nevertheless later resorbed and replaced by the new organelle produced in such an odd manner.

A stentor with single head but two tail poles and holdfasts, like a specimen found in nature by Fauré-Fremiet (1906), was produced when Balbiani (1891b) split the posterior end. This duplication can also be produced in *Condylostoma* (Tartar, 1941b), but in either genus it is much more usual for the two parts simply to fuse together again.

(c) RECONSTITUTION OF THE NORMAL SHAPE

Examples already given are enough to indicate the strong tendency of stentors to reconstitute the normal shape and contour of the cell. Later discussions will show that this capacity is indeed phenomenal, though easily passed over because of the slow pace with which it is pursued. For the present it is sufficient to say that no shape distortion of a stentor has yet been produced from which the animal could not recover in time. The gradual nature of the processes involved was emphasized by Schwartz (1935), who showed that minor discrepancies in the striping persisted for a long time.

Apart from such minute disruptions, the shape of a stentor seems to be strictly a function of the pattern of the striping (Tartar, 1954). When from aborted cleavage or for some other reason there is a break in the striping, the contour of the cell shows a corresponding deviation from normal (Fig. 28A) and if the

striping breaks into many patches the whole cell becomes knobby
when expanded (see Fig. 71B). Likewise, longitudinal fragments
remain thin and elongate until they recover the normal complement of stripes (see Fig. 12A). If two stentors are grafted together
at random, there is no arrangement from which they cannot shift
and integrate into a normal shape (Fig. 28B) (Tartar, 1954).

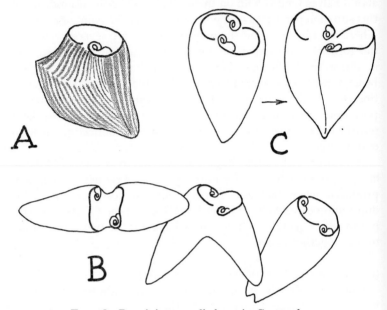

FIG. 28. Pertaining to cell shape in *S. coeruleus*.

A. Any discontinuity in the lateral stripe pattern results in
corresponding modification of cell shape.
B. Even head-to-head telobiotics can reconstitute a single
normal shape by jack-knifing and fusing. (After Tartar, 1954.)
C. Doublets with mouthparts proximate tend to form double
"cleavage" shapes.

Doublet stentors are usually wide, but if they become single, they
or their progeny recover the normal number of lateral stripes.
When doublets persist and retain essentially two sets of body
striping there is a strong tendency to develop a siamese twin shape
(c), showing again that cell shape depends on the disposition of
the ectoplasmic striping.

2. Nuclear behavior during regeneration

Not until the primordium is already half developed (stage 5) do the macronuclear nodes begin to coalesce; their fusion is not so complete as in reorganization and especially division. But Causin (1931) reported that regeneration is like abortive fission in that the macronucleus divides, the parts later rejoining. No one else has observed this. The point needs checking, in view of Yow's (1958) recent work on *Euplotes*, showing that in regeneration *two* ciliary anlagen are produced, just as in division, though one is promptly resorbed and hence was overlooked by previous investigators.

In any event, the compacted regeneration nucleus renodulates and the number of new nodes may not be the same as originally. Johnson, confirming Balbiani (1889), remarked that there is invariably a slight increase in the number of nodes after renodulation. The average increase was from 12·6 to 16 macronuclear beads. If the regenerating fragment was cut so as to contain few nodes to start with, there was a substantial increase during regeneration. Hence primordium formation in regeneration can be used for correcting a decreased nucleo-cytoplasmic ratio, just as Schwartz found for reorganization. This adjustment of the nuclear size to the size of the fragment was confirmed by Weisz (1949a) and is in accord with my own observations.

Prowazek (1904), too, found that the number of macronuclear nodes always increased during regeneration. He further stated that this increase might occur even if the stentor was only diagonally cut or injured, but he does not seem to have followed his animals closely enough to exclude the possibility that an intervening reorganization had not occurred. Evidently he believed that any substantial cut or deletion of oral parts resulted in a nodal increase which was also an increase in the absolute size of the macronuclear material, for he stated that after the invariable nuclear hypertrophy there then occurred a subsequent reduction to the normal nucleo-cytoplasmic ratio. Thus in some cases he found that one node of a series was absorbed, but it might have fused with another. These observations should be checked especially with regard to real changes in the macronuclear volume. Increase in the number of macronuclear nodes following regeneration was explained by Schwartz (1935) in the following manner. The macronucleus increases substantially as a rule only during cell division; therefore pre-division stentors, as they grow, will come to have a decreased nucleo-cytoplasmic ratio or the need for more nuclear material, which will be redressed only during subsequent fission. If regeneration is then brought about, a stentor can take this opportunity of primordium formation to make up its lack and increase the number of macronuclear nodes. Then he found that when this happened and the stentor was caused to re-regenerate there was now not an increase in nodal number because the normal nucleo-plasmic ratio had already been achieved; and if substantial parts of the cytoplasm had been removed there might even be a decrease in number or coalescence of nodes. However, in all this Schwartz doubted that there was an actual change in macronuclear volume and believed it more likely that the adjustment was largely an increase or decrease in the effective surface of the nucleus. Yet, in grafts of two stentors sharing but one macronuclear node I found an indubitable increase in nuclear mass at the end of regeneration (see Fig. 86B).

When a stentor is transected across the longitudinal axis the macronucleus is distributed about proportionally; the posterior fragment has to regenerate a new set of feeding organelles, while the anterior does not and serves as a control. Comparing these two, Weisz (1949a) found that in the posterior piece only does macronuclear coalescence occur, as an accompaniment of primordium formation. More recently, Guttes and Guttes (1959) have found that mitotic division also occurs only in the posterior fragment, or at least this was demonstrable in 17 out of 125 cases. No mitoses could be found in either the anterior fragments or in uncut controls not undergoing fission. If the exact time of mitosis is somewhat variable, this could account for their not always finding it. They noted the similarity between their results and those of Schwartz, who deduced that micronuclear multiplication occurs during reorganization along with macronuclear increase. The results showed that mitotic multiplication of micronuclei, as well as increase in the number of macronuclear nodes (see above) can take place in regeneration; for only the posterior fragments would have to form an oral primordium to replace the missing feeding organelles. This is in accord with demonstrations of mitosis in other ciliates during regeneration (Lewin, 1911; Suzuki, 1957; and Yow, 1958).

The Guttes assumed that both fragments regenerated. This is true only insofar as the anterior fragments had to regenerate the holdfast; but this makes no demands on the nucleus and can even occur in its absence. It has long been known (e.g., Morgan, 1901a) that anterior halves need not and do not form an oral primordium. Therefore the most important difference between the two types of fragment is that oral anlagen formation occurs only in the posterior ones, and this is somehow related to corresponding changes in both macronuclei and micronuclei.

To the Guttes, however, the only difference between the fragments was that the posterior halves lacked the feeding organelles. Their interpretation is accordingly highly questionable; for they suggested that in the posterior halves the phosphoryolytic energy utilized in membranellar beating could now be diverted toward promoting mitosis. Historically, this explanation stems from the Henneguy–Lenhossék hypothesis, 1898, of the homology between mitotic centrioles and the fibrogenic basal bodies of flagella and cilia. But the application cannot be valid if we accept Schwartz's deduction (see p. 103) that mitosis also occurs during reorganization of stentors, during which the original membranellar band is retained and continues actively beating as the new one from the reorganization anlage joins with it. Instead, it may be concluded that regeneration, reorganization, and division are so similar that each gives the cue for macronuclear and micronuclear increase; and it may be the developing primordium which provides this encitement, as in part suggested by Weisz (1951b).*

3. Effective stimulus to regeneration

That cutting injuries alone, without excision of parts, do not result in regeneration or reorganization has been pointed out many times. Morgan (1901a) tells how he cut the cell nearly in two without effect, even if the cut passed through the membranellar band. I have found, however, that if the feeding organelles are cut in two and displaced, or if for any other reason a good set of mouth-parts and a good membranellar band are present but not joined,

---

*According to Uhlig (1960) " regeneration " can occur without primordium formation, evidenced only by fusion and renodulation of the macronucleus and formation of a new contractile vacuole under the wide-stripe areas. Division also occurred without anlagen formation (cf. Fig. 18B).

regeneration will then ensue (Tartar, 1957c). Causin (1931) found neither primordium formation nor nuclear changes in *coeruleus* which were cut into repeatedly. Yet (if a repetition be allowed for completeness of this account) he remarked, without giving further details, that when so cut the "sectioned myofibrils degenerate and new ones appear in the pigment bands to replace them." Weisz (1949a) also spoke of an extensive reorganization of "contractile equipment" during regeneration and these hints deserve pursuing. Causin likewise considered that alteration of the nucleo–plasmic ratio would be a sufficient stimulus to regeneration, but whatever anticipations he may have had in this direction are probably covered by Schwartz's demonstration that reorganization follows excision of major parts of the macronucleus.

Even substantial portions of the lateral body wall and endoplasm can be removed without inciting regeneration, but removal of any portion of the feeding organelles is a sufficient stimulus to regeneration. Excision of all mouthparts of course produces prompt primordium formation. If the gullet or the oral pouch only is removed regeneration also occurs, or if in morphogenesis mouthparts are produced which lack either of these organelles, or are in any other way incomplete, they will be replaced by a new set through regeneration (Tartar, 1957c). The mere act of primordium formation therefore does not satisfy the requirements of regeneration, for there seems to be a feedback mechanism which informs the cell whether the resulting differentiation has been complete.

When only the aboral half of the membranellar band is removed regeneration is much delayed as a rule but does occur eventually. The only exception is that, if division intervenes, the abbreviated feeding organelles, now on the proter, may be approximately of right proportions for this smaller cell and then regeneration does not always occur. These results are reminiscent of Taylor's (1928) studies on *Uronychia*, in which he found that the removal of one cirrus, or the sectioning of critical neuromotor fibrils which could then not rejoin, constituted sufficient stimulus for regeneration.

Long ago Johnson observed that a double monster stentor regenerated doubly, on both sides, though it needed to renew only one of the mouths. Such observations were greatly extended with the technique of grafting two stentors together. In doublet animals with two complete sets of feeding organelles I found that if one of the mouthparts developed incompletely, or if one mouth was excised, or if one complete set of feeding organelles was removed without leaving remnants behind, then the remaining set, normal and fully formed, still did not prove sufficient. Regeneration always occurred on the defective side with simultaneous reorganization on the other. The only time when this did not take place was when the doublet was transforming into a single stentor and one of the primordium sites was disappearing (Tartar, 1954). Regeneration therefore may be said to occur whenever a primordium site is not subtended by a complete set of feeding organelles normally joined together in one unit.

4. Time for regeneration

Clocking the time for regeneration may afford some hint regarding the nature or the order of magnitude of the processes involved. At least we can designate the minimum period within which any postulated reaction must be able to accomplish a visible result, and this should offer some guide to hypothesis. A point which is obvious, yet perhaps deserving explicit statement, is that regeneration of lost parts is enormously more rapid in ciliates than in multicellular animals.

We have noted that an excised tail-pole and holdfast in *Stentor coeruleus* can be re-formed in one to two hours, and little or no synthesis of new structures may be involved. Relating oral as well as pedal regeneration to temperature, Weisz found that lowering the temperature 10 degrees increased the time by a factor of about 1·6. He also claimed that the presence of intact feeding organelles hastens foot formation, yet it is possible that such formations are retarded when the head is excised merely because an added burden is thrown upon the cell (Child, 1949).

Oral regeneration is by elaboration of a primordium and requires more time. An important distinction was emphasized by Weisz when he separated a preparatory period, as the interval between excision of parts and the beginning of anlage formation, from the time required for the development of the primordium itself. The former he found to require about 4 hours as a rule, though the figure can be pushed closer to three if one is careful to watch for the inconspicuous stage–1 anlage. Development then proceeds at the rate of about one stage per hour and the total time for regeneration from the moment of cutting is around 8 to 10 hours (Weisz, 1955). What may occur during the preparatory period is discussed later (p. 138).

In a study of several ciliates other than *Stentor* but including the spirotrichous *Spirostumum*, Sokoloff (1913) stated that the larger the fragment the sooner it regenerates, but his data indicate that differences appear only when there is a marked disparity in size of the pieces. The differences were explained on the basis that a hypothetical physiological harmony has to be established before regeneration and that this, rather than regeneration itself, takes more time to accomplish in tiny fragments. Weisz (1948a) did not find such differences in *Stentor coeruleus* and stated categorically that, other conditions being the same, the time for both oral and holdfast regeneration is independent of the initial size, provided the piece is large enough to permit any regeneration. In a recent series of tests I have found, however, that when the head and tail-pole of *coeruleus* were excised and regeneration times measured for the main cell body and its own polar fragment the time for the initial appearance of the oral anlage was with two exceptions always greater in the smaller pieces, and the difference was often considerable (unpublished). Size therefore may have a bearing on regeneration rates.

The same tests — in which the posterior fragment was "favored" by the holdfast — render questionable Weisz's (1948a) contention that the presence of a foot increases the speed of oral regeneration. Therefore, Child's (1949) criticism of this point also may be valid.

In aboral, longitudinal halves which lack the normal primordium site Weisz (1951b) found that oral, pedal, and contractile vacuole regeneration were much delayed — oral, as much as 30 to 40 hours. He attributed this delay to the time required for other stripes to assume the morphogenetic role normally played by those in the part removed. I too have found that the preparatory period in such fragments is usually very protracted, but there appear to be contradictions that need resolving because this was not always the case and some of these fragments did regenerate promptly (Tartar, 1956c). Likewise, when only the primordium site was removed along with the mouthparts, the time for beginning primordium formation was exceedingly variable, ranging from 5 to 12 hours (Tartar, 1956a).

It is relevant here that in doublet stentors, with only one set of feeding organelles removed, regeneration is usually prompt (Tartar, 1958b), again indicating that the remaining set of intact organelles offer no inhibition to a primordium site which is not subtended by one of its own. In single animals, however, the time for beginning anlage formation does vary inversely with the extent of oral ablations, recalling a similar rule by Zeleny (1905) for metazoa. Thus Morgan found that the more of the membranellar band removed the sooner regeneration followed, and Weisz (1948a) confirmed this. A similar relationship was demonstrated in the hypotrichous *Uronychia* by Taylor (1928). Even when there are no ablations, re-regeneration occurs if for any reason the differentiation of the oral primordium is incomplete, and the more incomplete the sooner (Tartar, 1957c). I also noted the time relation in regard to the length of membranellar band removed and found in addition (Tartar, 1959d) that if the gullet, buccal and oral cavity are neatly removed so as to leave almost the entire length of membranelles intact regeneration is still retarded. These experiments indicate that any portion of the feeding organelles is partially inhibitory of primordium formation, but all are required to prevent this formation entirely.

Sokoloff and others believed that the ratio between volume of nucleus and volume of cytoplasm cannot vary too greatly if regeneration is to be possible, but Weisz (1948a) found that regeneration times are the same in comparable fragments regardless of the number of nuclear nodes included, provided of course that at least one was present. He therefore discounted the idea of necessary nucleo–cytoplasmic ratios. With this I can agree in regard to the range of differences in the ratio which one finds in fragments from a single animal, yet it will be shown later (p. 306) that the extreme decrease in the ratio of nucleus to cytoplasm which is made possible by grafting experiments does indeed result in very tardy regeneration.*

*Uhlig (1960) emphasized the correlation between "age" and regeneration time: this period was shortest in young, post-fissional animals which were also more reactive in producing primordium formations at multiple primordium sites from disturbances of cell patterns.

5. Minimum size of regenerating fragments

Given at least one macronuclear node, how small may a fragment be and still regenerate? In the earliest cutting experiments on stentors, Gruber (1885b) had already found that not only halves and thirds but even smaller fragments of *coeruleus* regenerate and form tiny *Stentors.* The embryologist Lillie (1896) raised the question of the limits of divisibility of stentors as leading to significant theoretical implications. Fragmenting the ciliates by shaking, he found that no piece smaller than 1/24th the volume of a large *polymorphus* regenerated completely, and the minimal size for *coeruleus* was 1/30th. Lillie was impressed by the fact that such fragments are still of considerable size, since they were about 80 μ in diameter, and therefore emphasized that the cytoplasm is as important as the nucleus to regeneration, postulating that there is a "minimal organization mass" below which the complete, potential form of *Stentor* could not find representation. This size limit should be absolute rather than relative; therefore he expected that it would not be exceeded even if one started with smaller cells for cutting. Morgan (1901a) found that pieces no larger than 1/64th of the whole *coeruleus* could regenerate and this was later confirmed by Stolte (1922). Morgan's minimal fragments were in fact only slightly smaller than Lillie's but they were cut from larger cells. Recalling that there are also lower limits to the size of regenerates in *Hydra*, *Tubularia*, and *Planaria*, Morgan offered a first-order explanation for the failure in regeneration of very small pieces in both metazoa and ciliates, namely, that there is simply insufficient material to produce the typical form.

Sokoloff (1913) pursued this problem further in the ciliates *Dileptus* and *Spirostomum.* The first is suitable because the macronucleus is finely subdivided and widely distributed, and the second because the very elongate shape lends itself to cutting tiny fragments. Pieces 1/80th the volume of the whole cell could regenerate. Although fragments 1/100th of the normal size could be cut, these did not regenerate or survive for long. Therefore Sokoloff (1934) seems to have settled on the idea that there is really no theoretically significant limit to the divisibility of ciliates, and that in practice a limit is imposed only by the circumstance that in smallest fragments the wound surface with its exposed endoplasm is relatively so large that the pieces become vacuolated and soon disintegrate.

This conception was taken to the extreme by Weisz (1954) when he stated that size is not a limiting condition of regeneration in protozoa and that theoretically one molecule of deoxyribonucleic acid surrounded by a shell of cytoplasm should be able to re-constitute the organism. He therefore regarded the explanation of Lillie and Morgan concerning minimal size as untenable. Weisz (1948a) found successful regeneration in pieces of *coeruleus* as small as 70μ in diameter; yet he reported and later emphasized (Weisz, 1953, 1954) that even much larger fragments could be produced which are incapable of regeneration. The crucial point, he thought, was whether or not a fragment contains a portion of the normal primordium site and hence presumably specialized kinetosomes which alone can produce an oral primordium. Yet this explanation is contradicted not only by Causin's (1931) demonstration of the dispensability of the primordium site but also by Weisz's own experiments, mentioned above, showing that regeneration can occur in aboral halves, though much delayed. And I have found (Tartar, 1958b) that nucleated primordium sectors, or just the part of the stentor cell which contains the primordium site, can regenerate completely, with mouthparts, only if of sufficient size.

When a sample of *coeruleus* is set aside for a week or two without added nutrients the animals starve until individuals are produced which are much smaller than normal daughter cells. Starting with these starvation dwarfs, I cut off substantial portions of the posterior pole and found that pieces as small as 75μ in diameter or only 1/123rd the volume of large, pre-starvation stentors, could re-generate completely and survive for over 6 days (Fig. 29). Although these tiny stentors had much fewer than the usual number of membranelles, the width and length of these organelles when measured proved to be very nearly the same as in large animals, and these relatively oversized organelles caused the anterior end of the tiny animals to shake and shudder with their beating.

Therefore it seems to me, as previously suggested (Tartar, 1941b), that a limit to reconstitution of the normal form is imposed simply by the fact that the units of ectoplasmic structure are each of a nearly constant size or incapable of "miniaturization", so that with decreasing volume there will come a point beyond which the formation of anything like a normal set of feeding organelles

is impossible with such units. Failure of smallest pieces to regenerate would then be due neither to pathological changes nor
to insufficiency of material but rather to structural incompatibility
between the size of the parts and what is to be made from them.
Tiny fragments can produce some oral cilia and membranelles but
it may well be that there is a jamming when these parts attempt to
coil tightly inward to produce a gullet.

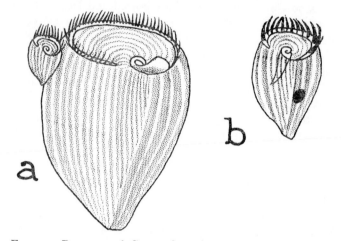

Fig. 29. Regenerated *S. coeruleus* of near minimum size. *a:*
Tiny and large stentors drawn to same scale. Note that membranelles are of same width and length in both. Pigment stripes
are also of similar widths, hence minute form had only about 20
as compared with 100 for the large animal. *b:* Enlarged view
of regenerant, which has but one macronuclear node and very
few stripes in the frontal field.

If units of ectoplasmic structure in ciliates, such as oral cilia,
body cilia, and trichocysts, are of a standard, nearly invariant size
for any species of ciliate (cf. Bonner, 1954; Ehret and Powers,
1959) this should simplify the problems of growth; for one would
then need only to explain their increase in number, and further
hypothesis regarding their adaptive size would not be necessary.
This seems to be one of the crucial theoretical points involved in
these small-fragment studies. The other resides in the amazing
fact that organic form is largely independent of size and, outside
the limitation just mentioned, it is possible for stentor shapes and

eeding organelles to be produced in an enormously wide range of izes. It seems that nature herself has already explored these possibilities, for the tiny, blue-green *Stentor multiformis* appears n almost every respect like the tiniest regenerate of *coeruleus*.

. Adjustments to proportionality of parts

Tiny fragments form primordia which are very short though pparently of normal width and therefore regenerate a set of feeding rganelles proportionate to their size except that the individual membranelles are relatively large. In the other extreme, Balbiani 1891b) noticed abnormally large mouthparts in some of his double monsters and I, too, have occasionally seen the same, as well as very large frontal fields and unusually long membranellar bands in the products of stentor grafting. Hence the normal upper limit in size of these organelles can also be exceeded.

When regeneration is induced by excising the mouthparts only, the new membranellar band joins with the old one. Therefore one might expect that when the entire head is removed the regenerated membranellar band would be smaller; but in this case the primor-

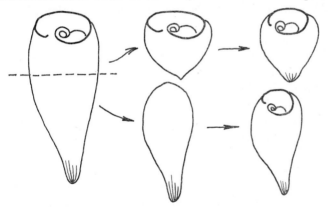

FIG. 30. Proportionality of parts in *S. coeruleus*.

Anterior half of transected stentor is at first too short and with too-large head. Membranellar band and frontal field are then reduced to half original size without primordium formation, as the cell extends and a new tail-pole and holdfast are formed. Posterior half is at first too long, then regenerates a smaller set of feeding organelles, as the posterior pole is proportionately reduced. (After, Morgan, 1901a.)

dium grows to a greater length, extending far forward, and so the size of the regenerated feeding organelles is the same and proportionate.

Of special interest is the finding of Morgan (1901b) that frag ments whose parts are rendered disproportionate by the cutting do not wait, as conceivably they might, for gradual differential growth to right the imbalance but adjust to proportionality relatively soon. Morgan cut unfed *coeruleus* in two transversely and observed in the anterior fragments that the stalk which was at first too short then gradually lengthened, while the original membran ellar band, initially too large, became reduced to half its starting size without formation of a new one, and proportionality of parts was regained (Fig. 30). In posterior fragments the stalk was at first too long, but it gradually came to assume normal proportion and the regenerated feeding organelles were of course of smaller and proper size. Reviewing his own studies, Morgan (1901b) then added the statement that the regenerated organelles on the posterior fragment are in fact too small and that they "later become larger until the characteristic form is reached". This would imply an improbable growth *in situ*, a question which will be dealt with shortly.

Prowazek (1904) said that he confirmed Morgan's original findings and noted that they imply, with reference to the anterior fragment, that there should be an imperceptible resorption of portions of the old membranellar band to make it proportionate in size. Such adjustment he thought was exhibited in a dramatic way in the case of a stentor which divided unequally, producing a smaller than normal proter which carried the now much too large original ingestive structure. The feeding organelles then gradually regressed until they appeared to be completely resorbed while a new primordium was forming to produce a head of proper proportions. Yet this behavior may be regarded as anomalous because it does not occur even in the most abbreviated anterior fragments in which there is more occasion for it.

Even in normal division the original head, which is passed on to the anterior daughter, is at first too large but on separation both the proter and the opisthe seem to have feeding organelles which are equal in size and proportionate. According to Weisz (1951b) adjustment occurs in the presumptive proter during the last stages of division, whereby the original feeding organelles are reduced in size. The partial regression of the mouthparts at this time, in which disappearance of the oral pouch as such is particularly conspicuous, may represent the initial steps toward a remodeling of the mouthparts on a smaller scale, but further changes are not easily followed.

We do not yet understand what determines the size or scale of mouthparts formed anew. Experiments here are contradictory. When a stage–3 regenerator was cut in two transversely through the primordium and the anterior half rotated 180° on the posterior the short anterior half anlage produced a tiny mouth while the posterior section of equal length was completely employed in forming a large one (Fig. 31A). If the two fragments were entirely separated, however, each portion of the primordium produced a small and proportionate gullet and oral pouch in addition to the membranellar band (B). An odd case, in which the regeneration primordium was unusually short, produced a tiny set of mouthparts in a large stentor (C); but when a nucleated primordium sector was isolated from a stage–4 regenerator the mouthparts were still proportionate to the fragment although the anlage was of normal length (D). When tail-poles were grafted into the frontal field and reorganization followed, the mouthparts produced on the graft were proportionate to its size, as were those on the host (E). Hence in some cases the length of the primordium and in others the size of the cell seemed to determine the scale of the parts produced.

The most exaggerated requirement for an adjustment of cortical organelles is occasioned by producing fragments which consist of the head only (Tartar, 1959d). By circumscribing the membranellar band and cutting carefully around the oral pouch and gullet so as not to disturb them, fragments were cut which contained only the feeding organelles intact, the frontal field, a little endoplasm, and usually one or two of the most anterior macronuclear nodes. Much shorter than the anterior fragments cut by Morgan, these pieces folded on themselves in healing to produce spheres in which the membranellar band was thrown into coils like the stitching on a baseball (Figs. 32 and 86c). In these specimens there was no primordium formation, but the membranellar band soon decreased in length as it became normally disposed and the mouthparts were later gradually reduced in size, while ecto-

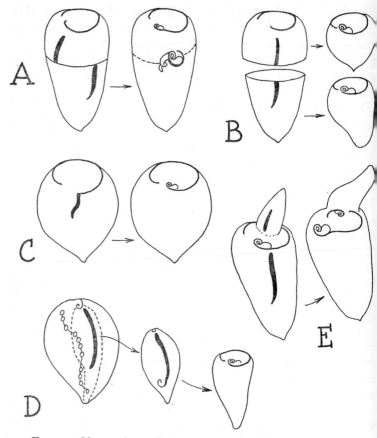

FIG. 31. Observations relating to proportionality of mouthparts in *S. coeruleus*.

A. Regenerator in stage 3 is transected and the halves rotated on each other. Both sections of the as yet undetermined primordium produce mouthparts. Those from the anterior part are very small; posterior anlage almost entirely used to form a very large set of mouthparts. Yet —

B. If the halves of such a specimen are separated, equal, proportionate and medium-sized oral differentiations are produced.

C. From deletions to the primordium site a very short regeneration anlage was produced, forming much too small a set of mouthparts for the size of the animal.

plasmic striping grew out and the normal form and proportions of a stentor were reconstituted on a small scale. But nothing of this happened if no nuclear beads were included and the fragment then remained until death about four days later just as it was after cutting and healing. It would therefore seem that the nucleus is essential in both the formation and the dedifferentiation of oral structures. These cases demonstrate how capable is *Stentor* in adjusting its parts to normal proportions.

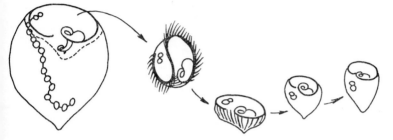

Fig. 32. Adjustment of size of parts in nucleated, isolated head of *S. coeruleus*. Feeding organelles and frontal field are excised without injury but with minimum lateral ectoplasm. In folding to cover the wound the fragment becomes much contorted. Membranellar band decreases in length and lateral striping gradually grows out to form a tail-pole. Later the mouthparts are also decreased in proportion. Adjustment occurs without primordium formation but only if nucleus is present.

7. Can mouthparts and membranelles be formed *in situ?*

In the normal course of life new feeding organelles in *Stentor* are formed only through the development of an oral primordium; yet there are hints in the literature that this may not be the only pathway to oral differentiation, although no really convincing demonstrations have been offered. In respect to the mouthparts,

---

D. Primordium sector isolated from a stage–4 regenerator. Development continues and size of mouthparts is proportionate not to the original cell or the length of the anlage but to the size of the fragment.

E. Tail pole was grafted to frontal field of a stage–2 regenerator. First sketch shows an additional anlage now induced in the graft. On developing, the primordia produced mouthparts proportionate to the size of the part in which they arose.

Morgan commented that if a portion is removed the remaining parts seemed to reconstitute the normal ingestive structure, though this was generally replaced later by a new one. In my experience an isolated gullet can attain a neat opening on the surface and attaches to the correct end of a remnant of the membranellar band, while the severed oral pouch with its membranellar border also does not remain as cut but coils sharply to form a pigmented depression with the shape of the inside of an abalone (Fig. 33A).

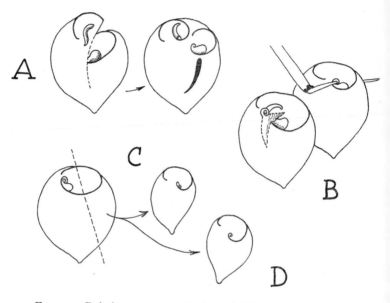

FIG. 33. Relating to reconstitution and formation *in situ* of mouthparts.

A. Gullet severed inside of stentor, isolated oral pouch widely displaced, gullet opening destroyed by anterior incision. Gullet finds neat opening to exterior and joins adoral end of adjacent membranellar band, while oral pouch coils sharply as if attempting mouth formation. Regeneration follows.

B. Two types of gross oral injury which are followed by mending without regeneration: sectioning mouthparts but leaving them close together, and thrusting an eyelash into the gullet and out through opposite side of the cell.

C. Before regeneration, adoral end of the membranellar band may produce a small pit, or a tight coiling (D).

Yet neither part reconstitutes a complete mouth, even if either one is completely removed. If the gullet is severed from the oral pouch and the structures are left adjacent, or if the mouthparts are severely injured in place, in the vast majority of cases the parts will rejoin and perfect mouthparts be reconstituted without the formation of a regeneration primordium. That some remodeling can occur *in situ* was indicated by the fact that in one case an unusually long and wide gullet was produced. In another case an eyelash was thrust down the gullet and out the side of the cell yet no regeneration followed and the stentor was later capable of forming food vacuoles (Fig. 33B).

Morgan also noted that some of his aboral, anterior fragments formed a small oral pit at the proximal end of the membranellar band remaining (Fig. 33C), and a similar effort toward oral regeneration was also observed by Causin (1931). I have observed these formations too, as well as the tendency for the cut, proximal end of the membranellar band to form at least a tight little coil (D). I further reported (Tartar, 1956a) a case in which good mouthparts were apparently reconstituted from the buccal pouch alone, as well as the formation at least of an apparently complete gullet instead of merely a pit at the end of an adoral band (Tartar, 1956b). One may at least conclude that the mouthparts are quite capable of repairing themselves.

This may also be said for the membranellar band. If the band is cut in two or small sections of it removed, the parts simply heal together and no regeneration ensues. Whether some compensatory growth of membranelles occurs if some are excised has not been precisely determined. Stevens (1903) found in oral longitudinal halves "some evidence" that the abbreviated membranellar band increased in length. But the formation of regeneration primordia in stentors from which half the band has been excised speaks against the formation of membranelles *in situ*. Were this possible, such regeneration would then not be necessary.

In Prowazek's important if miscellaneous paper of 1904, he first reported that the membranellar band in *coeruleus* is shed when the ciliates are subjected to a weak solution of table salt. Then he noted that after 24 hours a new membranellar band was regenerated in the same place (an derselben Stelle). This is all he says. The point is not developed further, nor was this remark italicized, as was his habit in emphasizing major issues in the remainder of the paper. Hence it seems to me that all later commentators have mis-interpreted this passage as a statement that membranelle formation can occur in place or without primordium formation. But this is not to exclude that such development may occur after a fashion, anomalous as this would be. Schwartz repeated Prowazek's salt-shedding experiments and stated that in some cases there was clearly a neo-formation of membranelles *in situ*. His explanation was that only the cilia of the membranelles had been cast off, leaving the basal bodies intact, from which new cilia may have grown; and he remarked that if this can occur, such replacement, rather than primordium formation, should be the method of renewing supposedly worn-out feeding organelles. I have myself noticed a few similar cases. In one of these, a stage–3 divider was treated with sucrose and it shed the membranellar band. The division primordium remained but showed abortive development, while around the anterior rim of the cell there appeared within about 4 hours shorter than normal oral cilia which beat in meta-chronal rhythm. Such cases indicate that if carefully graded treat-ments were employed, a renewal of the large oral cilia if not the entire membranelle might be firmly established. Yet it is certain that in most experiments of this sort the entire band comes off and the regeneration primordium is soon formed (see p. 252).

8. Repeated oral regeneration

Since the formation and development of an oral primordium involves the production of thousands of new, large, oral cilia as well as other parts, one wonders whether there is an inexhaustible reserve for such synthesis. Gruber (1885b) cut and presumably decapitated a *coeruleus* on 5 successive days and each time complete regeneration followed until the animal finally became necrotic and too small for further operation. With the same large species, Prowazek (1904) also performed successive cuttings. In one tabulated case an animal was cut nine times during which macronuclear beads were not removed, and this animal always regenerated. The material of the macronucleus seemed to have been substantially drawn upon, because it was finally reduced from 11 to only 2 nodes. He also reported 3 cases in which the animal was repeatedly cut or wounded and compelled to regenerate and that these then became able to regenerate without the nucleus. This surprising result was explained in terms of the then-popular chromidial hypothesis, whereby a nucleus can be stimulated to extrude chromidia, which can then substitute for it (see p. 299).

Hartmann (1922) posed the question of whether division could be indefinitely postponed by repeated cutting ablations on a feeding cell. That this is the case, he demonstrated for *Amœba* and the fresh water worm *Stenostomum*, as well as for *Stentor coeruleus*. Stentors were fed on *Colpidium* and allowed to grow but were cut before they attained division size. Hartmann noted that a cut could produce either oral or headless remainders and, although his account is not clear in this regard, I assume from his statement that regeneration occurred and that this was oral regeneration and not merely holdfast renewal or recovery of normal shape. In one tabulated case a stentor regenerated 25 successive times during 52 days, without fission, while the controls divided 35 times. These results indicated, that if there is an accumulation of some factor disposing the cell to fission, this factor is reduced by excisions; as well as that indefinitely repeated regeneration seems to be possible within one individual if fed, and that frequent fission is not essential to survival.

9. Blockage of regeneration

Although stentors regenerate with the greatest regularity and can even re-regenerate repeatedly or exhibit a succession of re-organizations in starved fusion complexes, I have encountered a half-dozen cases among thousands in which, for some unaccountable reason, otherwise healthy appearing *coeruleus* failed to regenerate the feeding organelles though surviving for many days. A similar number of instances were found among starving animals, which is enough to give the impression that stentors cannot form regeneration primordia without carbohydrate reserves as Weisz (1948b) asserted. Yet a direct pursuit of this question showed that even the most pellucid animals without food vacuoles or demonstrable glycogenoid granules were still quite able to regenerate (Tartar, 1959a). On the other hand, it is common enough to find that necrotic stentors or animals which have an apparently decreased vitality from being long isolated on slides are unable to consummate regeneration. Improper healing of cut animals is supposed to offer a blockage to regeneration according to Sokoloff (1924) and Weisz (1948a); but my experience is that the healing capacity of stentors is sufficient for neat repair after any cutting operation except an extreme reduction in the ectoplasm which alone prevents apposition of cut surfaces.

Nevertheless regeneration can be blocked in *Stentor* by treatment with certain chemical agents. Weisz (1955) tested the effects on regeneration of over 20 compounds, including substituted purines and pyrimidines and a variety of anti-metabolites. The most effective, in the sense of producing reversible blockages without toxicity, was acriflavin, a mixture of 2,8-diamino-10-methyl-acridinium chloride and 2,8-diamino-acridine. These compounds or their allies are bacteriostatic, and some of their effects on ciliates had already been explored (Robertson, 1925). Weisz reported that acriflavin has a graded sequence of effects on *coeruleus*, depending on concentration and duration of exposure. First there was some paralysis of ciliary beating and cell contraction, followed by more or less complete shedding of the pellicle. Oral primordium formation might then be merely delayed, or prevented entirely, the animals then dying. When primordium formation occurred there were graded effects in the completeness of the development of the anlage. The primordium might appear briefly and then be resorbed without any attempt at re-regeneration. Oral formation might be arrested at stage 4, producing a membranellar band which developed no further. Sometimes the band could assume the normal curvature but failed to coil inward and develop the gullet and associated mouthparts. These inhibitive effects could be reversed or counteracted by other agents: adenine, guanine, thymine, uracil, folic acid, RNA, and DNA, the two latter, presumably the commercial product from yeast, being the most effective. Interpreting these findings, Weisz postulated that development of the oral primordium is a series of separate morphogenetic events interconnected by acriflavin–sensitive transition reactions. Kinetosomes might be affected in several of their functions, first in the promotion of ciliary beating, then in their synthesis of new cilia, and finally in some morphogenetic activity by which membranelles and other complex organelles are produced. Application of compounds which reversed the effect of acriflavin had the same effect whether administered before or during the acriflavin treatment, and hence it appeared that inhibition by acriflavin is non-competitive. He could not say whether the effect is physical or chemical.

This inviting biochemical approach to cell differentiation as expressed in oral primordium formation in *Stentor* is being pursued further by A. H. Whiteley. He is finding (unpublished) that both the purine analogue, 8-azaquanine—which gave no effect for Weisz—and the pyrimidine analogue, 2-thiocytosine, completely block anlagen formation in *coeruleus*. The inhibition is reversible, and regeneration of animals returned to lake water indicates that this result is probably not due to toxicity but to interference with the formation of nucleic acids which incorporate purines and pyrimidines. Moreover, in the case of 8-azaquanine the effect is counteracted by the presence of normal components of nucleic acids, i.e., hydrolyzed yeast RNA or by RNA directly. And the implication of RNA in primordium formation is further indicated by Whiteley's finding that a certain concentration of the RNA-destroying enzyme, ribonuclease, can also block regeneration. The abolition of this effect by added RNA implies that the RNAase was in fact producing this blockage through destruction of ribonucleic acids.

Similarly, but at a wider range of concentrations, 5-methyltyrosine prevented regeneration without appreciable toxic side-effects. Since this compound is an antimetabolic analogue of adenosine found in most proteins, the result in this case was probably due to the blockage of protein synthesis. Therefore it appears that primordium formation in which thousands of new cilia are produced does involve extensive protein synthesis and not merely the translocation of proteins already formed, as well as that RNA is equally implicated, in accordance with the hypothesis that RNA guides protein synthesis (Brachet, 1957).

A satisfactory elucidation of the intimate material basis of the elaboration of cell differentiations is rendered promising in regard to *Stentor* by the fact that several treatments inhibit oral anlagen formation, presumably by affecting separate, essential aspects of a complex process. Even simple salts in very dilute solution also delay or prevent regeneration or inhibit primordium development (see p. 254). Moreover, regeneration may be blocked by morphological disarrangements without chemical additives, as when reversing the single primordium site often if not always precludes the formation of an anlage (p. 197).

Oral regeneration is thus often the preferred phenomenon for study because by oral ablations we can induce at will the biochemical and epigenetic processes involved in primordium formation. But there is no reason to suppose that the fundamental features of anlagen development in regeneration are different from those in the more autonomous performances of division and reorganization. Instead, it is perhaps reasonable to suppose that from the means providing for the basic requirement for reproduction by division were developed the capacities for reorganization and regeneration which seem far less significant for survival of the species.

CHAPTER VIII
ACTIVATION AND INHIBITION OF
THE ORAL PRIMORDIUM

WHEN a stentor which is in the process of developing an oral primordium is intimately grafted to a normally feeding partner not producing a new set of feeding organelles, both animals no longer continue on their original ways but now act upon each other with significant and visible consequences. These interactions were first explored in fusions of regenerating to non-differentiating stentors. Regenerators often caused the partner to produce a primordium and undergo parallel reorganization. This type of interaction may be called induced reorganization as formulated by Weisz (1956). Alternatively, the influence may proceed in the other direction, suspending the regeneration and causing the regenerator to resorb its anlage. This reaction may be referred to as induced resorption of the primordium (Tartar, 1958b). Another way of exhibiting these interactions is to graft cell sectors bearing primordia on to various hosts. When grafted to stentors which are themselves undergoing regeneration, the extra primordia are accepted, supported, and continue developing; but if implanted on to non-differentiating stentors primordia are resorbed though the patch itself is incorporated into the lateral striping of the host.

The range and basis of these reciprocal influences have been quite extensively explored (Tartar, 1958b, 1958c). The results can be explained in terms of two contrasting cell states: activation, in which something of the whole cytoplasm is involved in supporting primordium formation and development, and inhibition, which is equally pervasive and tends to block or counteract the processes of cell redifferentiation. Either of these states is sufficiently potent to spread from one cell to another with which it is intimately joined, in the one case to force a precipitous primordium formation, and in the other, to cause the complete resorption of an anlage which is already well begun.

K

135

1. The course and spectrum of cell interactions

Enlarging upon these statements, we shall at first and for the most part confine our account to regenerators and their parts interacting with non-differentiating stentors (Tartar, 1958b). When a sector bearing the primordium and a few macronuclear nodes is cut out of a regenerator, development of the anlage continues as the fragment regenerates a small stentor; or when the sector is grafted into the back of another regenerator, both host and donor primordia continue differentiating and produce a doublet or bistomial stentor. These tests show that such sectors contain all that is necessary for anlagen development and that the grafting operation itself has no effect on this process. But if a

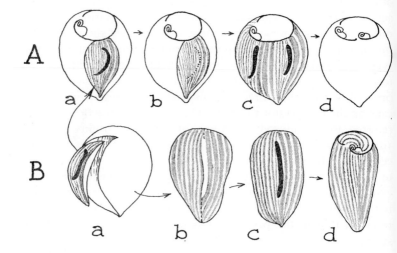

FIG. 34. A. Induced primordium resorption. Sector of a stage–3 regenerator grafted to a non-differentiating host (*a*). *b:* Anlage is promptly resorbed, but not the multiplied fine striping encompassed by it. *c:* Specimen undergoes regeneration-reorganization because added primordium site does not subtend mouthparts, and a doublet is formed (*d*).

B. Accelerated reformation of primordium after excision. *a:* Primordium and site removed. *b:* Rift soon appears in previously closed line of heal. *c:* Primordium appears in rift within an hour after operation and there is no multiplication of adjacent lateral stripes. *d:* Only relatively few and broad stripes are hence carried into the frontal field.

sector bearing a mid-stage primordium is grafted onto a non-differentiating stentor (without primordium and not in process of regenerating, reorganizing, or dividing), the primordium is promptly taken down and resorbed—not sloughed. Notice in Fig. 34A that the patch itself is not resorbed, nor are the newly multiplied fine striping to the right of the primordium site; instead, the sector becomes part of the lateral striping of the host.

This experiment shows that something besides cytoplasm and macronucleus is necessary for regeneration. The cell must also be in a state of activation. The nuclei of the non-differentiating host could have been replaced by others from an actively regenerating stentor and primordium resorption would still have taken place; likewise if the host's primordium site had been replaced with the grafted sector. Therefore the state of inhibition (or its opposite, activation) seems to characterize the cytoplasm; and not merely the part adjacent to anlage formation, but every part of the cytoplasm. For it is clear that an inhibiting influence was spreading from the host, across the grafted patch, to the primordium, resulting in its dissolution. There are indications, though not yet conclusive, that the endoplasm as well as the macronucleus is indifferent, with cell states characterizing the cortex alone.

A reciprocal influence appears to occur in the later history of this type of case; for now the grafted primordium site, lacking subtending oral structures, is incited to produce a regeneration primordium and brings the host along with it into activation, with the result that combined regeneration and reorganization occur to produce a doublet stentor.

Rapidity and success of induced resorption depends upon the stage of development of the imposed primordium. Early anlagen to stage 3 can be completely resorbed within about 2 to 4 hours. Stage–4 primordia which already have a well developed membranellar band can also be dissolved, but this requires many hours during which the anlagen crumples and is gradually taken down, though complete resorption may not occur. From stage 5 onward, the primordia do not seem to be resorbable under any conditions, yet they do not remain unaffected when grafted to non-differentiating hosts. Late primordia shrink in length or become compacted and convoluted as if the ectoplasm were not co-operating in their deployment, and mouthparts are not developed or remain incomplete. Examples of this abortive development will be noted later.

A state of inhibition can therefore adversely affect primordium development at any stage until final oral structures are formed, or conversely, a state of activation is essential during all this time. The initial appearance and preparation of the anlage also requires activation. For incipient regenerators at what may be called stage O will not even begin primordium development if grafted to inhibitive, non-differentiating partners. The inhibition is in fact then so strong that the regenerator usually does not begin regenerating until the following day.

Returning again to our typical experiment, consider now what happens to the regenerating stentor after the primordium sector has been removed. A new anlage can appear within one hour, although an hour and a half is closer to the average interval. This precipitous re-formation of the anlage is most simply explained on the basis that the cell was already activated.

An accelerated renewal of the anlage of a quite different order of magnitude (6 vs. 9 hours) was noticed by Weisz (1956) in comparing dividers, which had resorbed their primordia because of injuries, with injured pre-fissional animals. This time difference he attributed to the persistence of an " anarchic field " or multiplied store of new kinetosomes which remain ready to supply materials for the new primordium. Yet, when an anlage is resorbed there is no rift left in the ectoplasm to indicate that kinetosomes remain, and one would expect an "embryonic" anarchic field also to be resorbed since the earlier and more nascent the primordium the more easily it is resorbed. Moreover, in regenerators in which a new primordium could appear within the surprisingly short time of a single hour, a relatively large sector bearing the anlage was excised so that any anarchic field adjacent to the primordium would also surely have been removed. For in the related *Fabrea* the new kinetosomes lie between the kineties immediately adjacent to the anlage and in *Stentor* they seem to be coincident with the primordium itself (Villeneuve-Brachon, 1940), so it should be impossible to cut out the anlage without also removing its progenitors. I therefore cannot agree with Weisz's explanation, nor accept his claim to have effected this separation of primordium and precursors in other experiments. The long preparatory period of about four hours between inducement of regeneration and first appearance of the primordium is probably occupied, not by developing an anarchic field or other assemblage of formed materials for the anlage but in transforming the cell from a state of inhibition to one of activation (Tartar, 1958b).

In the rapid re-formation of anlagen in regenerators minus primordium sectors the primordia themselves are normal and lead to successful regeneration, but their manner of appearance is unusual. As shown in Fig. 34B, the line of heal simply reopens and an anlage appears in the rift. Apparently there is no time for concomitant stripe multiplication in the presumptive frontal field, and the primordium simply cuts out and carries forward some of the relatively wide striping on its right side. The frontal field is correspondingly abbreviated and reorganization therefore often follows.

A similar appearance is also found in induced reorganization. If a stage-3 regenerator is grafted to a smaller non-differentiation cell the latter exerts an initial influence by causing the arrest or even partial regression of the regenerator's anlage, though later the regenerator is dominant and induces normal primordium formation, with stripe multiplication, in the partner which then reorganizes simultaneously (Fig. 35A). But when a stage-4 regenerator is used no transient regression of the original anlage occurs, and the induced primordium may be forced to appear so rapidly that there is neither stripe multiplication nor normal growth in length of the anlage (B). As indicated in the first example, the impression is unmistakable that in mis-matched grafts there is a contest and conflict between primordium activation and inhibition, the final outcome of which is only decided after some time. Figure 35c illustrates a case in which an incipient regenerator was grafted to a small non-differentiating partner: a regeneration primordium soon appeared and an anlage was induced in the other component, then regression of both primordia occurred, after which both were revived and regeneration–reorganization went to completion. If in balance, with the forces of inhibition apparently equalling those of activation, neither resorption nor development occurs; the primordium is not merely arrested but seems abortive as it takes on a crumpled appearance, and so the graft complex remains for a half-day or more until an entirely new start is made

(D). Considering this case as a mid-point, the range of interactions was from one extreme of prompt and complete primordium resorption to the other, or precipitous induction of anlagen formation.

Where the final result will lie within this spectrum depends upon the stage of the original primordium, the relative volume of the two cells, and the intimacy of their union. As we shall see in

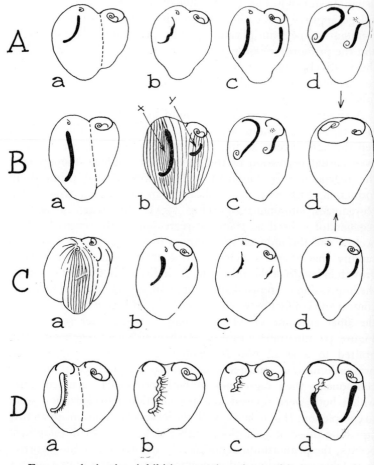

FIG. 35. Activation–inhibition reactions in parabiotic stentor grafts.

the next section, the stage of differentiation of the anlage is probably significant as marking the waxing and waning of a wave of activation. That this activation or the reciprocal state of inhibition characterizes some aspect of the whole cell is shown by the importance of the relative size of the two graft components. A large regenerator induces reorganization in a much smaller non-differentiating partner, if the latter is larger it forces the regenerator to back down and resorb its primordium. If the two cells are equal, anlage resorption also occurs, and this seems to indicate that the force of inhibition is stronger than that of activation. However that may be, the two forces or cell states are seen to be quantitative and potentially measurable.

On the other hand, the *stimulus* which starts the whole course of regeneration is stronger than the forces of inhibition, as indeed it must be if primordium formation is to be possible at all. Thus

---

A. Induced reorganization. *a:* Large stage–3 regenerator (activated) grafted to small non-differentiating partner (inhibited with respect to anlage formation). *b:* Initial partial regression of the primordium under influence of partner. *c:* Revival of regeneration primordium and induction of reorganization primordium in small partner. *d:* Regeneration–reorganization, with resorption and renewal of oral structures in the reorganizer, producing a doublet stentor.

B. *a:* Stage–4 regenerator grafted to small non-differentiating partner. *b:* More advanced regeneration primordium does not suffer partial regression and a reorganization anlage is induced so rapidly that no concomitant stripe multiplication occurs (*y*, cf. *x*). *c, d:* Regeneration–reorganization produces a doublet.

C. *a:* Stage–0 regenerator (stripes splitting in primordium site) grafted to small non-differentiating cell — immediately following operation to show how cells are split down the backs opened out and pressed together. *b:* Regenerator continues to stage 2, induced primordium in stage 1 (predominance of activation). *c:* Conspicuous regression of both anlagen (predominance of inhibition). *d:* Revival of primordia leading to doublet formation through regeneration on one side and reorganization on the other.

D. Abortive primordium development. *a:* Stage–4 regenerator grafted to non-differentiating animal of same or larger size. *b, c:* No induction. Advanced primordium arrested, shortened, crumpled — neither developing nor resorbing and showing no normal membranelles. *d:* Simultaneous regeneration and reorganization occurring much later.

if a large and a very small non-differentiating stentor are grafted together and the mouthparts then excised from the minor component, simultaneous regeneration and reorganization then occur in the graft complex (Tartar, 1954). For now the reorganization primordium is not to be regarded as induced by the regenerator; instead the stimulus to regeneration somehow passes from the small cell to the larger, causing it to produce its own state of activation.

Moreover, in some cases, stage–1 regenerators did induce reorganization in non-differentiating partners which were much larger than they. Here it is possible that something of the powerful original stimulus to regeneration, whatever its nature may be, lingers in the early regenerator to boost its inductive influence.

The relevance of the intimacy of union on the timing and final result of the interaction between a differentiating and a non-differentiating stentor will be important in analyzing the basis of the mutual influences (Weisz, 1956). When the two partners are firmly but not broadly joined, the reorganization primordium induced by a regenerator is noticeably tardy in appearing (Fig. 36A); when the joining is tenuous, there is no induction at all (B).

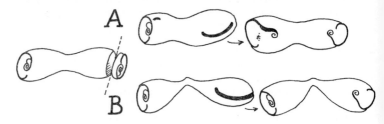

FIG. 36. Barriers to induced reorganization, shown in tail-to-tail telobiotics with one head excised.

A. When union is broad, regeneration in one induces reorganization in the other partner, but with considerable delay.

B. If connection is tenuous, no induced primordium formation occurs. (After Tartar, 1958b.)

2. Timing the period of activation

When a late stage–4 regenerator is grafted to a smaller non-differentiating stentor, there is usually the transient induction of a beginning reorganization primordium; but the regenerator now overtakes the reorganizer, and as the original primordium goes into its final development the induced anlagen is resorbed (see Fig. 38E). Stage–5 regenerators are no longer able to induce reorganization in a partner cell. Therefore we may say that as anlage development goes to completion the state of activation ceases and is replaced by a state of inhibition.

When does activation begin? This time can be determined by several tests. If a sector bearing the primordium of a regenerator is grafted into a regenerating stentor the transplanted anlage continues its development along with that of the host; but if the primordium is grafted into a regenerator in which the primordium has not yet appeared, the transplanted anlage is resorbed. When regeneration is induced by causing the membranellar band to be shed in salt solutions and when some of the salt is carried over with the specimen and regeneration is thereby much delayed, such cells are also not able to support primordia grafted to them although it may have been many hours since the stimulus to regenerate was given. And if stage–2 or 3 primordia are implanted on non-differentiating cells whose heads or mouthparts are then excised, the stimulus to regeneration in the host is not itself sufficient to support the primordium development and the anlage remains for a long time in arrested development or may even become partially resorbed, but is finally revived and continues differentiation as the host primordium itself appears and develops. Considering these results and allowing for an appreciable time-lag in the effects upon each other of host and graft, we can conclude that activation is not developed to an effective state until shortly before the primordium appears.

3. Relation of the macronucleus to activation and inhibition

The cell states relating to primordium formation and development seem to reside in the cytoplasm and are possibly restricted to the cortical layer or ectoplasm. The nuclei probably respond to changes in the cell state, as when macronuclear nodes condense and micronuclei undergo mitosis simultaneous with the passing of the cell from its state of activation to one of inhibition; but they do not seem to be the bearers or determiners of these cell states. The evidence for this is, briefly, that enucleated non-differentiating stentors cause as prompt and as complete a resorption of anlage in *nucleated* primordium sectors grafted to them as nucleated hosts, and the macronuclear nodes of an early regenerator can be replaced by those of a non-differentiating cell without stopping the course of regeneration (unpublished). In the latter experiment "non-regenerator" nucleus clumps and renodulates on cue just as the original nucleus would have done. It therefore appears that the nucleus simply responds to any demands made upon it by the cytoplasm without taking the lead in cell redifferentiation, though of course the macronucleus is essential to primordium formation.

Yet the presence of the macronucleus seems to be necessary for achieving a state of activation in the cytoplasm, as suggested by the following experiment. Both feeding organelles and macro-nuclei were removed from *coeruleus* and after five hours re-generation primordium sectors were grafted to them. Normally the hosts would have been in active regeneration by this time but now, lacking the nucleus, they behaved exactly like non-differentiating hosts, causing resorption of the grafted anlage. It follows that the nucleus is not only very probably essential to protein synthesis in the elaboration of the oral primordium but is also necessary for the achievement of the postulated state of activation in the cytoplasm. Another finding which points to the same conclusion is that if regenerators with early primordia are enucleated the anlage are then soon resorbed. Not only is there no further synthesis of ciliary proteins, or whatever is involved in the further development of the primordium; the developing organelles, in contrast to remnants of those already formed, are actually taken down and resorbed, so that it appears that the nucleus is necessary for the maintenance as well as the achievement of the state of activation.

4. Relation of intact feeding organelles to activation and inhibition

Because removal of all or of a substantial portion of the feeding organelles initiates their complete regeneration, it is natural to suppose that the formed parts had exerted an inhibition on the production of their like. Indeed, it is clear from the experiments recounted above that non-differentiating stentors are continually inhibiting primordium formation because they even cause resorption of already well-formed anlagen grafted on them. This relationship is common to regeneration in general, whether of plants or multicellular animals; for it is a general rule in regeneration and embryological studies that formed parts prevent neo-formations of their like and so allow the organism to attain stability and unity of form (see Child, 1941; and Rose, 1957). That there is specific inhibition between formed and potential structures can be demonstrated on the cell level in *Stentor* where it presents special problems as well as unusual opportunities for analysis.

The first exploratory experiment in this direction was performed by Prowazek (1904) when he cut dividing *coeruleus* in two transversely. If the animals were in an early stage of fission, the half of the primordium remaining in the anterior fragment was resorbed, but not in the posterior piece; yet he was not aware of the full significance of this simple test. Today we can say that the portion of the anlage in the anterior fragment was resorbed because of the presence of the intact feeding organelles, and conversely, that their absence in the posterior piece permitted the maintenance and continued development of its section of the primordium.

Weisz (1956) later found that it was sufficient merely to slice into an early divider to cause total resorption of the entire primordium. I have also found that a single slice into the cell, merely removing the tail tip (Tartar, 1958c), or even a too long exposure to the quieting agent, methyl cellulose, may cause stage 1 and 2 dividers to resorb the primordium. Even at stage 4 the anlage may be completely resorbed in the adoral half of dividers cut in two longitudinally. Early primordium sectors cut from these dividers, including the mouthparts but not much of the membranellar band, also resorb the anlage when isolated but not if the original mouthparts are also excised from the piece. The response of regenerators to cutting Weisz found to be entirely different, for the primordium is then never resorbed because of injuries. This point has also been adequately confirmed; following a standard maximal disturbance in which the regenerator was cut into three sections and spread out widely, the anlagen were never resorbed (Tartar, 1958c).

A simple explanation for this difference between dividers and regenerators is at once apparent. It is not because the division primordium is uniquely subject to reversal of its development

(Weisz, 1956), for we have seen that regeneration primordia can also be caused to be resorbed. The difference lies rather in the simple fact that dividers have an intact set of feeding organelles but regenerators do not. Thus if the injurious cut through a divider is such as to remove the entire feeding organelles or the mouthparts, then, as in Prowazek's original experiment, the division primordium is not resorbed. And therefore the simplest interpretation is that presence of intact organelles is the cause of resorption. Then, as Weisz himself suggested, in division (as in reorganization) the primordium site is somehow enabled to escape the inhibitive action of the existing feeding organelles and to produce an oral primordium in spite of their presence; and I would add that cutting injuries in some manner nullify this delicate escapement, thus enabling the formed parts to re-exert their full inhibitive force.

Inhibition by the intact feeding organelles would also explain why dividers do not produce a new primordium at once after anlage excision, as do regenerators.

The situation in dividers can be duplicated in regenerators by grafting a new head in place of the one that was removed (Tartar, 1958c). If the regenerator had not yet produced a primordium, it was prevented from doing so; or if it already had an early primordium, this was then resorbed (Fig. 37). When tails were grafted instead of heads, primordia were not resorbed. This is evidence that the formed feeding organelles exert an inhibitive action on primordium formation and development. With regenerators which had progressed beyond stage 2 the effect was not as marked and only partial resorption or merely arrested development occurred. But when the primordium was completely resorbed in recapped regenerators the majority of the specimens later reorganized. This suggests that complete healing may not have occurred, with complete union of lateral striping, and thus set the stage for later escapement of the primordium site in reorganization.

Similarly, it may be that in division, as in reorganization, there is some temporary and invisible severance of connection between the lateral body striping and the feeding organelles sufficient to break the path of oral inhibition and permit the formation of a primordium although intact feeding organelles are present.

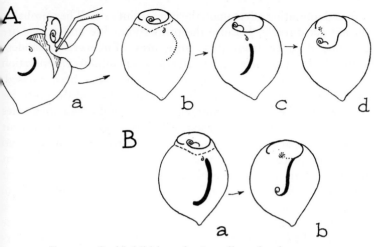

FIG. 37. Oral inhibition of primordium development.

A. Stage–2 regenerator is recapped with head from another stentor. By handling only pendent portion of donor, which is subsequently excised (*a*), injury to feeding organelles is prevented. *b*: Development is stopped and the anlage resorbed. This occurs neither on injury, alone, of regenerator nor after implanting tail poles; therefore a specific inhibition by formed oral structures. Most specimens reorganized later (*c*, *d*), and some divided instead.

B. When primordium was already at stage 4, it was not resorbed (*a*) and served for reorganizational replacement of the grafted feeding organelles. (After Tartar, 1958c.)

Reorganization and division would then be like regeneration in that the oral structures may be "self-excised", and if so, the regeneration response to cutting off the head or mouthparts would be not so much an adaptive behavior as a gross imitation or artificially induced performance of something that happens cryptically in the recurring processes of fission and reorganization. This in turn would at last answer Gruber's (1885a) question why stentors should be so capable of regenerating from injuries such as they are not likely to encounter in nature, as well as explain to a considerable extent his original conception of the close similarity between regeneration and division, a point repeatedly emphasized by later students of ciliate morphogenesis (see Balamuth, 1940).

We need to learn how these formed feeding organelles exert the inferred inhibiting effect upon the primordium site. They probably do not act directly, because the primordium site and anlage are at some distance from these structures. Moreover, in tandem grafts the head of the anterior cell effectively inhibits regeneration in the posterior partner, the head of which has been excised though the distance between ingestive organelles and the posterior primordium site is then abnormally great. Nor do these organelles give off some "inhibitory substance", since regeneration will occur if the mouthparts are merely cut and separated or the intact head rotated in place. Not the materials of the organelles but their proper pattern and relationship to the whole is essential to their inhibitory effect. Moreover, non-differentiating stentors from which the mouthparts have just been excised still can induce resorption of early regeneration primordia grafted to them. The tendency of the normal primordium site to form anlagen is apparently stronger than that of other loci in the lateral ectoplasm, and therefore requires a stronger inhibition. This is indicated by the finding that fusions of six aboral halves promptly regenerate whereas anlagen formation in these grafts without normal primordium sites is long delayed if one set of intact feeding organelles is present (Tartar, 1956a). In contrast, when one set of feeding organelles is removed from a doublet stentor, the remaining set is insufficient to prevent, or often even to delay, regeneration in the "unsaturated" primordium site left on the cut side.

As a working hypothesis it is suggested that formed oral structures act upon the lateral stripe pattern, with which they are connected, in such a way as to render this pattern inhibitive of primordium development. The entire cell-body ectoplasm would be involved in this inhibition, as indicated by the fact that the larger the volume of cytoplasm the greater the inhibition exerted. This state of inhibition could then be transmitted across the borders of a grafted sector, rendering the included striping in the patch also inhibitory and producing resorption of the primordium or the state of inhibition could be transmitted in a similar way over the ectoplasm of an adjoining cell. Conversely, when the head is excised or the mouthparts removed, oral inhibition is discontinued and the pattern of the body striping gradually transforms, with the aid of the nucleus, from a state of inhibition to one of activation which is to be characterized in the same way. The important point is that the development of the oral primordium is not a strictly local affair except in morphological terms, that the entire ectoplasm appears to be a continuum, that every part of this ectoplasm—even far from the primordium site—can affect the primordium development by either hindering or supporting it, depending on the intrinsic state of that cytoplasm.

5. Synchronization of developing primordia

In stentor grafts or complexes of more than one individuality there is a strong tendency for both or all oral primordia to complete their development together although they may have begun at different times. This synchronization was first indicated by Johnson in his observation of redifferentiation in an adventitious double-tandem monster of *coeruleus*. The anterior individuality had a complete set of feeding organelles but the posterior lacked the mouthparts. An anlage first appeared in the posterior component, then somewhat later primordium formation also occurred in the anterior component which had no need for regeneration; but in spite of the difference in the time of their appearances the two primordia soon fell into phase and developed simultaneously. This case may therefore be regarded as the first observation of a regenerator inducing reorganization in its partner; and it suggested that in such double systems both parts tend to do the same things together and at the same time.

Even within a single primordium the parts tend to develop together when they might do otherwise. Thus if half of an early anlage is excised there is a compensating growth in length of the primordium but a difference between younger and older developing membranelles is not detectable (Tartar, 1957c). Evidently the older part waits while the growth of the new part is accelerated. This effect is still more striking in cases in which an original primordium later extends into a new primordium site which is often produced by graftings. This and other examples described in Fig. 38 show how an anlage extension or an induced reorganization primordium may differentiate very rapidly in order to catch up with the first anlage, often apparently cutting short its growth in length in its haste to develop. Conversely, in the achievement of simultaneity of development, arrest and delay of one of the anlagen is often noticeable.

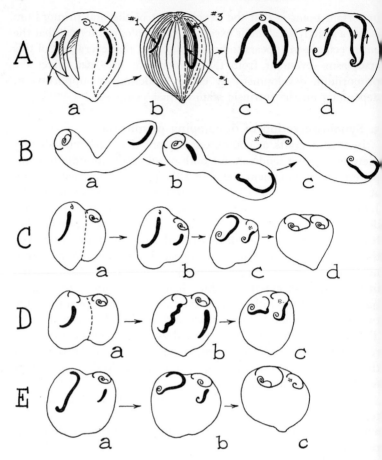

Fig. 38. Synchronization of primordia within a graft complex.

A. *a:* Anlage of a stage–1 regenerator excised and patch with stage–3 regeneration primordium implanted. *b:* Stage–3 anlage arrested while an extension occurs adjacent to wide-stripe area of host which forms a new primordium, both the latter in stage 1. *c:* All three anlagen synchronous by stage 4. *d:* Primordia join, with metachronal waves of membranelles continuous in direction of arrows. Implanted anlage, with its extension, forms a V-shape which undergoes stomatogenesis at the point and a doublet stentor is formed.

These are only a sample of many observations (unpublished) in which synchronous development within the same system by arrest of one primordium, or acceleration of the other, or both occurred. But if the phase difference between the two anlagen is great, simultaneity cannot be achieved and the older primordium overtakes the much younger one, causing the system to pass into a state of morphogenetic inhibition, resulting in resorption or very incomplete development of the younger anlage (Fig. 38E).

Synchronization of primordia, often involving astonishing accelerations and delays in development, should have important implications which are only coming into view. For one thing, it is clear that each primordium is not given a start and a source of substrates and a suitable environment to proceed on its own. Instead, the two primordia are as it were in continuous "communication" with each other though they may be at opposite sides of the cell. One suggestion that comes to mind is that there is a competition for substrates which the younger primordia are able to take up more avidly. But the supply does not seem to be limited, since induced primordia are formed and present anlage

---

B. *a:* Telebiotic with narrow connection has stage–3 anlage at end from which the feeding organelles were excised. *b:* Original primordium at stage 5; induced anlage appeared at other end and developed precipitously to stage 4. *c:* Both anlagen synchronized at stage 6 and regeneration with induced reorganization continues.

C. *a:* Smaller non-differentiating stentor grafted to stage–3 regenerator. *b:* Original anlage now in stage 4 and induced reorganization primordium has developed so rapidly that it is now in the same stage. *c, d:* Synchronous regeneration and reorganization to produce a doublet.

D. *a:* Stage–3 divider, with mouthparts excised, grafted to non-differentiating stentor of same size. *b:* Division primordium develops to stage 4 but becomes crumpled as it is arrested and waits for induced reorganization to attain the same stage. *c:* Synchronous regeneration–reorganization proceeds from stage 4 onward. The graft complex did not divide.

E. Stage–5 regenerator grafted to non-differentiating partner. A reorganization primordium is induced (*a*) in the partner, but the regenerator continues development and passes out of the stage of activation. Thereby induced anlage is "overtaken" and can neither develop to normal length nor produce mouthparts to replace those resorbed.

readily extend themselves into new primordium sites. Another possibility is that somehow the anlage does receive morphogenetic guidance from the surrounding ectoplasm which acts as a unit and that the ectoplasm as a whole gives "information" only one step at a time, instead of a single command to make a primordium. However this may be, we see again that the cell makes a strong attempt to act together in all its parts as a single integrated unit

6. Activation in reorganizers and dividers

It is natural to suppose that the state of activation which is not of the nucleus but of the cytoplasm and can be transmitted from one cell to another, or from a host cell to a grafted patch, is to be found whenever an oral primordium develops. Therefore reorganizers and dividers should also be in this state. This can be tested by determining whether they continue to support oral differentiation in regeneration primordia grafted to them, in the same way that regenerating cells do. They do. Reorganizers support regeneration primordia (Tartar, 1958b), likewise for dividers. But in the case of dividers the intact feeding organelles seem to exert a greater effect than in reorganizers and the mouthparts usually have to be excised if a grafted anlage is not to be resorbed along with the host's, following the injury of cutting Conversely, both division and reorganization primordia are resorbed when grafted to non-differentiating cells. We may conclude that oral primordia arising under any circumstance require the same type of cytoplasmic as well as nuclear support.

7. Rerouting the oral primordium

This state of activation, or readiness to support primordium development which is common to all re-differentiating stentors, points to a basic similarity of dividers, reorganizers, and regenerators which has often been remarked. It was Gruber who first noted that oral regeneration is accomplished through the formation of a lateral primordium like that appearing in the normal course of division. The unique characteristic of fission is not anlage formation but the development and constriction of a division furrow, and this aperçu of Johnson's is amply confirmed by the fact that dividers as early as stage 3 can proceed to complete separation after the primordium is excised. Otherwise, events in regeneration and division are very similar. In both, the macro-nuclear beads coalesce. Causin even described an instance of temporary division of this compacted nucleus in a regenerating stentor, though this is probably exceptional. In both there is mitotic division of the micronuclei (Guttes and Guttes, 1959).

Reorganization is obviously similar to regeneration in that a new set of feeding organelles is produced while the original individuality of the organism is retained, and the accompanying nuclear changes are similar. Schwartz (1935) commented on the resemblances between reorganizers and dividers: in both there is oral primordium formation in the presence of an already complete set of feeding organelles; and in reorganizers as in dividers there can occur the mitotic multiplication of micronuclei as well as an increase in the number of macronuclear nodes. A basic similarity in division, reorganization, and regeneration was recognized by Weisz (1949a) who conceived of these processes as alternative responses to a graded series of stimuli increasingly forceful in their extrinsic character.

In all three programs of morphogenesis, oral primordium formation occurs and a basic similarity is best demonstrated by the fact that the anlage can be rerouted to serve other ends than that for which it was originally "intended". In other words, morphogenesis can be "reprogrammed"; for it can be shown that a stentor is not irrevocably set upon one course from the start. Johnson, for example, described a case in which a reorganizing *coeruleus* seemed to have transformed itself into a divider. At first the primordium ran all the way forward to contact the original membranellar band, as is characteristic of reorganizers, but then a secondary contractile vacuole developed and the anterior portion of the anlage was resorbed, whereupon the cell divided. I read this report with some scepticism because I have never seen resorption restricted to one section of the primordium; although I have observed three instances in which a *coeruleus* which should have re-organized divided instead. These were from regenerating animals, the primordium and neighboring ectoplasm and endoplasm of which had been excised so that they had already suffered a con-siderable reduction in volume, which is supposed to preclude division (Weisz, 1956). A new anlage was then produced so rapidly that no stripe multiplication occurred and the resulting

frontal field and head was much too small in relation to the size
of the cell. This disproportion is almost always the occasion for
reorganization, defined as the spontaneous replacement of major
portions of an intact set of feeding organelles by a new one; but in

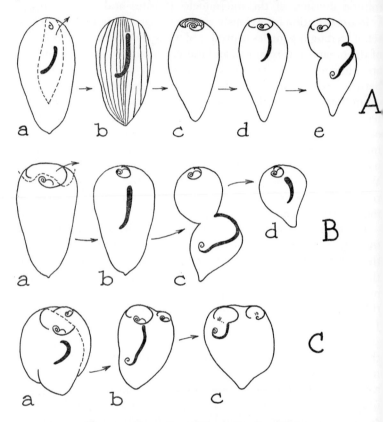

FIG. 39. Rerouting of the oral primordium.

A. Reorganization anlage presumably serving for division.
a: Primordium excised from stage–3 regenerator. *b:* New
anlage promptly formed in line of heal, without stripe multiplication. *c:* Hence regenerated frontal field and head are too small.
d: This disproportion is usually the stimulus to reorganization
and an anlage altogether like that of reorganizer (not Ɔ-shaped
as in divider) is formed. *e:* Yet animal may divide instead of
reorganizing, even though its original volume was considerably
reduced by excision.

these instances the stentors divided instead (Fig. 39). One may suppose that for some obscure reason the primordium which developed for the purpose of reorganization was used instead for the division, nevertheless, of animals considerably smaller than the maximum size.

It is also possible, but again not indubitably demonstrated, that regenerators can be converted into dividers. In experiments already described, all of the membranellar band but none of the mouthparts or all of the mouthparts but none of the membranellar band were removed from larger animals, with the result that division almost invariably occurred, thus representing cases in which an operation which would ordinarily be expected to incite regeneration led to fission instead. The primordia did appear at first exactly like those of regenerators, but subsequently the anterior ends of the anlagen bent to the right as division was accomplished in the typical manner (B).

Regenerating stentors can easily be converted into reorganizers. When a complete head is grafted to a regenerator to replace the one which was excised and the regeneration anlage is not resorbed, then this primordium finds attachment to the intact membranellar band and the preexisting mouthparts are resorbed as they are replaced (see Fig. 37).

Dividers are frequently converted into reorganizers by many types of operation which permit the continued development of the division primordium but somehow block furrow formation. Causin reported that mere transfer of dividing stentors onto a slide often resulted in their undergoing reorganization instead,

---

B. Regenerator becomes a divider. *a:* If either membranellar band (as shown) or the mouthparts only are excised, a regeneration primordium is called for and appears (*b*) but serves for division instead (*c*) even though ablation decreased cell volume. *d:* Proter regenerates proportionate oral structures later.

C. Divider becomes reorganizer. *a:* Stage–3 divider grafted to oral half of a small, non-differentiating stentor. *b:* No induced primordium in small partner; anlage of divider develops to stage 6 without commencing division or reorganization. *c:* Anlage finally used to reorganize larger animal; later the mouthparts of the partner were also resorbed though having no reorganization primordium from which to replace them. Next day the specimen performed double regeneration–reorganization.

and this was confirmed by Hetherington (1932b). When mid-stage dividers were greatly disturbed by cutting and spreading them out in a clover-leaf pattern, the separated parts then healed together and the primordium continued to develop, but almost all of the specimens reorganized instead of dividing (Tartar, 1958c). Division was usually only thereby postponed, and successful fission with a new primordium generally occurred some time later. Likewise, when heads of early dividers were circumscribed and rotated 180° on the body, there occurred an initial partial regression of the division primordia, probably due to the cutting injury as such, after which the anlagen continued developing but moved forward instead of posteriorly and the animals reorganized instead of dividing. In three cases a stage–3 divider was grafted to a small non-differentiating stentor or to the oral longitudinal half of such an animal. The primordium served only to replace the feeding organelles of the divider and, surprisingly enough, the mouthparts of the partner were also gradually resorbed though there were none to take its place (Fig. 39c). When early dividers were grafted to regenerators, regeneration proceeded on one side while reorganization instead of division occurred on the other as already mentioned in connection with dividers failing to induce division. Even when two stage–3 dividers were grafted together in homopolar parabiosis they reorganized doubly instead of dividing. It is clear that furrow formation is not determined from the beginning of the division process but is inaugurated much later, so that shifts from division to reorganization are possible.

Likewise dividers can easily be changed into regenerators. Causin had at least one case in which he cut off the anterior right hand corner with membranelles of an early dividing *coeruleus* the primordium of which then served for regeneration instead of division. When primordium sectors were cut and isolated from dividing animals, these pieces made no attempt to divide but used the anlagen to regenerate the missing ingestive organelles (Tartar, 1958c). It was also shown that if the head or feeding organelles are excised from dividing cells they then regenerated instead, postponed fission with the formation of a new division primordium usually occurring sometime later. In conclusion it may be said that in their beginning phases fission, reorganization, and regeneration are more similar than different, so that a stentor embarked upon any one of these courses is not irrevocably determined to pursue no other.

The experimental analysis reviewed in this chapter demonstrates that stentors alternate through at least two cell states involving some pervasive aspect of the cell. A prolonged state of inhibition of oral primordium formation which maintains the *status quo* of the formed organism alternates with another and more transitory state promoting redifferentiation of feeding organelles which prevails during regeneration, reorganization, and division. Moreover, the stimulus to regeneration appears to be another condition separable from the subsequent activation, transmissible to any grafted partner regardless of size and resulting in its parallel reorganization. Whether there is a "division state" or predisposition to fission which is likewise transmissible in fusion complexes is still obscured by contradictory evidence.

Besides clarifying the question of division, we next need to know in what parts of stentor these cell states reside. Present evidence suggests that the nucleus is not involved, since macronuclei can be exchanged between regenerators and non-differentiating stentors without effect. A nucleus or some nucleus is essential for primordium formation and development but this organelle apparently does not take the lead. Enucleated non-differentiating stentors are as capable of inducing anlagen resorption as nucleate. Preliminary tests in which stentors bereft of the endoplasm show the same inhibitive influence suggest that cell states reside in the cortical layer. If so, these states characterize the entire ectoplasm because the effect is quantitative and depends on the relative sizes of the joined stentors. Every part of this or some other pervasive feature of the cell may be involved in the cell states of activation and inhibition and somehow capable of affecting what occurs locally at the primordium site, as indicated by the quantitative relationships.

After those parts of stentor which "carry" or take the lead in establishing cell states are identified, the next step according to conventional procedure would be to obtain a biochemical characterization of the changes in these parts. It is natural to suppose that intercellular transmission in grafts would occur via the semi-fluid endoplasm which flows and mixes between the two partners. For instance, this endoplasm, during primordium formation and development, might be charged with an unusual amount of RNA in support of the extensive synthesis which then presumably occurs. But if it is the semi-solid ectoplasm which is involved, the transmission would be more probably something like an electrical excitation of a more novel character. Moreover, the synchronization of developing anlagen without indication of competition for substrates suggests that not one substance or state of excitation is concerned but a series, paralleling the stages in primordium development.

If nourished stentors are continually undergoing structural growth and not merely stretching or extending the distance between their formed parts as seems evident in the case of the lateral striping (see Fig. 11A), how is this possible when during the same period synthesis and morphogenesis in oral redifferentiation is being so effectively inhibited that a stentor can even cause the regression of the primordium of another stentor and even after that anlage has been well-started? Yet extensive nodal increase in the macronucleus does seem to require the state of activation or its final phases, since this increase occurs only during the last stages of primordium development and it appears that reorganizers may instigate anlagen formation in order to accomplish this nuclear increase. Evidently the different parts of the pattern of cortical differentiations, however, constitute a very precise responding system in respect to growth; and this is also indicated by specific resorption of extra mouthparts or in a disproportionately long membranellar band, when all other parts remain apparently unaffected.

In the resolution of such problems relating to cell states in *Stentor* I think we may expect interesting discoveries which may in turn prove relevant to cell differentiation in general.

CHAPTER IX

PRIMORDIUM DEVELOPMENT

AN ACUTELY FELT omission in our data on *Stentor* is the lack of silver-stain or electron micrographic studies of the developing oral primordium. We have therefore no idea of what happens on the level of fine structure during the most dramatic act of cyto-differentiation. Yet much can be said in simple description of the forming anlage and its relation to the pattern of lateral striping. This relationship is two-fold: first, some of the ectoplasmic stripes and bands adjacent to the primordium join with it to complete the integrated parts of the ingestive apparatus, and second, the anlage arises in definite correlation with the topography of the cell surface.

1. Normal location and development of the primordium

At its inception the oral primordium seems to violate the cortical pattern because it makes its appearance as a break in the ectoplasm, cutting across the striping. The unpigmented rift suggested to Johnson that the primordium originates in the endoplasm and breaks through to the surface. He further argued that the ectoplasm is too thin to supply the materials needed for this extensive elaboration, besides being too highly differentiated to participate in such "embryonic" formations. In the related *Bursaria truncatella*, Schmähl (1926) also found that the primordium gives the appearance of breaking through the ectoplasm, yet his cross-sections clearly showed him that the anlage lay entirely in the surface. On the basis of other ciliate studies (see Lwoff, 1950) it is probable that the anlage is formed entirely in the ecto-plasm and requires cortical derivatives such as kinetosomes for its composition. Villeneuve-Brachon (1940) described accumula-tion of kinetosomes in the early primordium, and these, in *Stentor* as in the related *Fabrea*, seem to arise by multiplication of granules in the existing ciliary rows.

159

If the anlage has to cross the striping, it is apparent that the structural components of the clear stripes would have to be sundered and the pigment granules pushed aside to make room for the primordium. Much simpler would be merely to have the stripes spread apart and permit the anlage to form parallel to them; and this does occur in *Folliculina ampulla*, in which the primordium follows the contour of the stripes (Fauré-Fremiet, 1932). In this and other forms (see Lwoff) one could speak of a " stomatogenic kinety ", if all kinetosomes of the primordium arise in connection with a single kinety. But even in the related *Semifolliculina*, Andrews (1923) described the oral primordium as cutting across the lateral striping. Also like *Stentor*, there is in the Ophryoglenids no single kinety which produces the primordium, according to Mugard (1947). In the latter there seems to be good reason for this type of development. Where the primordium site cuts across the lateral stripes these are bent and a small section cut out of each kinety, the sections then combining to form the anlage. This does not occur in *Stentor*, and there are certainly more membranelles produced than kineties which are cut by the anlage. Although the anlage of *Stentor* may come to lie largely parallel to the lateral striping, even those of the "French school" did not maintain that it arises from a single "stomatogenic kinety" (Chatton and Séguéla, 1940). All we can say at present regarding the elaboration of the membranellar band is that kinetosomes appear from somewhere in the rift provided for them, sprout cilia, and align themselves in a series of parallel rows to make the membranelles. This corresponds to Schmähl's descriptions of *Bursaria* in which he observed first single cilia with separated basal bodies later coming together as membranelles.

Normally, the primordium always appears on the ventral side of the cell at about one-third the distance in contracted animals between the mouthparts and the posterior pole. This precise localization of the anlage was emphasized by Schuberg (1890) who correlated it with local differences in the pattern of lateral striping. Thus the primordium appears in what he called the ramifying zone, a zone of abbreviated striping bounded right and left by bands which do run from pole to pole. Schwartz (1935) however has pointed out that as the primordium increases in length its anterior end may overstep the left boundary stripe, so that there is nothing magically restrictive about the ramifying zone as far as primordium formation is concerned.

In fact, Morgan (1901a) soon found that oral regeneration occurred readily enough even after the normal site of the anlage was removed, and Stevens (1903) confirmed this by showing that in longitudinal aboral halves lacking this site entirely the oral primordium appeared in the line of heal. Fauré-Fremiet then posed explicitly the question of whether, if the primordium always appears at the same place in stentors, there is some specialized potential restricted to this area; but his student Causin (1931) likewise found that the normal primordium site could be completely eliminated without preventing regeneration. Therefore there are not localized potentialities for oral differentiation in one region of the cell. This point has been amply confirmed by later students of *Stentor*, including myself. Weisz regarded the oral primordium as arising from a single stomatogenic kinety next to the left boundary stripe of the ramifying zone. He stated (1953, 1954) that not only tiny fragments but also pieces larger than half the cell can be cut which do not regenerate because they lack the specialized kinetosomes of this meridian; although reporting that longitudinal aboral halves can regenerate and that in division the primordium bends so that it *eventually* touches the left boundary stripe, from which it follows that the anlage originates away from this stripe. That the ectoplasm is virtually totipotent throughout as regards oral differentiation will become even clearer as our discussion proceeds, and this is not contradictory to the fact that the oral primordium usually appears in a certain place.

Stages of visible change in the anlage in regeneration have been defined (Tartar, 1957c) and are altogether comparable to those of division (Fig. 40). The first sign of primordium formation as seen in *coeruleus* is a scooping of the pigment granules to each side as a rift crosses about 10 granular stripes (Moxon, 1869). A groove with slightly projecting flanges is evident at later stages in cross-sectioned view, as shown. Stripe multiplication also occurs with the splitting of granular bands both immediately above and below the primordium. The primordium extends from both ends, cutting across more stripes posteriorly, the anterior end reaching forward. Now the anlage has a glistening appearance, presumably due to cilia growing out from kinetosomes included within it.

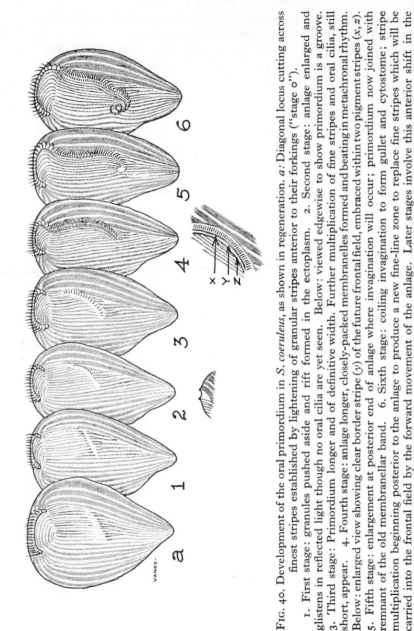

FIG. 40. Development of the oral primordium in *S. coeruleus*, as shown in regeneration. *a*: Diagonal locus cutting across finest stripes established by lightening of granular stripes anterior to their forkings ("stage o").

1. First stage: granules pushed aside and rift formed in the ectoplasm. Below: viewed edgewise to show primordium is a groove, glistens in reflected light though no oral cilia are yet seen. 2. Second stage: anlage enlarged and 3. Third stage: Primordium longer and of definitive width. Further multiplication of fine stripes and oral cilia, still short, appear. 4. Fourth stage: anlage longer, closely-packed membranelles formed and beating in metachronal rhythm. Below: enlarged view showing clear border stripe (*y*) of the future frontal field, embraced within two pigment stripes (*x*, *z*). 5. Fifth stage: enlargement at posterior end of anlage where invagination will occur; primordium now joined with remnant of the old membranellar band. 6. Sixth stage: coiling invagination to form gullet and cytostome; stripe multiplication beginning posterior to the anlage to produce a new fine-line zone to replace fine stripes which will be carried into the frontal field by the forward movement of the anlage. Later stages involve this anterior shift in the

This I have called stage 2. At stage 3 the anlage has become somewhat longer and the cilia are clearly visible in it but they have not attained their final length. Even so, as Johnson observed, the cilia begin beating on their first appearance, at first slowly and without coordination. Oral cilia then attain their definitive length, and transverse stripes in the rift indicate the formation of membranelles which now beat slowly but in metachronal rhythm. The membranelles are at first very close together and they will produce a membranellar band longer than the primordium as the distance between them later increases (Stevens, 1903; Schwartz, 1935).

As now deployed, there runs immediately to the right of the membranellar row a pigment stripe and to the right of this a clear band (the border stripe of Schuberg), and further to the right another pigment stripe, which three will form the border stripes of the frontal field. In the meantime, in an extensive area to the right of these, considerable stripe multiplication has usually occurred with formation of many kineties separated by very fine granular stripes, as Moxon first noted. It is these fine stripes which will form the new frontal field, as well as the lining of the buccal pouch and of the gullet in part. At stage 5 the posterior end of the anlage enlarges a bit and begins to make a sharp bend to the right in the initiation of mouthparts formation. A spiraling ingrowth of the end of the primordium forms the gullet (stage 6). In this invagination the terminal membranelles are carried down inside the cell, as well as the posterior ends of the fine striping, and shortly a gullet lined with bright refringent oral cilia and pigmented ectoplasm is produced. It seems likely that there are some further additions at this time to produce the complete lining of the gullet, but this is not known for sure.

At stage 7 the ectoplasm adjacent to the membranellar band and just forward of the spiral gullet begins, in *coeruleus*, to depress and form the oral pouch as the anlage starts shifting into its final position. With further development the entire anlage moves into its final position, carrying the new stripes with it as the enclosed frontal field (stage 8). In this migration the primordium which at mid-stage was roughly parallel to the lateral striping comes to assume a position at right angles to it and this may involve cutting and shifting of stripes, as Moxon remarked, as well as compensating growth in length of the stripes below the new mouthparts

(Schwartz, 1935). As the two ends of the new membranellar band approach each other the enclosed fine stripes are bent into arcs in the frontal field.

There are certain modifications of the primordium in different types of morphogenesis. Speaking teleologically, the primordium in reorganization needs only to replace the original mouthparts which will be dissolved, and, as Schwartz emphasized, there is accordingly less multiplication of fine stripes than in either division or regeneration. In dividers the anlage, already at stage-2, may appear semicircular as its anterior end also bends to the right and cuts across lateral striping, and stripe multiplication may be observed along both ends (see Fig. 15A). On the contrary, in regenerators and reorganizers the anterior end of the primordium usually runs straight forward to the anterior pole or to a pre-existing adoral membranellar band. The Ɔ-shaped primordium is usually diagnostic of dividing animals. All primordia begin in stage 1 at the same site and level of the cell. This was remarked in reference to regenerators and reorganizers by Johnson. My impression is that it is also true of dividers, Weisz (1951b) to the contrary.

Earlier students of *Stentor* in the heyday of the recapitulation theory saw an evolutionary significance in the lateral origin of the oral primordium in stentors. Both Schuberg (1890) and Johnson (1893) regarded this as a return to a more primitive design in heterotrichous ciliates. *Spirostomum*, presumably more primitive, retains the lateral disposition of the membranellar band and resembles regenerating stentors in stage 6. In *Fabrea* the mouthparts would be shifted half-way forward from their original posterior location having the appearance of stage 7 in stentors. In *Stentor* itself they would eventually achieve the wholly anterior disposition. Finally, in Folliculinids the highest development would be achieved, in which there is an enormous extension of the membranellar band in two folds projecting outward from the anterior end.

2. Primordium development under abnormal conditions

Such is the normal development of the oral primordium so far as we now know. Its behavior under unusual circumstances may give us some insight into the processes involved (Tartar, 1958b).

First, multiplication of lateral striping is not essential for anlagen formation, as shown when a large regenerator, for example, induces the precipitous formation of a reorganization primordium in a small, non-differentiating animal grafted to it. An anlage appears which cuts across several stripes which show no splitting whatever and an extensive presumptive frontal field is not produced (see Fig. 34B). Dissociability of stripe multiplication and membranellar band formation is further indicated by the reciprocal process of induced primordium resorption; for when this occurs the new band disappears entirely but there is no regression of the newly-multiplied fine stripes and ciliary rows which then contrast sharply with the neighboring stripes remaining (Fig. 34A). When a newly forming membranellar band is caused to be shed by treatment with salt solutions at a relatively late stage in anlage development, the multiplied fine striping can still be moved forward to form a new frontal field, indicating that these stripes are not merely shifted passively by the migrating adoral band (Fig. 41B).

The disposition of the original anlage rift at stage 1 is not rigidly fixed. It may run almost perpendicular to the striping or its course may sometimes be considerably canted at about 30° to the striping. In one case it slanted downward instead of upward though this did not interfere with normal oral formation (Fig. 41A). The primordium opening need not cut across the lateral striping at all. Thus Stevens (1903) observed that in longitudinal half fragments the anlage appears in the line of heal which runs from pole to pole. But this type of development is shown most clearly when the primordium, excised from a regenerating animal, is replaced at once. The line of heal, at first tightly closed, opens to permit the formation of a new primordium entirely parallel to the striping (see Fig. 34B). Since such specimens were already in regeneration, the new anlage develops very rapidly and there is apparently insufficient time for stripe multiplication. After stage 6, posterior ends of such replacing primordia curl to the right, cutting through some of the relatively large preexisting stripes which are carried forward to form new frontal fields of abnormal appearance.

The primordium need not develop as a unit or single entity from the start. When through abortive fission a head-like structure remains athwart the primordium site, anlage development

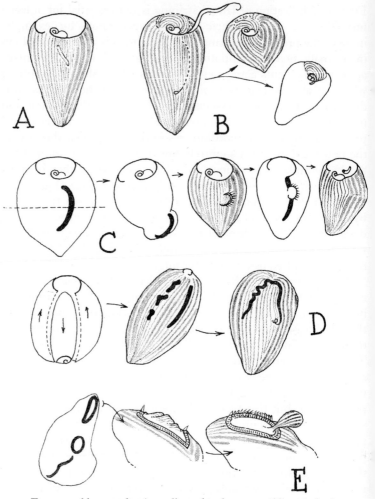

FIG. 41. Abnormal primordium developments (*S. coeruleus*).

A. Anlage slanting in direction opposite from the normal, satisfactory reorganization nevertheless accomplished.

B. Stage–5 divider treated with dilute sea water to cause shedding of membranellar band and all but posterior end of the division primordium. Though the posterior daughter formed only a gullet, this organelle and the multiplied striping of the prospective frontal field moved anteriorly to their normal positions. Both cells then regenerated.

C. Stage-4 divider transected and posterior fragment discarded. In continued "division" the anterior half of the anlage was shifted to the posterior end of the anterior fragment, later moving forward and forming a crescent of membranelles. After the mouthparts were excised, a regeneration primordium appeared which bridged the interrupting crescent. A nearly normal animal was regenerated (though with an extra tube in the frontal field) either by resorption of the crescent or its incorporation into the new membranellar band.

D. Island primordia formed when post-oral sector was reversed 180°. Anlagen formation on both sides of the patch. Islands of membranelles joined with each other and with the second primordium but complete mouthparts were not formed. After several transformations the specimen eventually became normal.

E. Capacity for erosion of ectoplasm shown in narrow-loop primordium. Graft of 4 *coeruleus* produced one normal, one ring- and one loop-primordium. Enlarged view of latter in second sketch shows "erosion", lifting and buckling of ectoplasmic striping enclosed within the membranellar band, leading eventually to the separation of a bleb of ectoplasm. Only membranelles and oral pouch were formed

F. Etching of clear band alongside an oral primordium. *a:* Stage-4 reorganizer (anterior) grafted in tandem with a stage-1 regenerator. *b:* Anlagen synchronized at stage-5, interrupted by oral remnant of the regenerator and stomatogenesis confined to the posterior primordium. *c:* Oral remnant either resorbed or incorporated. Clear band to right of primordium, apparently from dissolving of ectoplasmic structures, permits viewing through the interior of the cell with its food vacuoles to the ectoplasm on the far side. An elongated singlet produced which soon reorganized with two anlagen.

G. Dissolving of ectoplasmic striping in presumptive oral region (*x*) at stage 5—observed in experimental animals but may be an exaggeration of a normal process preceding oral invagination.

H. Divider in stage 2 transected through the anlage and halves rotated. Essentially there was no growth in length of the sections of the primordium, as if blocked by abutting stripes. Oral differentiation was incomplete in both halves, but the original mouthparts incurred reorganizational resorption.

I. Development of a V-shaped primordium. These are formed in addition to the host primordium when a fine stripe sector (*x*) is implanted into the back of a regenerator. The point of the V invaginates to form a good cytostome and gullet though two membranellar bands are involved. Resorption of subtended portion of old peristome permits entrance of new fine stripes into the frontal field.

M

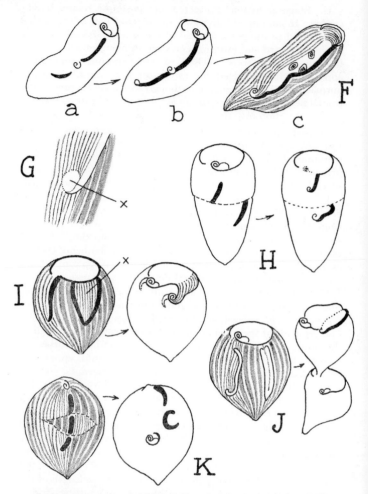

J. Development of a loop primordium. To a stage–3 divider was grafted a stage–2 regeneration primordium. As shown in first sketch, the host anlage is developed to stage 5 and the implanted primordium extended to form two parallel membranellar bands separated by only a single stripe. The specimen divided, with the loop primordium going to the proter, resorbing one of the bands and forming no mouthparts but only a curl.

K. Polarity in early stage–4 primordium. Mid-section was reversed *in situ*. Parts did not rejoin, as when merely transected, but developed separately.

may occur both above and below it with a single mouth produced only in the lower segment (Fig. 41C). In one unusual instance, in which the cell was cut in two longitudinally and the halves rotated 180° on each other, an adventitious primordium appeared first as a series of islands of oral cilia which later connected to produce a good membranellar band though mouthparts were not formed (D). These cases suggest that primordium formation is the result of local episodes of elaboration along its length rather than a differentiation proceeding from a single center.

Other observations indicate that dissolving or etching of formed parts may be involved in the later stages of primordium development, as if in this way space is provided for the evolving parts. Thus in *Bursaria truncatella* (Schmähl, 1926) and in *Condylostoma magnum* (Tartar, 1941b) the oral groove seems to be scooped out of the cytoplasm by an active process of dissolution. Something like this was seen in the development of an unusual stentor primordium in the form of a pinched ring. The enclosed striping was dissolved and cut out as a pendent tongue of cytoplasm (E). In two cases the breakdown or dissolving of ectoplasmic structures along the whole length of the primordium was conspicuous, and one of these is shown (F). This was in a tandem graft of two *Stentor coeruleus* in which, at stage 6 in development of the joined primordium, a wide break in the striping was seen to the right so that one could clearly see through the transparent plasma membrane into the cell interior, and the gap was later covered by scattered pigment granules not in rows. This may have been an exaggerated picture of what happens when a place is provided for the clear border stripe to the right of the membranellar band, as well as a demonstration that pigment granules tend to invade any open or unstructured area of ectoplasm. The case is also reminiscent of normal events in primordium formation in *Folliculina*, already mentioned, in which a gape or spreading of the longitudinal striping to a distance of 15 μ occurs. When primordium formation occurs without stripe multiplication there is sometimes the appearance at stage 5 of a dissolving of the ectoplasm near the posterior end of the anlage (G) and this might be regarded as a localized etching of the structured cortex to permit the inward invagination of the anlage in gullet formation.

Lengthening of the primordium can be blocked by incompatible striping. Thus when cell and primordium were cut transversely and the anterior half of the stentor rotated 180° on the posterior, there was no extension of the primordium from the cut end and very short membranellar bands were produced (H). This suggests that increase in length occurs in all parts of the primordium and not merely at its ends.

When the stripe pattern is abnormal after certain grafting operations V-shaped and even looped primordia may be formed (Fig. 41, I and J). The former can produce mouthparts of normal appearance, and the latter make an attempt to do so, though the conditions for invaginations are certainly quite atypical.

These and other types of oral development show that cyto-differentiation is not so delicately precise a process that interferences cannot be surmounted. They also demonstrate the important point made by Driesch that the same result in organic development can be achieved by several routes, even exceeding the usual experience of the organism.

3. Determination, or the progressive specification of the oral anlage

Only early-stage anlagen are resorbable (Weisz, 1956; Tartar, 1958c). Stage 3 appears to be the time of transition, after which oral primordia become self developing systems resistant to resorptive influences, though some early stage–4 anlagen, not actually resorbed, developed astomatously or with incomplete mouthparts. Weisz cut off the tails of late dividers including the posterior end of the primordium and found that the anlage then produced no mouthparts. Similarly, Lund (1917), working with *Bursaria truncatella*, stated that minor injury to the anlage of the gullet did not prevent development of the oral primordium but led to abnormality in the oral structures produced. He concluded that " there appears to exist in the anlage of the gullet a definite part which corresponds to a definite structure in the fully differentiated gullet ".

These isolated indications led to a comprehensive demonstration on the cell level of something very much like the determination of parts in developing embryos (Tartar, 1957c). It is well known that embryonic anlagen are at first modifiable but later not. This developmental principle seems to be simply a statement that once a complex is well underway it cannot be modified and there is no turning back, which is a rather universal generalization; yet in the development of the relatively new science of biology it was very important to find that the elaboration of the organism is not magical and immutable but is a process which occurs in time and is subject to some analysis by operative manipulations. In many respects it can be shown that this principle also applies to *Stentor*.

First we shall discuss deletion experiments on the oral primordium. Minimal excisions of parts of the oral primordium, always necessarily including some of the surrounding ectoplasm and endoplasm, were performed on regenerating stentors in stages 4 and 5 when the membranellar band is already well formed but there is still no visible indication whatever of developing mouthparts. When the anterior halves of such anlagen were removed, development continued and complete mouthparts were formed but the membranellar band was only half its normal length (Fig. 42A). Re-regeneration then occurred about a day later to produce a set of feeding organelles in normal proportion to the size of the cell. If the posterior half or third of the primordium was excised, only a considerable length of membranellar band was produced and no mouthparts at all, with re-regeneration now following sooner (B). Extensive removal of all but the posterior end of the anlage could lead to formation of a perfect set of mouthparts without any membranellar band at all (C); and removal of only the posterior tip, at stage 5 or early stage 6, resulted in complete absence of the gullet although oral pouch and membranellar band were normal (D). Finally, by removing a penultimate section of the anlage at stage 5 it was possible to produce heads in which a normal gullet terminated the membranellar band but the oral pouch was missing entirely (E). Therefore, it is clear that by stage 4 the oral anlage is determined and any ablation of its parts results in corresponding deletions in the organelles formed.

The same operations were then performed on early primordia. Even when extensive sections of the anlage were removed, the lack was then compensated by additions to the primordium, increasing it to its normal length, and complete, proportionate feeding organelles were produced (F). At stage 3 some specimens showed corresponding defects while others did not, so that it may be concluded that fixity or determination of the primordium occurs in late stage 3.

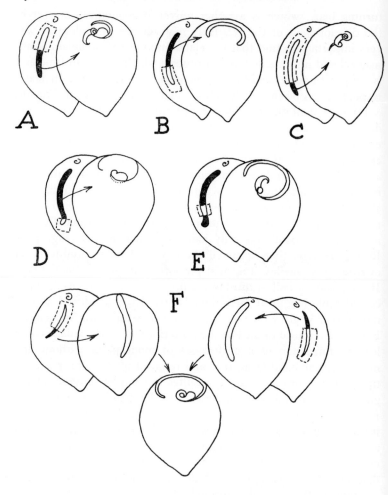

Fig. 42. Developmental determination of the oral primordium.
Removal of portions of the stage–4 anlage results in corresponding deletions: A. Posterior half produces mouthparts and
short membranellar band. B. Anterior two-thirds forms no
mouthparts, only peristome. C. Posterior fourth forms only
gullet with opening.
Removal of parts at stage 5, before stomatogenesis has visibly
begun. D. Excision of posterior tip of anlage results in absence
of gullet and cytostome, only membranellar band and oral pouch
being formed. E. Penultimate deletion results in absence of oral

Now it is very suggestive that it is just at this time that the primordium becomes susceptible to sloughing when stentors are treated with salt and other solutions (see p. 253). This shedding response indicates that the anlage has become disconnectable from the surrounding ectoplasm and this in turn suggests not only that the primordium has become an integrated unit but also that it may now be isolated from morphogenetic influences emanating from its immediate surroundings. As will be developed shortly, there are strong indications that mouthparts are induced at the posterior end of the anlage by reason of its relationship to the surrounding parts at the posterior end of the cell.

Parenthetically it should be noted that in one salt treatment of a stentor with a stage–4 primordium it happened that only a section of the membranellar band in the region of the presumptive oral pouch was sloughed, and again there was formed a perfect set of feeding organelles except that the pouch was missing. Since the ectoplasmic striping alongside the anlage is in these cases never affected, it may be assumed that the lining of the presumptive pouch had not been removed. From this it may be inferred that a certain section or bend of the developing primordium induces pouch formation in the adjacent ectoplasm on its right and that in the absence of this influence this material remains unaltered.

Progressive determination of the oral primordium is also demonstrated by shifting its location on the cell. When stage–2 primordia were circumscribed and shifted to the anterior pole they developed without forming mouthparts (Fig. 43A), but when this operation is performed upon later anlagen, oral development is then complete. Early primordia shifted to the posterior end developed adequate mouthparts and a well-formed though somewhat shortened membranellar band (unpublished). In one case a grafted anlage developing at the posterior pole even showed an additional gullet formation (B).

It therefore appears that the normal surroundings of the

---

pouch only, with adequate gullet attached to a long peristome.
F. Removal of large portions, whether anterior or posterior, of stage–2 primordium has no effect; remaining section of the anlage elongates and forms complete set of feeding organelles. (After Tartar, 1957c.)

posterior end of the primordium act upon it to cause formation of mouthparts and that when the anlage is shifted away from this environment such induction is missing. Later primordia in stage 4 or 5 have already received this influence and are then semi-autonomous systems capable of complete self-differentiation regardless of their surroundings.

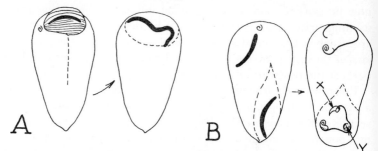

FIG. 43. Oral induction associated with the posterior pole.
A. Stage–2 primordium of regenerator shifted to the anterior pole develops no mouthparts but only membranellar band.
B. Stage–3 regeneration primordium implanted heteropolar on a stage–3 regenerator. Primordium patch slips to posterior end where it forms good mouthparts and an extra oral pouch (y) and gullet (x) in addition.

4. Induction of mouthparts formation

As just indicated, there is accumulating evidence that the posterior end of the cell in *Stentor* has an inductive action on the end of the developing membranellar band which causes it to invaginate and form mouthparts. Perhaps the first indication of this relationship was in experiments in which a sector bearing the primordium site was reversed *in situ* and the original mouthparts excised to initiate regeneration (Tartar, 1956b). An oral primordium then appeared in the reversed patch but mouthparts now were formed at both ends (Fig. 44A). Formation of the normal mouthparts at the original posterior end of the anlage may be regarded as due to the influence of its own surroundings of "posterior" ectoplasm, and that of the additional formation at the other end as being produced by an influence of the adjacent tail-pole, passing across the graft and affecting the originally anterior end of the anlage. This experiment has been confirmed by Uhlig

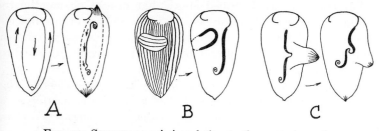

FIG. 44. Stomatogenesis in relation to the posterior pole.

A. Primordium site reversed *in situ* and mouthparts excised. Regeneration anlage forms best mouthparts at its posterior end (above) but oral formations are also induced at the other end by adjacent posterior pole. Polarity of primordium prevails as metachronal beat of membranelles proceeds from posterior to anterior (arrows). (After Tartar, 1956b.)

B. Wide stripe patch implanted transversely in mid-region develops a primordium but forms no mouthparts as does the other anlage in the normal primordium site extending to the posterior end. (After Tartar, 1956b.)

C. Lateral graft of an extra tail-pole induces abortive mouthparts formation in the middle of the primordium.

(1959) who emphasized that the symmetry of the induced mouth is always that of the inducing pole, i.e., the anterior end of the primordium shows a double curvature which results in its coiling in the normal direction. This was also shown in fusion masses in which for some reason mouthparts formed at the "wrong" end of the primordium yet coiled in the normal direction (Tartar, 1954, Fig. 11). The pattern of the posterior ectoplasm therefore determines not only that coiling and invagination shall occur but also the direction taken. Uhlig also noted that in these double-ended formations the original polarity is functionally dominant, for the metachronal beating of the membranelles originates at the normal mouth and progresses without interruption to the other.

Several other observations gave evidence that mouth formation depends on the geometric relationship of the anlage to the topography of the cell. Ectopic primordia, developing in primordium sectors grafted transversely across the lateral striping of the host did not form mouthparts (Fig. 44B). Sometimes when primordium sites or primordia were reversed in place there was not a bipolar differentiation, as described above, but instead no mouthparts were formed at all. In these cases, as in the absence or incompleteness of oral formation in stentors grafted in complex, random orientation, the failure of oral differentiation may be attributed to the mutual cancellation of polar gradients (Tartar, 1956b).

Starting from these implications, Schwartz's student, Uhlig (1959, and unpublished thesis), has pursued this matter in a demonstration of morphogenetic gradients in *Stentor coeruleus*, suggestively similar to those which have been postulated for the cleaving sea urchin egg. To mention only two of his experiments, Uhlig found consistently that when primordia were grafted transversely across the axis of the cell they never formed mouthparts, suggesting that although the anlage arises in this manner the assumption of its later anterio-posterior position is for more than " historical " reasons, namely, to align it with a morphogenetic gradient which will insure its complete and proper development. He also found that when an extra tail pole was grafted laterally alongside a developing primordium this had the effect of inducing an additional if somewhat incomplete formation in the middle of the anlage (Fig. 44c). The interpretation that this induction may be due to the operation of some gradient steepest at the posterior pole will be discussed in a later section on polarity (p. 202).

Hence there is good evidence that the oral anlage is induced to form mouthparts by its normal surroundings. Once this interaction has taken place and although there are yet no beginnings of mouthparts, the primordium is then determined and can develop completely regardless of where it is placed.

5. Repair, mending, and joining of primordia

The oral anlage can endure drastic cutting injuries without total blockage of development (Tartar, 1957c). For example, a stage-3 primordium was transected in many places yet produced an apparently complete set of feeding organelles, though these were later replaced by a new set (Fig. 45A). Usually, however, this operation, or the comparable one in which the whole length of the anlage is slashed through several times with the point of a glass needle, generally did not prevent the formation of a good membranellar band but the mouthparts were lacking (B), especially when later-stage primordia were used. As in continued develop-

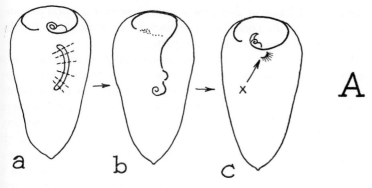

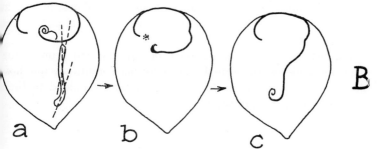

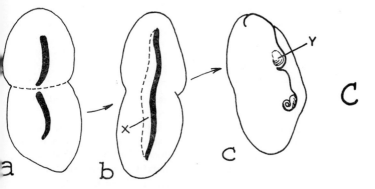

FIG. 45. Rejoining in oral primordia.

A. After cross-cuts. *a:* Stage–3 primordium of a divider transected 6 times. *b:* Anlage continues developing in normal time, severed parts rejoining as the animal reorganizes instead of dividing. *c:* Perfect but tiny mouthparts formed, possibly

ment after deletion of parts, these tests show that the oral primordium need not be complete or remain always continuous for the
full differentiation of its separate parts.

It is equally clear that in these interrupted primordia there is a
strong tendency for the parts to rejoin. This association is perhaps
best shown by tandem grafts in which the ends of two separate
primordia were made approximate (unpublished). Two stentors
could be grafted together in homopolar telobiosis without any
disturbance of the lateral striping or injury to the primordia, which
were brought into alignment. In almost every case in which the
anlagen were in mid-stage development, they fused together as a
continuous membranellar band (c). A complete set of mouthparts
was formed only at the posterior end, although almost always at
the point of joining there appeared an accessory oral pouch (see
also Fig. 41F).

We have therefore learned much of how the oral primordium
develops under both normal and abnormal conditions, but how
the precise and elaborate feeding organelles are guided to their
perfection remains a mystery.

---

because one section (x) which may have been pushed into
heteropolar orientation was not incorporated.

B. After splitting. $a:$ Stage–5 reorganizer with anlage sliced
through three times. $b:$ Reorganization proceeds, and a well-
formed membranellar band is produced but no mouthparts. $c:$
Specimen regenerating because differentiation was incomplete.

C. Joining of tandem primordia. $a:$ Tandem graft of two
stage–3 regenerators cut just beyond the ends of the primordia.
$b:$ Anlage join though not originally touching, development
continues, and a space clear of lateral striping (x) develops
alongside as in Fig. 41F. $c:$ Complete mouthparts formed only
at posterior end, only an extra oral pouch (y) being produced at
mid-level. (After Tartar, 1957c, in part.)

CHAPTER X

THE PRIMORDIUM IN RELATION TO THE STRIPE PATTERN

WE RETURN now to the site of the primordium to learn what peculiarity this region may have that it should serve as the place where the new feeding organelles always normally originate.

1. Nature of the normal primordium site

Schuberg in 1890 had already described a special geometry for this area which he called the ramifying zone. There he noted especially that the lateral striping does not run all the way to the posterior pole and his figures clearly and correctly show that in this region the granular stripes are the narrowest of any on the cell and the ciliary rows correspondingly close together. Causin (1931) and others have clearly seen and depicted these differences in the striping but it is not uncommon to find pictures of *Stentor* which completely ignore this distinction. That the oral primordium always appears at a definite position on the cell was Schuberg's main point. It soon became apparent that the narrow granular stripes are found in the region posterior to the mouth because the wide stripes to the left have been split to permit the interpolation of new clear stripes with their kineties and attendant structures. The primordium site is thus also the region of stripe multiplication, and indeed both processes run simultaneously during anlage formation

Morphologically, the ventral area may be characterized as the place where the oldest and broadest granular stripes meet the newest and narrowest in a locus of sharply contrasting stripe widths. This asymmetry of the lateral striping is found in all species of *Stentor*. That the kineties are not equidistant in other ciliates, and close together in the region of oral formation, may be the case in some, though this is by no means obvious. In the related *Folliculina*, Fauré-Fremiet (1932) could find no ramifying zone and described the pigmented stripes as not being graded in width. Yet in *Paramecium* the oral anlage does appear near the junction of two differently patterned areas (Ehret and Powers, 1959).

2. Production of supernumerary primordia

If the crucial feature of the primordium site lies in something correlated with the visible appearance of contrast between wide and narrow granular stripes, then it should be possible to elicit primordium formations in atypical loci by creating such areas of contrast by operative manipulation. This has proved to be the case, for a wide spectrum of experiments has shown that primordia appear wherever and however wide- and narrow-stripe areas of the ectoplasm come together to create a locus of sharp contrast in stripe widths (Tartar, 1956a, b, c).

First it was shown that the primordium site need not be in the normal position in order to produce an anlage and that a single animal or simple *coeruleus* graft complex can produce and develop more than one oral primordium. Thus when an extra primordium site cut from one stentor, and not necessarily carrying any macronuclear nodes, was grafted into the back of another animal and regeneration induced by excising the mouthparts, anlagen appeared simultaneously in both normal and ectopic sites and a doublet or bistomial stentor was always produced (Fig. 46A). It was then found that when only the sector characterized by fine pigment stripes in which the primordium first appears at stage 1 is implanted, an extra primordium still appears and it forms on the side of the graft where the narrowest stripes of the implant lie adjacent to wide stripes of the host (B). If such a patch was reversed and implanted heteropolar the extra primordium then appeared on the other side where the contrast in stripe widths was now the greatest (c). This anlage soon assumed the polarity of the host, but on forming the gullet the posterior end curled to the left instead of the right and an incompletely developed set of mouthparts of reversed asymmetry was produced. In the controls in which sectors bearing wide stripes were grafted into the back, or wide stripe area, no extra primordium formation occurred.

Taken together, these experiments are enlightening. The suture as such, produced by grafting, is not the cause of anlagen formation. Instead oral differentiation occurs only if and where an area characterized by fine striping lies adjacent to an area bearing wide stripes. The fine stripes need not be to the right of the wide, as is normally the case, but can lie to the left in an arrangement which is just as effective. Yet in the reverse arrangement the direction of coiling is reversed, as if the anlage always bends away from the wide stripes and into the fine, even though this results in a primordium of reversed asymmetry. And finally, it is evident that the wide- and fine-stripe areas are able to interact even though heteropolar.

One of the most convincing demonstrations of the correlation between primordium formation and locus of contrasting stripe widths (l.s.c.) was provided by splitting the fine line area of the primordium site by introducing a narrow sector bearing wide stripes. Now there were three loci of stripe contrast, the original primordium site and on each side of the implanted patch, and on regeneration three anlagen were produced, one in each l.s.c.(D). In further development the two primordia on the left usually joined to form a V-shaped anlage which might not form mouthparts. It should be added that control tests showed that neither a mere splitting of the fine-line zone nor the implantation there of an additional fine-line sector had the effect of producing supernumerary primordium formations.

Many other types of graft were made to produce juxtapositions of wide- and fine-stripe areas in all possible combinations, and these are also illustrated in Fig. 46. They showed that primordium formation is always correlated with this juxtaposition but is independent of the orientation of the striping; for in addition to the modifications already mentioned, the contrasting stripes may lie at right angles, or abut end to end homopolar or heteropolar. This shows not only that the two types of area can interact regardless of orientation but also implies that the developing oral cilia and their kinetosomes are autonomous in their precise alignment into membranelles, because normal membranellar bands were always produced regardless of the disposition of the adjacent ectoplasmic striping. For example, when anterior halves of regenerators were rotated 180° on their posterior halves (G) membranellar differentiation which was to all appearances normal occurred at the new l.s.c. where the lateral striping lay at right angles to the primordium instead of roughly parallel to it.

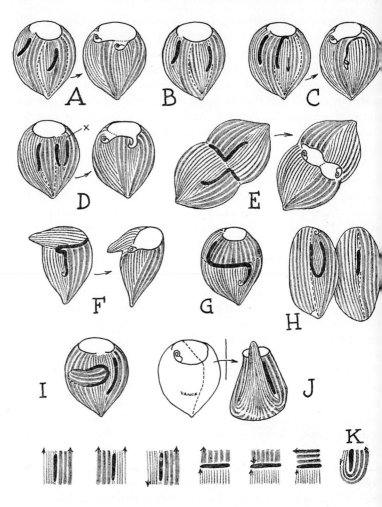

FIG. 46. Experiments establishing empirical correlation between primordium formation and loci of stripe-width contrast.

A. Sector bearing primordium site grafted into back of the host. On excision of mouthparts, primordia are formed both in the host's and in the implanted site.

B. Sector of fine-stripe grafted into wide-stripe area produces extra regeneration primordium on the side with the finest stripes.

Such cases also illustrate another point. In the normal primordium site the anlage appears in and across the fine-stripe area *near* that part of the cell which carries the broadest pigment stripes. Broad and fine stripes as well as the kineties between them are of course homopolar and presumably in intimate continuity since the wide-stripe zone is continually transforming into the fine-line zone by stripe splitting. If there is interaction between the two areas, this would seem to be an action at a distance and not something

---

C. Same, implanted heteropolar. The anlage now forms on the other side where the stripe contrast is greatest. Initially, the ectopic anlage bends at its posterior end, but later the polarity of host predominates and mouthparts are induced at the other end, incomplete and of reversed asymmetry.

D. Fine-line zone of host split by an implanted sector of wide striping. Three anlagen are formed in correspondence to the three loci of stripe contrast: one in the host primordium site (x) and one on each side of the graft. Adjacent anlagen join to form V-primordium which may or may not produce mouthparts.

E. Pair of stentors grafted by wound surfaces from removal of the heads develop primordia in the normal sites but extending around the suture where wide abut narrow stripes in heteropolar orientation.

F. Head of one stentor replaced by fine-line zone of another, grafted at 90°. Anlage extends from primordium site into the newly created l.s.c.

G. Anterior half rotated 180° on posterior. Anlagen appear in separated halves of the primordium site and are joined by extension which may run halfway around the specimen where wide stripes abut fine stripes end-to-end.

H. Left half rotated 180° on right. First sketch shows anlage formed in normal primordium site and extended to new l.s.c. where fine stripes meet wide-stripe area of the other half. Second drawing shows third primordium induction in minor l.s.c. produced on the opposite side.

I. Wide-stripe patch implanted transversely into fine-line zone of host develops an extra primordium, which however forms no mouthparts, probably because too distant from posterior pole.

J. Aboral half, folded upon itself, develops regeneration primordium where the widest stripes lie next to their narrowing prolongations.

K. Summary diagrams showing primordium formation (indicated by bar) to be correlated with loci of contrasting pigment stripe widths but independent of the orientation of those stripes. (After Tartar, 1956a, b.)

immediately taking place between the materials of the " last " fine stripe and the " first " wide stripe. In certain graft combinations one obtains what may be called the locus of stripe contrast in the strict sense of the term. For instance when the anterior half is rotated on the posterior, wide stripes abut fine stripes but careful examination shows that wide and narrow bands do not fuse together even though they are homopolar, and this may also be true of the associated ciliary rows. In heteropolar telobiotics (E) it is even more obvious and probable that joining does not occur, as a definite suture persists. When patches are grafted parabiotically but in reverse orientation, the fact that they usually retain their original polarities and slip on or creep away from each other, is indicative that heteropolarity of adjacent striping prevents the most intimate structural union, although the line of heal may appear quite perfect. Now, in such cases the anlage seems to appear within the suture and therefore at an l.s.c. in the strict sense rather than in the sense of mere adjacency, as in the normal primordium site. In either type of formation it is clear that there is something about the juxtaposition of wide- with narrow-stripe areas which locates primordium formation. Extra anlagen can be produced at will in an almost mechanical way which is not teleological, for the *Stentor* may form primordia which it could better do without. Moreover, the number and length of oral formations is clearly not limited by some " critical metabolite " sufficient only for one. Both repeated and multiple regeneration are possible for this cell.*

3. Abnormal primordia correlated with abnormal striping

If primordium formation is reliably correlated with loci of contrasting stripe widths, then this should also be manifested in aberrant stentors with unpremeditated misalignments of the patterns of cortical striping, leading to primordia of very abnormal forms. A sampling of such cases is shown in Fig. 47. Perusal of these sketches will show with what persistence all loci of stripe contrast are filled out with primordia, often exceedingly bizarre. Even though the l.s.c. may be very contorted or of extraordinary

---

*According to Uhlig (1960) the size of the anlage is also directly correlated with the degree of stripe contrast at the primordium site.

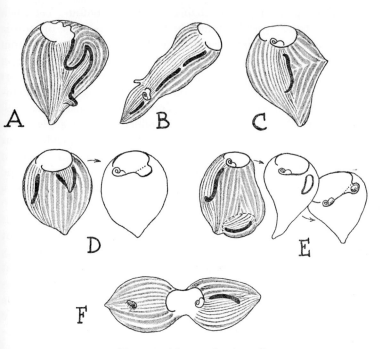

FIG. 47. Abnormal primordia.

A. Odd specimen found in culture and showing how the anlage follows the contortions of the locus of stripe-width contrast.

B. Elongate specimen from aborted fission now regenerating with extensive primordium formations in long l.s.c.

C. Dividing stentor showing how anlage follows contour of the fine stripes and not the broad, which are considerably misplaced.

D. Short V-primordium from small, anterior patch of fine striping forms no mouthparts and merely replaces a portion of the original membranellar band.

E. Stage–2 regeneration primordium grafted posteriorly into a stage–5 reorganizer. Regeneration anlage extended and formed a loop primordium which moved to the anterior end, broke into the peristome and formed good oral pouch.

F. Reorganizing double stentor with odd anlage in one half consisting only of an oval of long oral cilia, not organized into membranelles. Specimen then died.

length, anlagen formation reliably follows its contour. Yet when the wide stripes were bent and the fine stripes not, the primordia was normal and straight, confirming that the anlage comes from the fine-line zone. Neighboring sectors of fine striping put in wide-stripe areas usually result in V-shaped primordia. If short and far anterior, such anlagen contribute only a section of membranelles to the regenerant; if long and extending posteriorly, well formed mouthparts are generally produced at the angle, even though this involves the co-operative coiling of two membranellar bands in a way that does not naturally occur (see Fig. 41I). When a small patch of fine striping becomes surrounded by wide-stripe areas the patch is encircled by a new membranellar band as a continuous ring. Especially when in the form of a loop, such anlagen still attempt to form mouthparts toward the posterior end but these are never very complete (Fig. 41J). When in the form of small rings, they contribute at most a section of membranelles enclosing an extra oral pouch. Schwartz informed me (1958) that the same occurs when small patches of wide striping find themselves surrounded by a fine-stripe area, and that this may occur even though the patch is very small, suggesting to him that the materials of the primordium probably do not come from wide-stripe areas. Perhaps the case shown in Fig. 47F was of this origin; at least it carries the same implication.

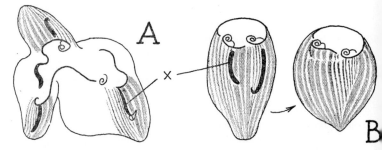

FIG. 48. Cases of primordia (*x*) curving in the wrong direction: into the wide stripe area. A. In main portion of a graft of 12 *coeruleus* reorganizing on the fifth day. Only one of the anlagen is abnormal and it formed only a short tube and no adequate mouthparts. B. In a doublet stentor, but in this case the abnormal primordium apparently formed good mouthparts notwithstanding.

In four instances it has been observed that the primordium curved in a paradoxical direction, the posterior end bending toward the wide-stripe area instead of the narrow. Two cases are shown in Fig. 48. They remain entirely unexplained.

One of the most remarkable relationships between the stripe pattern and oral anlage development is found in cases of reversed asymmetry. For these are always correlated with a reversed position of wide- and narrow-stripe areas (Tartar, 1956b, c). My best case is shown for the first time in Fig. 49. This was from a

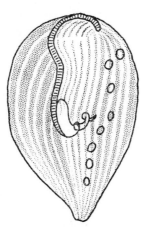

FIG. 49. Reversed asymmetry in *S. coeruleus*. After rotating left half on right and anterior half on posterior, stripe pattern reconstituted with stripes graded in opposite direction from normal. The primordium appears in the l.s.c. but coils into the fine-line zone which is now to the animal's left. Macronuclear chain is also on reversed side from normal. Fair but incomplete mouthparts formed and specimen reorganized four times without achieving an adequate oral differentiation.

specimen of *coeruleus* which had been " drawn and quartered ", i.e., the anterior half was first rotated 180° on the posterior, then the animal was cut longitudinally and the left half rotated on the right. Naturally, this operation resulted in great disturbance of the cortical stripe pattern and when realignment was achieved the area bearing widest stripes lay to the right instead of to the left of the fine-line zone. Correspondingly, the anlage coiled in the reversed direction but it was never able to form a complete set of mouth-parts even though it undertook 5 successive regenerations. Every time the primordium persisted in coiling in the "wrong" direction and the oral differentiation could not be perfected. The character of the stripe pattern therefore not only determines where the primordium will be formed but also the direction of its asymmetry. Still to be explained is the barrier, possibly on the level of molecular asymmetries, which blocks the completion of cytodifferentiation. Other ciliates are able to produce what appear to be complete mouthparts of reversed asymmetry (Lund, 1917; Fauré-Fremiet, 1945a; Tartar, 1941b; Yagiu, 1952), yet they are incapable of feeding, possibly because the ciliary organelles beat in the wrong direction, and hence reproducing lines cannot be established.

4. Primordium formation in loci of minor stripe contrast

One naturally asks how great the difference between two ecto-plasmic areas must be in terms of visibly different pigment stripe widths in order to occasion primordium formation. Longitudinal aboral fragments lack both the widest and the narrowest stripes, but they give evidence that stripe widths are graded in an orderly manner all the way around the cell because in the line of heal the bands on the right are slightly narrower than the ones on the left, and it is here that the primordium always appears. During and after anlage formation there is multiplication of stripes in this region and a normal primordium site is regenerated. When two such fragments are grafted together in homopolar parabiosis there should be two minor l.s.c., and if regeneration occurs rather promptly two primordia are accordingly formed and a doublet is produced. One such combination was made with very narrow fragments in an attempt to eliminate all stripe differences, but one primordium did finally appear at 19 hours in a minor l.s.c. which contained no fine striping (Fig. 50A). It would appear that any stripe difference, however minor, is sufficient to locate the place where the primordium will break through.

As a rule, but not always, the regeneration of longitudinal aboral halves is delayed as compared with whole animals in which the mouthparts have been excised. Causin regarded this delay as due to the necessity for first regenerating a typical primordium site,

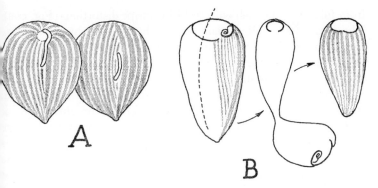

FIG. 50. Consequences of minimum contrast in granular
stripe widths.

A. Graft of halves of two stentors with fine-stripe areas
removed. After delay of 19 hours two primordia finally formed
in the sutures with very minor stripe contrast.

B. No regeneration without stripe contrast. Aboral side with
medium-width striping is isolated by a cut but left attached to
oral portion so that the latter, in swimming will draw out the
aboral fragment and keep it from folding. The parts soon
separate. Last sketch shows fragment which failed to regenerate,
presumably because it lacked a l.s.c., though it lived and was
active four days.

but primordium formation occurs before. Weisz (1951b) ascribed
the delay to time required for the transformation of the ciliary
row next to the widest stripe into a stomatogenic kinety, but there
is no evidence for a key kinety in normal oral differentiation.
Instead, it may well be the case that minor l.s.c. are quantitatively
less potent in exciting primordium formations and therefore do
so more gradually, and further evidence for this surmise will be
given in the next section. If so, a quantitative time factor would
be available for investigation in connection with anlage induction
by l.s.c.

An attempt has been made to produce nucleate longitudinal
fragments which are so narrow as to contain no significant contrast
in stripe widths (Tartar, 1956c). A longitudinal cut was made far
to the right of the central axis of a stentor but the two parts were
left joined at the tail pole. This was in order that the larger portion
by active swimming would draw out the smaller and prevent it

from folding upon itself with resulting stripe distortions (Fig. 50B). The pieces soon pulled apart but not before straight-line healing had occurred. In 4 cases, the narrow fragments did fail to form primordia though they had no mouths, retained sufficient macronuclear nodes, and survived and were active for about 5 days. It is therefore possible that in an almost completely symmetrical system there may not be sufficient difference or anisotropy of pattern for oral differentiation. Such specimens presumably were entirely capable of producing primordia, since much smaller fragments do, but apparently failed to do so because of the absence of any guidance in where to produce them. The attempt to produce anisotropic systems by grafting together patches of fine striping from the center of the cell and comparable patches of wide striping, however, was not successful; always sufficient l.s.c. remained and primordia were formed at these places.

5. Competition among loci of stripe contrast; regeneration and obliteration of primordium sites

Although the number of primordia is usually equal to the number of loci of stripe contrast, this correspondence is apparently modified by competition among primordium sites. Thus it usually happened that in grafts of two longitudinal aboral halves in which membranellar band remnants remained and delayed the onset of regeneration a primordium was formed in only one of the minor l.s.c. and a single stentor resulted, as if one site became dominant over the other (Tartar, 1956a). This effect could work either way. Two aboral halves were grafted with a complete primordium site and regeneration was delayed; two primordia were produced, instead of one in the major primordium site. This was explained by noting that in tardy regeneration one of the minor l.s.c. had time to regenerate something like a normal primordium site with major stripe contrast. When a number of aboral halves were grafted together with a single normal primordium site, the latter produced the sole initial anlage and only one set of mouthparts was regenerated. In later reorganizations the minor l.s.c. had their effect in multiple oral differentiation, and eventually the original primordium site disappeared (Fig. 51A). This decline of one primordium site appears to have been by a shifting forward and gradual absorption of the fine-line zone, but in most cases the same is accomplished simply by a widening of the narrow striping so that the contrast with neighboring areas disappears (see Fig. 58B). Stentor graft complexes in general often show a waxing or waning of supernumerary l.s.c., always tending eventually toward the single form.

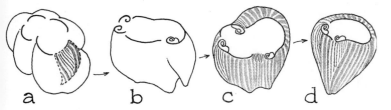

FIG. 51. Resorption and formation of loci of stripe-width contrast. *a:* Graft of 6 aboral halves without fine striping plus one primordium site. *b:* Initial oral regeneration only from the site with its maximum l.s.c. *c:* Reorganized now from three primordia as fine striping multiplies in two sutures with minor l.s.c. Original fine-line zone being resorbed. *d:* Re-reorganized from the two new l.s.c. only, original l.s.c. nearly obliterated. (After Tartar, 1956a).

6. Exceptions

The correlation between loci of contrasting stripe widths and primordium formation is not without its puzzling exceptions. Primordia have on rare occasions been observed to be formed where no l.s.c. was evident, and still less frequently the primordium appeared at some place other than the good primordium site which was present. These exceptions were so few that almost all of them can be presented in Fig. 52. In two cases of doublish or mixed up stentors, as explained in the caption, the single or secondary primordium appeared far from the major locus of stripe contrast (A and B). Another case showed a primordium in the primordium site but also another on the opposite side of the cell where there was no significant stripe contrast (C). Other cases showed primordium formations or extensions in regions where the stripe widths were apparently uniform (D, E, F, G). A special case was a double primordium with a single kinety or clear stripe separating the two halves which also appeared in an area without significant stripe contrast (H).

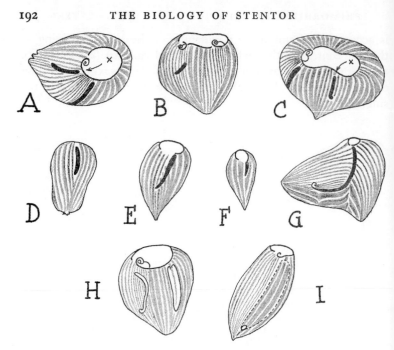

FIG. 52. Exceptions to formation of primordium in association
with a locus of stripe-width contrast.

A. Anterior half of a stentor, with intact feeding organelles,
was grafted to two minced stentors. Next day two division
anlagen were formed, one in the l.s.c. and another (*x*), paradoxically, amidst medium-width striping.

B. Specimen resulting from rotating anterior half 90° on the
posterior developed primordium only in the minor l.s.c.

C. Fifth day reorganization in a regenerator to which an
additional regeneration primordium had been grafted.
Secondary anlage (*x*) appeared where a primordium site had
been but which no longer showed contrasting stripe areas.

D. Regeneration in posterior tip cut from a stage–2 divider,
the anlage appearing in a site of negligible contrast in stripe
widths.

E. Anterior aboral corner fragment of a *coeruleus* bearing
anlage without significant l.s.c. but showing some branching of
striping. Later normal primordium site was formed by further
stripe multiplication.

F. Tiny fragment with regeneration primordium developing
amidst a few uniform granular stripes. Stomatogenesis did not
occur and the specimen died 2 days later.

Although primordia form at sutures where wide-stripe areas lie heteropolar to fine striping (Fig. 46H), local reversing of the wide-stripe half of an l.s.c. completely blocked anlagen formation and no regeneration occurred though the specimens lived for a week or longer (1).

These apparent exceptions may point up the fact that the correlation between primordium formation and loci of contrasting pigment stripe widths is a purely empirical one. It is probable that the granular stripes as such have nothing whatever to do directly with primordium formation. They contain no kinetosomes as possible progenitors of the basal bodies of the primordium. Instead of narrow-stripe areas we might just as well have spoken of close-together areas, referring to the fact that the clear stripes with their kineties here are not so far apart and their opposite would then be " wide-apart areas " (cf. Uhlig, 1959). At stages 1 and 2, in fact, the anlage arises wholly within the fine-line zone which is not an area of stripe contrast, but the point is that this place is near a wide-striped area and that experiments show this to be significant. All we can say is that there is a condition which is usually *associated with* the juxtaposition of areas bearing wide stripes with areas bearing narrow which is conducive to primordium formation. In the exceptions to the rule this crucial condition may well be present though not in its normal association with contrasting stripe widths. Yet the whole question of interaction at the l.s.c. still remains to be explored.

It is attractive to regard the wide-stripe areas as inducing primordium formation in fine-stripe areas adjacent or near by.

G. Two stentors grafted at right angles. Anlage develops in the only intact primordium site but extends in suture toward remnant of membranellar band along locus without contrasting stripes.

H. Regeneration primordium in narrow sector grafted to a divider. At stage shown the division anlage is developing, while the grafted one extended to form two membranellar bands separated by a granular stripe and surrounded by uniform medium-width striping. (Further development shown in Fig. 41 J.)

I. Wide-stripes alongside primordium site reversed in place and no primordium formation occurred though the specimen survived for a week without mouthparts.

Conditions of embryological induction seem to be fulfilled: a fine-stripe area remains morphologically inert as ventral ectoplasm until it is brought into association with a wide-stripe area. The latter itself never produces further elaborations, but in its association with a fine-stripe area there are produced the oral structures of *Stentor*.

Whatever the difficulties to be resolved as we learn what actually happens at the primordium site, the concept of the l.s.c. is a useful guide. It explains why a graft complex produces more than one primordium—because it has more than one primordium site or l.s.c.—and this is not explainable in terms of either cytoplasmic or nuclear volumes. It explains why any nucleated fragment cut from locations far from the normal primordium site can nevertheless regenerate: because of the graded stripe widths around the cell, it is almost impossible to produce a piece which on healing will not bring stripes into juxtaposition with other stripes that are not so wide and hence produce a sufficient anisotropy to occasion primordium formation.

It is therefore remarkable that on the cell level in *Stentor* we find something very much like induction as manifested in the embryogenesis of amphibia. In both cases there is the evocation of a major elaboration determining the principal axis of the organism—neural tube in salamander and feeding organelles in *Stentor*—around which a new individuality can be organized (see Fig. 55D). This evocation in both can be brought about by the juxtaposition of certain parts, and is followed by a regionalization or secondary induction, which in amphibia determines which end of the tube will form the brain and in stentors is represented by mouthparts formation under the influence of the posterior end of the cell. What the significance of this striking parallel may be we cannot yet say, but the consequences of the fact that induction need not be intercellular could be of considerable theoretical importance.

CHAPTER XI

POLARITY

POLARIZATION as a graded " difference " is probably a precondition for the achievement of persisting organic form, for we cannot imagine how potentialities for development could begin in an entirely anisotropic system. Although specific form is not explainable in terms of polarities, which are almost universal in the organic world, the guidance of development is traceable thereto; and polarity may well be intimately involved in the first stages of differentiation itself (see Bonner, 1958). For radially symmetric organisms like *Acetabularia*, cellular slime molds, and higher plants, antero-posterior polarization may be sufficient, but *Stentor* is asymmetric in the position of its mouthparts and the pattern of the lateral striping. In the ciliate we may therefore expect to find transverse as well as axial gradients in some intimate property of the cortical cytoplasm; and in addition, the structural elements of the ectoplasm, which persist in fragments and in whole cells in reorganization and division, have a built-in polarity and asymmetry.

The importance of polar differences in explaining form has been emphasized above all by Child (1941). Consciously or not, the tradition he established has continually been drawn upon. Child also included *Stentor* in the scope of his investigations, yet his findings in this context are here considered in a different chapter because they seem, for the most part, to be more indicative of structural differences. In the autonomous differentiation of stentors there is better evidence for gradients than in responses to external agents.

1. Fixity of structural polarity

There is abundant evidence that structural polarization characterizes the formed components of the ectoplasm. As already described, ciliary rows or kineties are intrinsically polarized because they follow the general rule of desmodexy in ciliates: the fiber or fibers connecting the cilia in *Stentor* are always to the right of the ciliary meridian so that one cannot turn a kinety upside down and have the over-all pattern remain the same. Endomyonemes or M–bands also show graded differences in tapering widths and in density of lateral connections. Polarity may even characterize the granular stripes, for in pigmented forms grafted in heteropolar orientation there is always a white line or space where granules are not continuous at the place of abutment. Since we do not conceive of a polarity in these granules themselves, it follows that the ectoplasm in which they reside may itself be polarized, though little differentiated otherwise.

Balbiani (1893) recognized that original polarities were retained in *Stentor* fragments as shown by the direction of their swimming; and Prowazek (1904) made the same claim on the basis that folded longitudinal halves eventually draw themselves out in correspondence with the original polar axis. Causin (1931) found that triangular fragments cut from the middle of the cell retained their polarity although the " bulk axis " was at first at right angles to this, but Weisz (1951b) provided a more convincing demonstration. He cut stentors in such a way that the future site of the primordium was bent around over the anterior end of the cell, or conversely, part of the general striping was bent around so that its forward end pointed backward toward a much-shortened primordium site. When anlagen appeared they followed the striping, as did the general reconstruction of shape, in complete disregard of the " bulk axis ". It is in fact difficult to conceive how a fluid endoplasm could have an axis at all. The main point is that intrinsic polarity persists in the striped ectoplasm, no matter how oriented. Weisz's inference, that the polarity of the so-called stomatogenic kinety determines the polarity of the oral primordium and that of the entire cell cannot be the case, however, because the primordium first appears at nearly right angles to the striping and at a considerable distance from the kinety in question, and because reversing the whole sector containing the primordium site does not result in reversing the polarity of the entire cell.

For intrinsic polarity within the ectoplasm is best demonstrated by altering the orientation of parts of the cell or separating parts and turning them around. The simplest response is that the disarranged parts shift into homopolar alignment. If a patch is

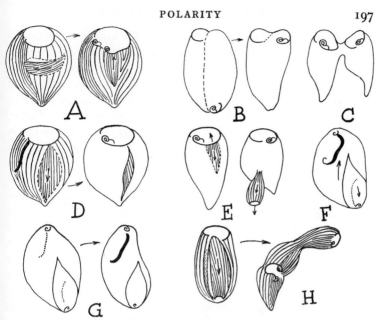

FIG. 53. Adjustments correcting heteropolarity.

A. When primordium site is implanted transversely it rotates into harmony with axis of the host, striping of the latter accommodating.

B. Left half rotated 180° on right, but parts eventually come into homopolar alignment.

C. Same operation performed on doublet stentor leads to homopolar alignment of the two individualities.

D. Fine-line zone grafted heteropolar into host with mouthparts removed. In this case regeneration anlage formed only at the host primordium site, possibly because the reversed patch was gradually resorbed *in situ*.

E. Wide-stripe sector implanted heteropolar often shifts forward or posteriorly, being resorbed or isolating itself from the host pattern.

F. Early primordium may fail to develop even when grafted to a regenerator in same stage of development if implanted heteropolar.

G. Alternatively, both early primordia may be resorbed but when re-formation occurs there is no anlage induced in the reversed primordium site.

H. Reversed primordium-site sector commonly leads to formation of three individualities, the lowest in the figure being of reversed asymmetry. (In part after Tartar, 1956b, 1957c, 1958b.)

grafted transversely across the striping of the host it will rotate in correspondence with the host axis (see Fig. 44B), and even when a stentor is cut in two longitudinally and the halves rotated 180° on each other they often rotate back into their original alignment (Tartar, 1957c), as shown in Fig. 53. Grafted pairs could shift into homopolar orientation from any initial arrangement (Tartar, 1954). The original polarity of the components is obviously retained and becomes the basis for their extensive movements with reference to each other in the reorientation (see Fig. 28B).

Another response which sometimes occurs when patches or sectors are completely reversed is that the misoriented piece becomes resorbed in place (Fig. 53D) (Tartar, 1958b). Commonly the ectopic patch creeps towards the anterior or posterior end of the host where it is gradually resorbed (E). A less drastic expression of this way of resolving the conflict in polarities is observed in the suppression of such pieces, as when early primordium sectors are grafted heteropolar on to regenerating hosts and the anlage then fails to develop, or when the induction of a secondary primordium fails to occur in an additional primordium site implanted in reverse (Tartar, 1958b) as we show in (F) and (G). These cases may be of great interest for their implication that the instigation and support of primordium development involves geometric relationships in the entire cortex and are not solely the result, say, of a substance like RNA being released within the cell and affecting formative loci regardless of how they lie.

Reversed sectors may not be resorbed but creep to one end of the host and establish new individualities (Tartar, 1956a) clearly demonstrating the autonomous polarity of the implant (H). Alternatively—and most intriguing for the problem of polarity— the patch may remain in place and produce an astonishing disturbance of the form and morphogenesis of the cell (Tartar, 1956b). In Fig. 54A is shown one case of four in which regeneration never occurred though the animals survived 6 days—striking instances of inhibition of regeneration apparently due to polar conflicts; and (B) is an example of the transient chaos which may develop before polar discrepancies are resolved. Nuclear nodes also are often abnormally located, indicating that the overlying ectoplasm guides the movements of the macronucleus. From these extraordinary disturbances it may be inferred that, although the polarity is intrinsic within each part, there is an interaction of some sort by which heteropolarity may lead to extensive disharmonies beyond the original misalignment.

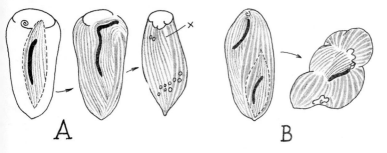

FIG. 54. Disturbances in heteropolar systems.

A. Primordium sector of stage–4 reorganizer reversed *in situ*. Absence of stomatogenesis associated with posterior end of anlage lying now in the frontal field. The inverted patch (*x*) apparently was gradually resorbed but no regeneration occurred during 7-day survival. Nuclear distribution abnormal.

B. Stage–2 regeneration primordium sector grafted heteropolar to regenerating stentor in same stage. Both anlagen were resorbed; then two new ones produced the incomplete oral differentiations shown in the second sketch as the shape became grossly abnormal. Specimen is re-regenerating with single primordium.

Polar conflicts may be resolved by the larger part becoming dominant (Fig. 55A). A compromise may result in heteromorphosis, in which a secondary polarity is responsible for the formation of an extra set of feeding organelles but the lateral striping has, throughout, the polarity of the major portion of the specimen so that the secondary oral differentiation is of reversed asymmetry (B). These forms are however less frequent and less well-developed in *Stentor* than in other ciliates. When the major mid-section of the cell is reversed, all parts retain their original polarities and multiple formations occur (C).

Shifting the head to the posterior end does not result in reversal of polarity. The most frequent result (unpublished) was that a new set of feeding organelles eventually regenerated at the original anterior end of the major cell body, and the displaced head became

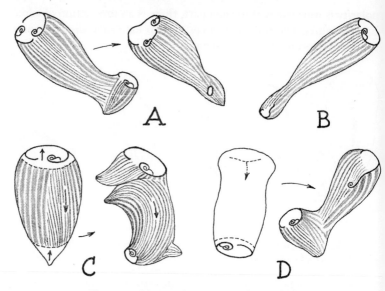

Fig. 55. Observations concerning polarity.

A. Heteromorphic specimen from abortive fission of a divider grafted to a regenerator, showing tendency toward resorption of conflicting part.

B. Heteromorph with continuous striping and therefore reversed asymmetry in the smaller part, consequence of heteropolar implant (later separating) which set up a secondary polar axis.

C. When major portion of stentor is reversed (head and tail trade places) all parts retain their polarities and mid-portion regenerates separate head (x) and tail (y).

D. Head excised and grafted to replace tail at posterior end does not reverse the cell polarity nor prevent regeneration of the "host" but organizes a new individuality.

the center of organization and growth of a secondary cell shape (Fig. 55D). From the standpoint of oral inhibition these cases were also interesting as showing that a displaced set of intact feeding organelles can much delay primordium formation but not prevent it entirely.

All these experiments so attest the fixity of polarity in every part of the cortex that one wonders whether reversal of polarity is ever possible. It would seem that the best place to look for such a reversal is in folded aboral halves in which the striping bends and breaks to form a new holdfast (see Fig. 27), for in these cases both posterior and anterior ends of the severed striping meet at the new posterior pole. Yet such specimens will have to be followed very closely to determine whether the stripes in reversed orientation are not subsequently resorbed.

2. Rate of regeneration in relation to the polar axis

A further manifestation of polarity is of course to be found in the fact that heads are always regenerated at anterior ends of fragments and tails at the posterior. As in regeneration of metazoa, the organism can produce either anterior or posterior structures from almost any level of the body, the choice depending on the original polarity. Although cœlenterates and turbellarians may produce heteropolar heads on very short pieces, this does not occur in stentors. Isolated heads do not become heteromorphic (see Fig. 32) nor do disc-shaped fragments whose longitudinal dimension is brief (Fig. 25A). Nevertheless, it is conceivable that the rate of oral regeneration might vary with level of cut, as in flatworms (Brønsted, 1955). That this is not the case within a single cell such as *Stentor* was first shown by Gruber (1885b) who found that animals, minus the head only, regenerated a new set of feeding organelles as rapidly as posterior fragments. This was confirmed by Weisz (1948a), who also found (1948c) that the relative growth rates of fragments from any region were the same. Contrary to the experience with stentors, Sokoloff (1913) reported that middle pieces of *Spirostomum* regenerate faster than the ends but I think this work requires checking.

Although denying an axial gradient in speed of regeneration, Weisz (1948a) stated that oral regeneration is hastened by the presence of a holdfast, mid-pieces regenerating more slowly than posterior fragments. Child (1949) regarded this difference as probably incidental to the fact that middle fragments have to accomplish two regenerations, of both head and tail. This could be tested in other ways, as I have done (unpublished). If the presence of a holdfast hastens oral regeneration, then stentors from which the head only is excised should regenerate sooner than animals from which head and tail are removed, but they do not. On Weisz's assumption, the former should also regenerate in the same time as small tail pieces since both have holdfasts, but I found the regeneration of the latter to be always slower. Slower regeneration of oral parts in tail pieces may be the consequence of another aspect of polarity which will now be discussed.

3. Gradients in head and tail formation

Popoff (1909) had found in abortive fissions of *Stentor* that even though the daughters did not separate, a new tail pole with hold-fast, projecting laterally, was produced for the anterior cell because the lateral striping had been severed by the fission line. Weisz (1951b) then showed that foot formation could be brought about by excisions of post-oral striping, but the nearer the anterior end the more incomplete and temporary was the pedal differentiation (see Fig. 26A). Notice that the holdfast forms not merely where the stripes come together (at the posterior pole) but also differentially along the whole side of the cell, wherever ablation creates a new terminus of polarization.

Uhlig (1959) confirmed that there is a gradient in tail formation, highest at the posterior end and diminishing anteriorly. This gradient is strongest on the ventral side where the oral primordium is also formed, as shown by the appearance of a secondary tail projection in this region when anterior halves are rotated on the posterior (see Fig. 26B). The polar pedal gradient is therefore involved with the circumferential gradient in stripe widths, since it is on the ventral side that the locus of stripe width contrast determines both the location of the oral anlage and the side on which the new tail-pole will appear.

Now, the polar gradient in foot formation is also coincident with that responsible for the induction of mouthparts formation. Whenever, but only when, an end of the oral primordium lies near a part of the posterior end, or its entirety, are mouthparts produced. This inductive relationship has already been discussed (p. 202) but should now be considered further within the context of polar gradients.

Following the implications of double oral differentiation in reversed primordium sectors (see Fig. 44A), Uhlig (1959) has explored this matter thoroughly and concluded that the inductive action is strongest just beyond the posterior pole, diminishing anteriorly. Because his detailed report is not yet available, I have supplied sketches from my own experiments (including Fig. 44), which may therefore be regarded as generally confirmatory.

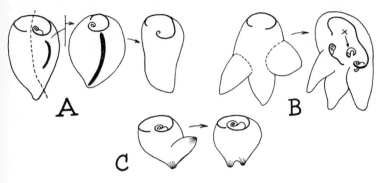

FIG. 56. Observations regarding induction of stomatogenesis by the posterior end.

A. In an oral half of a stage–3 divider the anlage was not resorbed but extended all the way to the posterior pole and produced no mouthparts, presumably because inducing region is anterior to the pole itself.

B. Two extra tail poles engrafted led to multiple stomatogenesis, with complete but ectopic gullet (x).

C. Specimen with two tail poles due to shift of primordium site produced a stentor with unusually large mouthparts, possibly due to the double tail.

Primordia far from the posterior end produce no mouthparts (Figs. 47D, and 26c). That the oral-inductive gradient stops short of the posterior pole is indicated in Fig. 56A, showing incomplete oral differentiation in a primordium extending too far posteriorly. It is possible, also, that inductive action may be compounded by the presence of multiple posterior ends. When three tails were grafted, double mouthparts were produced in the host (B), and in another case three posterior poles may have been responsible for unusually large mouthparts formed (c). Astomatous oral differentiation in large fusion masses may be due to the mutual canceling of oral induction gradients in these random grafts. A similar initial astomatous development in isolated sectors bearing division primordia (Tartar, 1958c) may likewise have been due to the fragments at first containing insufficient polar regions, a situation later corrected by regeneration of the posterior pole.

Uhlig also regards the appearance of a primordium or new membranellar band in connection with the locus of stripe width contrast as expressing a circumferential gradient in propensity for anlage formations, and this may be a fruitful way of regarding these events. Certainly the granular stripe widths, or as he perhaps more pertinently states, the distance between the fibrous clear stripes, form an orderly gradient around the cell. Primordium formation might therefore be regarded as always occurring at the " head end " of this gradient, or where the finest pigment stripes are found. Whatever explanatory virtue the polarity or gradient concept may have would then be applicable to happenings in this region. Yet there are some difficulties which still need to be resolved, for example, how primordium formations at transverse sutures (see Fig. 46G) can be regarded as expressing a gradient.

A harmonious co-operation between the circular gradient manifested in graded stripe widths and the polar gradient of mouth-parts induction is, according to Uhlig, necessary for complete oral development. The former guides the location and longitudinal development of the membranellar band, later invagination of its posterior end to form the mouthparts being induced by some influence having its high point near the posterior end of the cell.

When a stentor divides or is cut in two, there would be, in Uhlig's conception, readjustment to a new equilibrium in which the original single polar gradient is converted into two. As inti-mated above, short tail-pole fragments may therefore be slow in regenerating because of their need for greater readjustments before significant polar differences can be re-established. When stentors are cut in two and rotated so that anterior and posterior stripe systems cannot rejoin, a conflict between double but homopolar gradients apparently ensues, which is resolved in various ways to be described later (p. 227).

Stentors therefore may be said to bear within the structure of every part of the cortex an antero-posterior and a left-right polarization. In addition, there is experimental evidence for polar and circular gradients of paramount importance in the elaboration of major ectoplasmic organelles.

CHAPTER XII

FUSION MASSES
OF WHOLE STENTORS

REPEATED and cumulative grafting of stentors made possible the formation of relatively huge fusion masses of stentor protoplasm. These cytoplasmic continuums made from many cells are unique among biological phenomenon, and their potentialities for contributing to our understanding of the organism have by no means been exhausted. At present we can at least describe the response of *Stentor* when confronted with the problem of organizing a far greater than normal mass of protoplasm. The same forces of mending, adhesion, and integration which hold the single stentor together conspire in masses to make enduring unions, and there is little indication that pathologies arise which would obscure or preclude the expression of morphogenetic potentialities.

In fact, *Stentor* masses often live longer than single individuals under the same circumstances, perhaps for the reason that larger aggregates have more substance to draw upon under conditions of relative starvation. Up to the last day or two of their life, the masses remain active and apparently healthy, and there is no reason to suspect that they die from any other cause than starvation. Large masses may not even suffer from reduced surface in relation to volume as interfering with exchange of oxygen and carbon dioxide; for they take the shape of pancakes about as thick as the normal cell so that, as in the erythrocyte, every point of the interior retains a fairly normal access to the surrounding medium. The problems of these complexes therefore seem to be more morphological than physiological and they survive long enough to show much of what they can do.

1. Simple masses and biotypes

We begin with the simplest combinations of only two or a few more cells, something of the behavior of which has already been indicated in our previous discussions. Double animals are already well known in ciliates (see Fauré-Fremiet, 1948a) and were encountered in *Stentor* cultures by early observers (Balbiani, 1891b; Johnson, 1893; Stevens, 1903; and Fauré-Fremiet, 1906). Such as these can therefore arise in nature. They probably originate by the incomplete separation of daughter cells during fission, tandemly joined daughter cells later shifting alongside each other, often with apposition of feeding organelles and tail-poles. In some ciliates, notably *Colpidium* (Sonneborn, 1932) and especially *Paramecium* (Calkins, 1911) growth without fission may continue and produce monsters or very large multiple individualities. In general, however, studies on these abnormal forms have revealed two tendencies: first, that doublets, and to a less extent triplets, become stable biotypes which can reproduce themselves as such, and second, the complexes eventually become single individualities again by the gradual integration of their multiple morphologies; and it is the same in *Stentor*.

From the chance encounter of these forms, the next step was to produce them at will. This can be accomplished by a variety of means which block the final stages of cell division—to mention only one, the dilute formaldehyde treatments of Fauré-Fremiet (1945a). Possibilities of experiment were then greatly extended when it was found that stentors could be fused together by grafting in almost any number or arrangement desired (Tartar, 1941b).

In the simplest complexes, grafted pairs or 2–masses could form 1, 2, or 3 primordia on regenerating (Tartar, 1954). The number of sets of feeding organelles produced was called the oral valency. In the first case, the graft reverted almost at once to single individuality; in the rarest instances in which 3 anlagen were formed, temporary triplets resulted. But the great majority of 2–masses remained double for a long time. This corrected Weisz's (1951a) first impression that pairs always revert to singles within 18 hours through the dominance of one partner over the other.

All indications are that the oral valency of small masses is strictly correlated with the number of effective primordium sites available, as earlier intimated (Tartar, 1954). Neither total volume nor amount of nuclear material was determinative. The number of anlagen produced corresponded with the expected probability with which, in random grafting, the original sites would remain intact, one would be obliterated, or grafting would produce an extra juxtaposition of wide- and fine-stripe areas.

At first, multiple sets of feeding organelles often remained separated by lateral striping, and such complexes were called doubles or triples. There was a strong tendency for feeding

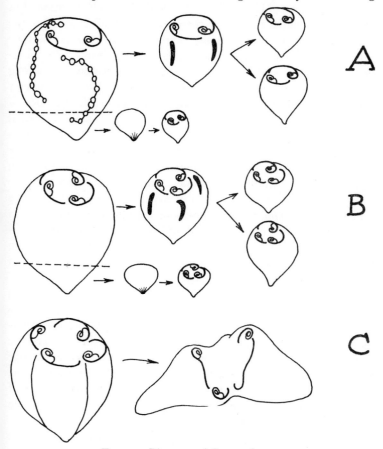

FIG. 57. Biotypes of *S. coeruleus*.
A. Doublets regenerate and divide as doublets, forming two anlagen in correspondence to the two primordium sites or l.s.c.
B. Similarly for triplets.
C. Quadruplet formed by grafting four oral, longitudinal halves does not persist as such but transforms into transition disequilibrium forms.

organelles to associate around one frontal field as the grafted animals shifted to produce a normal, homopolar, conical Stentor shape as persisting doublets and triplets. The latter forms may be called biotypes because they regenerated and reproduced as such (Fig. 57).

One doublet could produce thousands by multiplication, but after 1 or 2 months cultivation there was a gradual reversion to the normal single form. Triplets also reproduced themselves and they generally reverted to type in a shorter period, always " stepping-down " first to doublets and then to singles. Persistence for a long time of these biotypes may be related to their bilateral symmetry and unity of form as expressed, for example, in the presence of but one tail-pole and holdfast.* Fauré-Fremiet (1948a) regarded the balance between the two halves of a doublet as imposing a " structural constraint " on labile transformation back to the single type; for in such forms as *Leucophrys patula* he found that cutting injuries or the diminution of one component led promptly to reorganization as a single individuality. The application of this principle to *Stentor* is not immediate because the removal of a single set of feeding organelles in doublets merely leads to regeneration on the cut side and reorganization on the other, producing the doublet type again. Yet asymmetric doublets are the most likely soon to revert spontaneously to the single type.

It is doubtless significant that the quadruplet biotype could not be produced. This limitation has also been found in other ciliates (Fauré-Fremiet, 1945a). Grafts of 4 stentors could produce transient quadruplets but these did not persist and quickly reduced the oral valency. Unlike triplets, quadruplets could transform at once to giant singles (Fig. 57c) and this was the first indication of the tendency to reduction of oral valency in relation to the number of components grafted, which became increasingly prominent as the size of masses was enlarged.

The problem of organic individuality is confronted when we ask whether doublets are single or double individualities. They swim and feed and reproduce in a co-ordinated manner like single cells, and there is no further evidence that the two sides of a

---

*Uhlig (1960) reported that the one holdfast in doublets is nevertheless doublish or larger than normal, and similarly for triplets.

doublet contract independently as Balbiani (1891b) first described. Doublets generally show the single conical shape ending in one holdfast, but there are two contractile vacuoles, two macronuclear

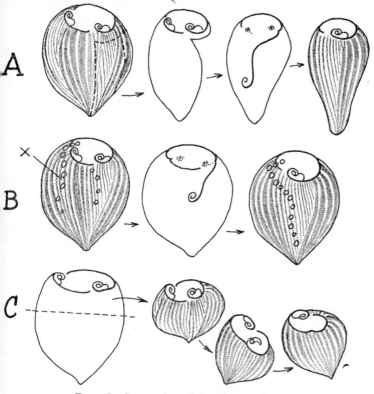

FIG. 58. Conversion of doublets to singles.

A. Doublet becomes single by removing one of the primordium sites or major loci of stripe contrast. On reorganizing, both sets of original mouthparts are resorbed and the excised l.s.c. is not reconstituted.

B. Spontaneous conversion, in which one (*x*) of the two original loci of stripe contrast disappears and the specimen reorganizes singly, also achieving a single macronuclear chain.

C. Isolated head end of doublet shows first a proportionate shortening of the membranellar bands, then cutting out and resorption of one of the mouths and obliteration of one primordium site, becoming a normal stentor even without primordium formation.

chains, and two complete sets of feeding organelles. Above all, the pattern of lateral striping is double, with two primordium sites or loci of stripe contrast; and this is seen to be crucial, for whenever doublets revert to singles there is always the obliteration of one primordium site, after which all other aspects of the complex become single. And doublets could be converted at once into singles by excising one of the primordium sites, even if the bistomial head was left intact (Fig. 58A).

It was difficult in cultures to catch doublets in the act of transforming into singles, but something of how this occurs may be indicated in the following. Figure 58B shows an asymmetrical doublet which was in fact not a 2–mass but produced by grafting a primordium site into a single animal. Such specimens remained as doublets for several days, but then one of the primordium sites disappeared as such, either the host site or that of the graft transforming into uniform lateral striping, for there was no evidence of stripe resorption. The transformation illustrated in (c) was instigated in the anterior half fragment of a broad symmetrical doublet. Reduction to half the original size resulted in the length of the membranellar bands being greatly reduced *in situ* until they became proportionate to the new cell size, but the mouthparts remained large. One primordium site then disappeared as its contrasting pigment stripes became of uniform width. While this was occurring the mouth subtending these stripes separated from the membranellar band and moved into the frontal field where it was gradually resorbed. The two bands then joined together and the final result was a single stentor produced even without the formation of a reorganization primordium.

Although there is evidently a strong tendency towards unification of shape, one may speak of a reversed propensity of sets of lateral striping to establish separate shapes, as if a complex which cannot achieve complete singleness then settles on a frank expression of its multiplicity. Doublets, especially when so oriented as to have two frontal fields, become double cones or siamese twins and enduring triplets also develop " cleavages " making them triple shaped (Fig. 59A and B).

A single animal even converted itself into a double shape when the tail-pole was bent and directed forward (c). These examples show again that there is no mysterious unity in the endoplasm and that cell shape is an expression of the cortical stripe pattern, following its unity, distortion, or multiplicity. In other words, one never finds a normal cell shape imposed on a grossly abnormal stripe pattern.

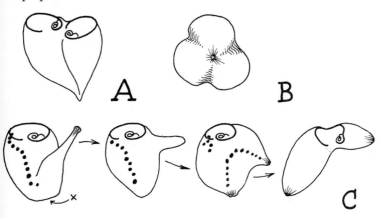

FIG. 59. Formation of multiple cell-shapes.

A. Persistent doublets often show tendency to produce parallel bodies.

B. The same tendency to "cleavages" shown in a triplet (posterior end view).

C. Tail folded into wound left by removing the division primordium. A new tail was produced at the bend (*x*) and each pole organized a separate cell shape. The nuclear chain is relocated accordingly.

2. Adjustments among formed ectoplasmic organelles

Correlated with the reconstitution of the normal stentor shape are shifts and adjustments of formed feeding organelles and holdfasts. Figure 60 illustrates the major tendencies.

Separated organelles migrate together, like to like, in spite of the intervening ectoplasmic striping. In fact, the lateral striping co-operates or may even produce these shifts by resorptive shortening between the parts and extension elsewhere. Isolated mouthparts and membranellar bands may travel a long way to join with or even break into a major set of feeding organelles. Stentors in which the left half was rotated 180° and healed securely to the right nevertheless could sometimes gradually return to the

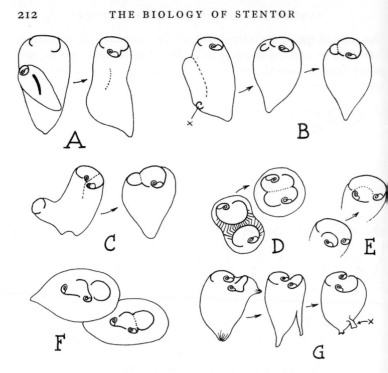

FIG. 60. Adjustments among formed ectoplasmic organelles.

A. Regeneration primordium sector with intact mouthparts grafted to stentor from which mouth was excised. Graft shifts its alignment, anlage is resorbed and mouthparts join with membranellar band to form a complete set of feeding organelles so that no subsequent regeneration occurred.

B. Grafted patch with wide striping and section of membranellar band (*x*). The peristomal remnant travels all the way to the anterior end of the host and is incorporated into the host's band, even with resorption of a part of that band to permit entrance.

C. Small stentor, with mouth excised, grafted to another whose mouthparts were cut in two. Mouthparts mend as completely normal structure, separate membranellar ring moves to anterior end of larger animal and is incorporated, no regeneration following.

D. In parabiotic graft of two stentors the feeding organelles fuse in spite of intervening striping and parts of both membranellar bands are resorbed to make a single frontal field.

normal orientation (Tartar, 1957c) and, remarkably, the same behavior is shown in operated early sea urchin embryos (Hörstadius, 1950). These shifts are as if like parts exert a strong "attraction" for each other, and their coming together is an important step in the unification of a fusion mass.

Selective resorption of parts occurs not only on the lateral stripes but also within the joined heads. When two sets of feeding organelles become tightly apposed, first those sections of the two membranellar bands are resorbed which permit the formation of a single ring and frontal field. Extra tails are resorbed or sloughed, or they may lose their separate identities by fusion. In all these precise adjustments between the parts of grafted cells we see the specific acts by which wholeness is achieved.

3. Larger masses and reduction of oral valency

Grafts of 5 to 100 animals were necessarily of random orientation and displayed several interesting emergent characteristics which are shown in Fig. 61.

Most obvious is that grafts of 6 or more animals cannot attain the unitary shape and giant individualities are not achieved. Instead, the general impression is that of bas relief sculpturing, as if each set of stripes were able to make an individual hump in the over-all contour. Although *Stentor* is able to make perfect forms in tiny fragments, it is apparently unable to cope with a mass much larger than it would ever encounter in nature. This is not because such masses are necrotic. Their limitations seem to be morphogenetic rather than physiological. Either they represent simply a self-defeating jumble or the upper size limit to form development and regulation bears in itself important theoretical implications. Lillie's "minimal organization mass" seems to have lost its

---

E. Similar, showing integration accomplished by resorption in only one membranellar band. Apparently, parts of the band are resorbed when they do not subtend lateral striping.

F. Adjustment in a graft complex, showing how just those portions of the membranellar bands are resorbed which make for an integrated frontal field.

G. Product of graft of two stentors in early division. Accessory tail-pole and holdfast move posteriorly but are eventually resorbed (*x*).

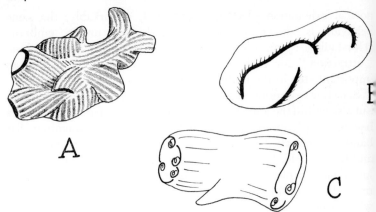

FIG. 61. Large fusion masses of *S. coeruleus*.
A. Graft of 12 stentors, heads removed, indicating bas-relief
sculpturing or partial emergence of constituent body shapes.
B. Graft of 14 stentors, regenerated, showing unusually long
garlands of membranelles without formation of mouthparts.
C. 15–mass, now organized into a bipolar system and with oral
valency reduced to seven. (After Tartar, 1954.)

significance from the consideration that the limit to size of regeneration is simply that complete animals cannot be made of very few
parts of invariant size, but there may well be a maximum organization mass beyond which anything like the typical stentor form
cannot be realized.

Although they do not organize into single giants, larger masses
show a tendency towards unification in the reduction of their oral
valency, number of primordia formed decreasing greatly with the
number of individuals grafted. A 15–mass for example produced
only 7 primordia, and a 55–mass had between 5 and 10 anlagen in
successive reorganizations. These great reductions in the number
of oral differentiations have yet to be adequately explained.
Perhaps some of the primordium sites join together as one. Or it
may be that in larger masses there is for some reason a competition
between primordium sites, with fewer becoming effective in producing anlagen. Partly responsible, too, may be the fact that oral
differentiation favors the upper surface; for these large masses did
not wheel about through the water but remained on the bottom
always with the same side uppermost.

4. Incomplete oral differentiation

When fifteen or more stentors were grafted together there was no longer adequate mouthparts formation. Primordia were few and unusually long, forming extensive garlands of oral cilia stretched across the mass (Fig. 61B). There was some indication that the membranelles in these bands were not completely formed, though this has not been ascertained. But it was obvious that formation of mouthparts was inhibited. Since induction of these parts is determined by a normal relation of the anlagen to the axis of the cell, the presence of numerous cell axes running in random directions and canceling each other in their polar influences may be responsible for the astomatous development of the feeding organelles in large masses.

5. Absence of fission

Random masses containing more than five stentors never showed any attempt to undergo fission. This is rather surprising for two reasons. First, the masses are very large and, although increase in size is not in itself invariably stimulative of division, one might expect that a very exaggerated volume could be so. Second, multiple fission would seem to be the easiest way for a mass to resolve its difficulties, yet this does not occur. But when masses are cut into pieces about the size of a normal stentor they promptly regenerate normal singles, a test which shows that no irreversible pathology occurs within large fusion complexes. Fauré-Fremiet (1945a) attributed similar failure in simpler complexes to their heteropolar arrangement, which permits the establishment of no single plane of fission. Whatever the reason, the elimination of the capacity to divide should make the study of fusion masses fruitful in searching for the basis of fission. In this connection one is reminded of an hypothesis by Berglas (1957) that cancerous proliferation might be stopped by capitalizing on the avidity of cancerous cells, causing their overgrowth to such a size that division is no longer possible.

6. Tubes and ciliated vacuoles

In these unique intracellular formations the morphogenetic capacities of *Stentor* seem to be extended beyond what is ever normally expressed. The tubes extend deep into the endoplasm

P

but usually open on the surface, while the vacuoles are wholly
internal though they may break through the surface later. Both
are lined with apparently normal ectoplasmic structure: pigment
stripes alternating with ciliary rows, and contractility was
sometimes noticed in the tubes.

These remarkable structures were first observed in masses of
stentors (Tartar, 1954). The tubes, at least, can occur in single
individuals. One day I isolated a very abnormal *coeruleus* which
was apparently the result of an incomplete fission, and on the next
day the cell was seen to be filled with elaborate internal tubules
(Fig. 62A). One tube opened where the mouth should have been
and was therefore like an exaggerated gullet. There seemed to be
other tubes with many convolutions which arose separately and

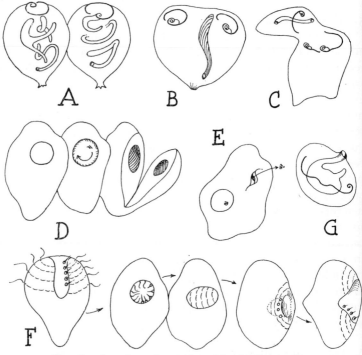

FIG. 62. Interior tubes and vesicles in *S. coeruleus*.
A. Front and back views of case apparently from aborted
fission which developed complex system of multiple tubules,
blue-green in color because lined with ectoplasm.

opened to the outside through the ectoplasm near the posterior end. These tubes were blue-green in color and obviously lined with ectoplasm. In grafted pairs one or two tubes sometimes appeared adventitiously (B). Sometimes the tubes had a neat opening through the ectoplasm at both ends (C). Usually they opened near the posterior pole and extended forward, suggesting gullet formation in the normal site of oral differentiation. Their appearance may represent acts of gullet formation entirely dissociated from anlagen development.

Internal ciliated vacuoles are equally surprising. These were often found in large fusion masses and may have been due to the accumulation of water inside. The vacuoles seemed at first to have structureless walls, but they soon became lined with typical striped, ciliated ectoplasm, as could easily be demonstrated by slicing

---

B. Graft of two enucleated stentors which developed a single tube, opening posteriorly, extending forward through the endoplasm, and lined with ectoplasmic striping. The tube contracted and extended with the mass, twisted through a 90° arc autonomously, and seemed to "breathe" by independently enlarging and narrowing. Elaboration of the structure in absence of a nucleus is paradoxical.

C. Tube with neat opening through the ectoplasm at each end, developed in a 3–mass.

D. Appearance of vesicle in a fusion mass. Initially the vacuole seems to consist of a simple membrane enclosing fluid. Later it becomes lined with ectoplasmic structure demonstrated by ciliary circulation of mass of shed pigment granules within and by transection to expose ectoplasmic striping.

E. Mass with two vesicles, one of which has broken through the surface, the collapsed lining becoming continuous with outside ectoplasm and forming deep, ear-like cavity.

F. Reorganization in *Cyathodinium*. Cortical ciliary apparatus is resorbed and a new one formed inside as a vesicle, lined with cilia and endosprits, which evaginates through the lateral surface and produces a new cell axis at right angles to the old. In division 2 endocellular ciliary anlagen are formed which move to opposite side. (After Lucas, 1932).

G. Odd formation of tubes and vesicles lined with pigmented ectoplasm and resembling an "archenteron" with one opening. Differentiation of the oral anlage was incomplete. (After Tartar, 1954).

through them. Invariably there was a shedding of pigment granules into the interior and these clumps of blue-green debris circulated around continuously in an orderly manner by action of the ciliary lining (Fig. 62D). There was no evidence of oral cilia or of mouthparts differentiation. Several vacuoles could be present together in one mass, and individual vesicles sometimes increased in size as if growing and subjecting the mass to great tension as indicated by the spherical form assumed. After attaining considerable size the vacuoles often broke through the surface and their ectoplasm became continuous with that of the outside, giving the appearance of " ears" because of their depth and folds (E).

In this evagination, as in their origin, the ciliated vacuoles strikingly recall the unusual mode of cytodifferentiation in *Cyathodinium* as described by Lucas (1932). During normal reorganization and division in this ciliate one or two ciliary anlagen arise internally, develop cilia projecting into the vacuolar space, then evaginate to the outside in orderly manner so as to produce a new ciliation at a different axis for the reorganized animal or the two daughter cells (Fig. 62F). In both *Cyathodinium* and *Stentor*, development of internal ciliation quite separate from contact with the ectoplasm poses a test of the hypothesis of the genetic continuity of kinetosomes. But whether the basal bodies of the cilia arise *de novo*, or develop from division products of the surface kinetosomes wandering into the interior, would be difficult to decide.

It is also possible that tubes and vacuoles may have arisen from bits of ectoplasm thrust into the interior during the process of grafting stentors. In several instances (unpublished) when I tucked pieces of ectoplasm inside the cell, tubes and ciliated vacuoles resulted. This observation is especially interesting as suggesting that internal ectoplasm can grow and even undergo an orderly disposition into tubes and spheres. Growth, naturally, would be from the morphologically inner surface of such pieces. Cannibalized stentors, though not at first enclosed in food vacuoles, are digested instead, since their " growth surface " never contacts the endoplasm of the predator. And conversely, ciliated vesicles can persist and develop because they are " turned inside out ".

In a special case, tube and vacuole formation seemed to have combined in a most unusual mass which showed a structure resembling an " archenteron ", with an " appendix " and a tube connecting to the exterior (Fig. 62G). Although fusion masses of stentors become increasingly unable to reconstitute the normal form, they seem for this very reason to be set free to express unusual types of cytoplasmic differentiation.

CHAPTER XIII

RECONSTITUTION IN
DISARRANGED STENTORS

CILIATES are often cited as achieving in complexity of structure and multiplicity of function the highest elaboration of the cell as a unit, choosing *Epidinium* as the ultimate. Stentors, with their elaborate feeding organelles, complex kineties, ribbon bundles and M–bands in the clear stripes, and granular bands of varying width and taper such that any part of the ectoplasm is theoretically identifiable with reference to its position in the orderly whole, are not far behind. Yet in spite of the cogency and high development of the cortical pattern, stentors can sustain and recover from drastic disruptions of this exquisitely organized ectoplasmic structure. Nor is reconstitution accomplished by the easier way of resorbing existing cortical differentiations and starting afresh, as in *Bursaria truncatella* in which excessive injuries lead to encystment followed by complete reconstruction, according to Lund (1917). Instead, the cut up and disarranged parts of stentors largely persist as such and apparently perform remarkable shifts and reorientations and rejoinings in a usually highly successful recovery of the normal pattern of the cell. This performance in fact suggestively parallels the reconstitution by dissociated sponges and disaggregated tissue cells of organized, functional units.

1. Minced stentors

The most drastic operation conceivable with *Stentor* is rather easily accomplished. The ectoplasm can be cut into as many as a hundred separate patches by slashing deeply through the surface of the cell with the sharp point of a glass needle. After many cuts, large patches will have been circumscribed and " float " free on the endoplasm. When these in turn are repeatedly transected, the needle not only severs the formed structures but also pushes the patches into gross disarrangements with reference to one another and the striped surface comes to have the appearance of fields seen from the air. Randomness can be increased by first cutting the cell transversely and rotating the anterior half 180° on the posterior; after healing, then recutting longitudinally and rotating the left half on the right. Quarters of the cell are thus transposed and disoriented before the mincing.

In some of the first experiments of this type (Tartar, 1941a, b) it was found that stentors with two heads or two tails could be produced from singles, and an analogy was drawn between this result and the consequence of inverting embryos in the 2-celled stage, by which twins are produced. Weisz (1951a) had found that excessive cutting injuries in grafting only resulted in death of the specimen, but evidently the conditions of experiment were not optimal. Further studies (Tartar, 1956c) revealed remarkable reconstitutions and allow us to say something of how they are brought about.

After minceration a stentor has a knobby or fascetted appearance from the patchiness of the striping, which again substantiates that the over-all shape of the cell is determined by the arrangement of the ectoplasmic striping (Fig. 63A). Within a few hours the patches begin reorientation, with their striping becoming more or less parallel. Although this point could not be tested, it seems likely that the arrangement of pieces becomes homopolar, like so many tiny magnets. The gradual nature of this process suggests that the position of the new polar axis is established statistically at first, by any group of patches which by chance happens to be similarly oriented and therefore can form a " field " whose influence might then spread to adjoining sections to bring them into corresponding orientation. With this shifting, patches soon appear much larger than originally, and this can be attributed to their joining together as they come into parallel and homopolar orientation. Areas bearing wide pigment stripes do not form a continuous structural union with fine-stripe areas, but only like with like. Although it would be difficult to observe minor resorption of patches, it is apparent that there is no large scale dedifferentiation.

As the cut areas move so their stripes become parallel, a visible polarity appears as the mass elongates in one direction and a hold-fast appears at the end of a projecting point. Oral regeneration never begins until a definite locus of stripe contrast of considerable

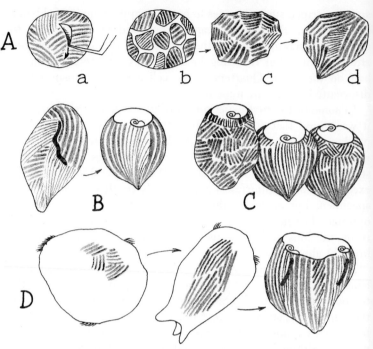

FIG. 63. Reconstitution in minced *S. coeruleus.*

A. Realignment and rejoining of pattern. *a:* Operation, consisting of repeated cutting with point of a glass needle until lateral striping is reduced to scattered patches. Holdfast and feeding organelles were removed. *b:* Patches, numbering about 50 are at first separated by endoplasm. *c:* Patches healing together and cell-shape knobby because of striping running in multiple directions. *d:* Indication of a tail pole and axis with patches aligning in parallel and joining when of the same type (e.g. wide-stripe areas with wide striping).

B. Subsequent regeneration in a similar case. An oral primordium appears as soon as a sufficient locus of stripe-width contrast was re-established (6 hours) and the anlage follows the course of this l.s.c. Second sketch shows nearly normal specimen one day after operation.

C. Intact head grafted to minced mass of two stentors minus heads and tails. Three days later the specimen became as shown, striping normalized on ventral (oral) side, still irregular anteriorly on dorsal side. Axis seems to be established by the engrafted head but head and bordering stripes apparently have length appears. Even if the head had previously been excised and the animals minced just before the anlage was due to appear, the primordium was still not formed until considerable reorientation had occurred. But if a stentor is minced and the mouthparts excised at the same time the primordium can and often does appear within the normal time of 4 hours, so that cutting of the striping and its subsequent rearrangement does not seem to interfere in any way with the activation and preparation of the cell for primordium formation. All the fine-stripe patches may not aggregate in one place and therefore two primordia may be formed producing a double stentor from a single. Oral regeneration seems to proceed normally whenever an l.s.c. is established to determine where the anlage is to be placed and it was noted that without exception the primordium does appear in an l.s.c. Such loci may be much distorted due to the original disarrangement, and the anlage faithfully follows their contorted contour (Fig. 63B). The specimen therefore does not wait until it has reestablished perfect order in the striping but regenerates as soon as possible and makes further adjustments later.

When all but the primordium of regenerating stentors was thoroughly minced there was no resorption of the anlage, which continued to develop, though often slowly; but the membranellar band formed was usually distorted. This indicates that the state of activation is not nullified by severe cutting, but that orderly striping is required for normal deployment of the developing feeding organelles. Even if the regeneration primordium itself was cut in two, the parts usually rejoined and development continued to rather successful regeneration.

Specific inhibition of oral primordium formation by intact feeding organelles occurred even though the cell was minced. This was demonstrated by grafting intact heads to singles and 2–masses

---

no strong orienting influence on adjacent patches. Specimen survived 8 days without reorganizing, and hence oral inhibition of primordium formation was effective though lateral striping cut into patches.

D. Mince graft of 5 whole stentors achieves axis by 6 hours, regenerates as a doublet and begins dividing as a doublet 2 days later. Integration of shape is better than in grafts of 5 not minced.

after they were minced. Often no primordium appeared (Fig. 63c), or only days later. The grafted head became harmoniously integrated with the minced host, and yet grafting of heads or primordium-site sectors or large areas of intact striping did not seem to hasten the gradual re-alignment of the patches.

Minced 2–masses like grafted pairs produced 1, 2 or 3 primordia upon regeneration. In most cases two were formed, in some cases only one, and very rarely 3. Again, the oral valency seems to be simply an expression of the probability of obtaining more than one area of fine striping in the reconstituted graft complex. Mincing a fusion mass in fact definitely favors attainment of unitary shape. A minced 25-mass formed a rather unified fan shape with single axis (Tartar, 1954, Fig. 33b), though large, unminced masses never achieved anything like the normal form. Two 5–masses, minced, became doublets with single conical shapes, much in contrast to the bizarre forms produced when such masses are not minced (Fig. 63d). Minced masses, unlike minced singles, seem to have a better chance of producing a single shape when all traces of the original axes have been obliterated, and this inference is substantiated by the confusion of mildly disarranged stentors, presently to be described. The response to these operations demonstrates an astonishing capability of thoroughly disorganized stentors to regenerate and to reconstitute the normal, orderly arrangement of the ectoplasmic pattern, even within a single day, after all the complex ciliary, contractile, conductive and other differentiations of the ectoplasm have been cut into tiny pieces scattered at random.

Remarkable, too, is the possibility of the reverse process, in which organization is sacrificed to autonomous disorganization. Several instances have been found in which individual *coeruleus* responded to certain treatments by spontaneously transforming the orderly striping into a generally disarranged patchiness much as if the cell had been minced (unpublished). The two instances from cutting operations are shown in Fig. 64. The same effect was sometimes produced by treatment with dilute salt solutions (see Fig. 71). If these responses are reproducible, we have an opportunity to explore the significance of this peculiar break-up of structure, so greatly in contrast to the general tendency of stentors to integrate themselves into an orderly pattern. This behavior

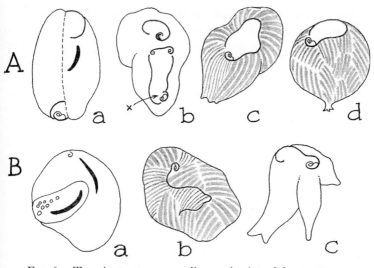

FIG. 64. Transient autonomous disorganization of shape pattern.

A. *a:* Left half of stage–3 divider rotated on right. *b:* Fission blocked but further primordium formation, leading only to 3 incomplete oral differentiations in addition to original mouth-parts (*x*). *c:* Reorganized singly, with fair stomatogenesis and good striping. *d:* On day 4 the lateral striping except in the oral meridian was broken into patches quite as if minced. This condition was later corrected to normal; and the specimen eventually divided, one of the products also then dividing, therefore apparently an instance of postponed fission.

B. *a:* Sector with stage–3 regeneration primordium and 8 nuclear nodes grafted transversely onto an enucleated stage–3 regenerator. Both primordia were, paradoxically, resorbed. Two new anlagen appeared, joined and gave fair differentiation of feeding organelles (*b*) but the striping became noticeably patchy. *c:* Reorganized now with striping aligned but with four tail-poles. Further normalization occurred later.

recalls, in a possibly significant parallel, the normal fragmentation of the cortical striping and kineties in large forms of the ciliate *Ichthyophthirius*. Patches so produced then become the ciliation of multiple daughter cells, according to the account of Mugard (1948). But in *Stentor*, the animals seemed to be able to recover after passing through a period of self-trituration, as they do from minceration.

2. Other disarrangements of the normal cell pattern

When gross parts of the stentor cell are shifted with respect to one another in operations much more simple than total mincing, the effects on form are usually far more enduring and bizarre. Original longitudinal and transverse axes are apparently retained in the large parts and fall into conflict with each other. Gruber (1885a) had shown that in stentors suffering a single cut the parts could shift upon each other to produce doublish forms, and Ishikawa (1912) produced these and large lateral flanges by slicing into *coeruleus* and holding the split parts separated for a few minutes so that they then did not heal in place. Here we shall simply offer two new cases which are typical.

Figure 65A shows a *coeruleus* which was simply split longitudinally yet it never recovered the normal form before it eventually died of starvation. The other case (B) was of a stentor which had been " quartered " with the result that each fourth of the cell was maximally misplaced. Gross abnormality resulted, finally leading to the formation of a double animal. In a previously cited case the same operation produced a doublet with reversed asymmetry on

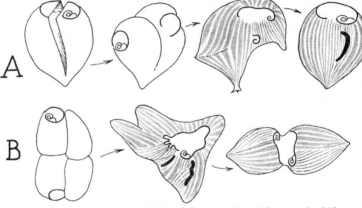

FIG. 65. Gross abnormalities of shape produced by simple shifts of large stripe areas.

A. When stentor is split to tail-pole, and halves shift by contraction, healing irregularly, aberrant form is produced but later corrected.

B. Anterior half rotated 180° on posterior then left half 180° on right. Quartered animal became very abnormal in shape, later converting to a telobiotic double stentor.

one side (see Fig. 49). Also to be recalled in this connection is the great confusion of shape when cell sectors are implanted hetero-polar in stentors (see Fig. 54). Disarrangement of large areas of ectoplasm therefore leads to much more confusion than mincing. Reorientation of such areas may simply be more difficult, or their polar " fields " may be so strong as to engender major conflicts within the cell.

The neatest and best studied disarrangement of the pattern of *Stentor* is that in which the anterior half of the stentor is rotated 180° on the posterior (Tartar, 1956a; Uhlig, 1959). When *coeruleus* is selected for this operation, the pigment stripes with their varying widths can be used to identify the cortical patterns of the two halves and to follow the changes which occur in them.

The nature of these transformations of the striping depends in part on whether and where the severed stripes may join. Using these cases, stentors grafted heteropolar by the headless anterior ends, and observations on minced animals, we can formulate provisionally a rule for the union of lateral stripes. It will be recalled that the complex fibrous structure lies in the clear bands and that the pigment stripes appear to be merely the spaces between these which are filled in with the colored granules. Yet if discontinuities in pigment stripes, appearing like the colorless fission line, can be taken as a criterion that the fibers of the adjacent clear bands are also discontinuous, then it seems that intimate structural union between two sections of ectoplasm occurs only when the abutting pigment stripes are of equal width, approxi-mately parallel, and homopolar. Thus in heteropolar grafts there is no joining of pigment stripes even when they are of equal width (see Fig. 46E). In mincerates, as well as in parts of the normal " ramifying zone " of Schuberg, it is indicated that pigment stripes of equal widths do not join if they are at an angle to each other (Fig. 63B). And in anterior-rotated-on-posterior grafts there is a discontinuity where the wide stripes of one half abut the fine stripes of the other, while in those places where stripes are of equal width they join and become continuous (Fig. 66A). As will be noticed in the figures, even though wide and narrow pigment stripes do not join, there is the appearance of a strong attraction between the two. Characteristically two fine stripes move so as to subtend one wide stripe, although a non-pigmented line continues to separate them.

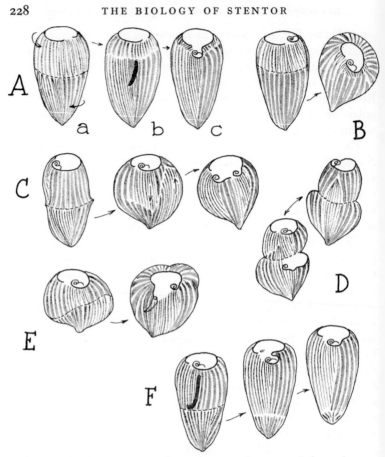

FIG. 66. Consequences of rotating anterior part 180° on the
posterior.

A. Equal halves rotated, mouthparts excised. *a:* Pigment
stripes of like width join and mend, wide and narrow stripes
match up, 2 to 1, without joining. *b:* Regeneration is delayed
because membranellar band left intact, hence single primordium
arising only in relation to the extending posterior striping,
anterior stripes resorbing. *c:* Completion of regeneration with
anterior striping nearly replaced by growth of posterior striping.

B. Stentor transected somewhat anterior to center; anterior
striping resorbed though no primordium is formed since feeding
organelles left complete. Head therefore does not make anterior
striping dominant yet effectively inhibits anlage formation in
the posterior portion, isolated by rotation.

The operation of rotating anterior on posterior halves was first used to demonstrate that primordium formation can occur in such loci of stripe contrast (Tartar, 1956a), but it was also observed that stripe disharmonies were resolved by resorption of the anterior striping and extension of the posterior to take its place. If regeneration was delayed by leaving the membranellar band intact, the forward resorption of the anterior ectoplasm occurred so rapidly that when an anlage was formed it appeared only in the primordium site from the posterior half (Fig. 66A). Even when regeneration was not induced, anterior striping could be dissolved as it was replaced by the posterior (B). Alternatively, in some cases in which regeneration was not induced the striping of anterior and posterior halves appeared to interpenetrate, parts of both anterior and posterior striping being preserved.

Later it was found that grafts with this astonishing interpenetration of stripes could be produced quite readily (Tartar, 1959b). Figure 66C shows how the fine line zone or primordium site of each half plows through the striping of the other half as it extends in length and gradually reaches the opposite pole. Specimens with two good primordium sites which reorganize as doublets are therefore generally produced. Later readjustments, in which the fine lines of either side become wider, then lead to eventual recovery of the single form. In one instance the animal divided.

C. Stentor cut in half, fine-line zones interpenetrating next day to reach opposite poles of the cell, with result that two loci of stripe-width contrast are extended and specimen becomes a doublet.

D. Front and back views of dividing specimen with interpenetrating stripes, showing how fission line forms indifferent to suture between stripes of the rotated halves.

E. Racial difference in interpenetration of striping. Same operation as in C, but with Elletsville race. First sketch: two days after operation with striping still unchanged. Second: 11th day, with striping now running pole to pole forming two primordium sites, one with reversed asymmetry and therefore producing anlagen which gave incomplete stomatogenesis.

F. Stage–3 divider cut with anterior part larger. Specimen reorganizes instead of dividing, with only anterior portion of the primordium developing, the posterior part resorbed. Posterior striping is gradually resorbed as anterior stripes extend.

Division occurred while the stripes were interpenetrating and the fission line did not follow the suture but cut indiscriminately across fine and broad striping, following a course which may be called typical (D). The latter, with similar cases, shows that abnormal disharmonies and discontinuities in the lateral striping do not preclude division and suggests that the fission line is determined by some agent other than the lateral stripes themselves. Thus the same subcortical forces which cause predivision of the carbohydrate reserves in the neat manner already described may impose a severance of the striping lying exterior to them regardless of the nature or disposition of that striping.

Yet the most interesting questions concern how the highly structured ectoplasm can permit stripe areas to slip by each other, as well as the bearing of stripe extensions in limited places on the control of growth throughout the cortex. Moreover, it appears that races of *coeruleus* vary in the ease with which stripes interpenetrate after this operation, specimens of one strain remaining as grafted (E) long after those of another had formed doublets.

Uhlig (1959, and unpublished) has developed this type of experiment much further, by transecting *coeruleus* at different levels before rotating the two parts. He substantiated that when the cut passes through the place of origin of the primordium producing approximately equal halves for rotation, the anterior striping is generally resorbed as the posterior stripes extend and take over.* When a posterior cut produces an anterior component about four times the size of the posterior, anterior striping now predominates and extends posteriorly, replacing the original tail-pole striping which is resorbed. The case shown in Fig. 66F confirms this finding. A dividing stentor was transected across the oral end of the division primordium and the smaller posterior part rotated on the larger. The tip of the anlage was then resorbed; the larger portion continued development and led to reorganization as the original posterior striping gradually disappeared. But these cases were not uniform and sometimes there was an interpenetration of stripes. Therefore it appears that in these grafts there is a delicate balance between the two systems which may be tripped to favor the

*Uhlig (1960) claims that resorption of the anterior striping proceeds from the anterior ends of this striping and not from the suture.

dominance of one or the other or may result in equilibrium, with the striping of both halves retained and interpenetrating. A fine and unnoticeable difference might swing the balance one way or the other. When the cell was so cut that the ratio of anterior half to posterior was about 3:2, Uhlig found that dominance was exerted by neither part and doublets resulted which could divide and produce more doublets. He states that then each primordium site " reorganized " completely, but perhaps he also observed what seems to me to be the case: that there is an extension of each half of the original primordium site as it penetrates through the stripes of the other half. He interpreted the various responses as an interaction between the head–tail gradient and the transverse or circumferential gradient in stripe width. For instance, when only the posterior end of the cell is rotated, its circular gradient in the immediate neighborhood of the steepest end of the tail-to-head gradient is apparently obliterated.

Experiences with this type of operation will have a bearing on the analysis of axial gradients in *Stentor*. From a more general standpoint it is shown that stentors have still further resources, in the selective resorption or interpenetration of stripes, for the reconstitution of their normal form and pattern.

CHAPTER XIV

ANALYSIS OF STENTOR THROUGH ITS RESPONSE TO EXTERNAL AGENTS

VARIOUS chemical and physical treatments of living stentors have been used to reveal and analyze otherwise inaccessible aspects of their structure and behavior. These studies are classified according to objectives of the investigation, types of effects produced, or the agent used.

1. Action of the membranellar band

To immediate observation, the most impressive activity of attached stentors is the orderly beating of the large membranelles in beautiful waves of metachronal rhythm. For the membranelles do not all beat together in the same phase but in succession, so that at any one instant membranelles in the effective beating stroke are followed by others successively relaxed in the recovery stroke and these are again followed by organelles in the effective stroke, giving the impression of waves originating in the gullet and passing along the membranellar band to its terminus. Hydrodynamically, this type of beating is probably the most efficient, because groups of cilia work together to move the water toward the mouth but this action is distributed so that there is a continuous flow, whereas if all membranelles beat in the same phase the medium would move by starts and stops.

The types of action of which the membranelles are capable and the variables involved are shown diagrammatically in Fig. 67. First, the membranelles may all be stopped and pointed forward and somewhat inward, when stentor is swimming backward or has momentarily ceased feeding (B). When they resume beating they do so at first individually and at random, soon falling into metachronal rhythm. Hence each membranelle is capable of independent beating. The number of strokes per second is the *frequency* of beating. Presumably the *amplitude* of the effective stroke may vary but this would be difficult to detect. The distance between membranelles in the same phase is the metachronal *wave length*. Speed with which metachronal rhythm passes along the band is the *wave velocity* and is equal to the product of frequency

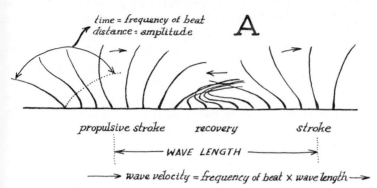

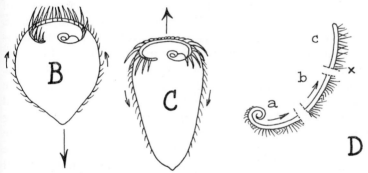

FIG. 67. Actions of the peristomal membranelles.

A. Analysis of successive beating or metachronal rhythm.

B. Swimming backward with ciliary beat reversed and membranelles stopped and pointed forward.

C. Forward swimming with membranelles active and pointing backward.

D. Coordination in transected sections of the peristome. *a:* Metachronal rhythm maintained, moving distally from pacemaker in the oral region. *b:* Isolated section sets up independent rhythm, pace set by proximal membranelles. *c:* Beating of membranelles still independent, as in the whole peristome when beating recommences. Rhythm will be re-coordinated by new pacemaker at *x.*

of beat and wave length. Each of these factors is variable. In addition, the membranelles can be oriented to point outward and backward as they do in forward swimming (c).

It will be recalled that the membranelles are rooted in triangular basal plates all of which are connected by an inner fiber. It was natural for early microscopists to have supposed that the impulse producing metachronal rhythm passed along this fiber, exciting one membranelle after the other; but there are at least two arguments against this supposition. The wave velocity (roughly 700μ per second) is slower than any known neuroid transmission (Sleigh, *vide infra*). And second, on resuming their beat the membranelles do not start at once in metachronal rhythm, which is only later established after a brief period of irregular beating.

Coordination in the membranellar band of *S. polymorphus* was the subject of astute investigations by Sleigh (1956, 1957). By several approaches he shows that the frequency of beating of the membranelles is dissociable from the wave velocity or rapidity of transmission of the impulse from one membranelle to the next. Both frequency and wave velocity decreased with lower temperature but the decrease was more rapid in the frequency of beating. Increasing viscosity of the medium by addition of methyl cellulose resulted in decreased frequency of beating but no change in the wave velocity. This corresponds to expectations, for external resistance should decrease the frequency of stroke without affecting internal mechanisms of transmission. Magnesium chloride increased the frequency of beating without affecting the wave velocity; and with aluminum chloride the trivalent ion was several times more effective in producing the same response. If these metal cations may be regarded as reducing the internal viscosity of the protoplasm in cilia, increased frequency would be explained as due to lower internal resistance. Digitoxin greatly increased the wave velocity but only slightly increased the frequency of beat and the shape of the effect-vs.-concentration curves was different. Finally, cutting the membranellar band interrupted the wave conduction but did not prevent the reappearance of metachronal rhythm in separated sections distal to the gullet (Fig. 67D). This experiment at once excluded that metachronal waves originate only in the gullet region and can be stopped by cutting the fiber which connects the basal plates of the membranelles.

Following incision, the first membranelle distal to the cut established a new frequency of beating, which was then taken up by all the membranelles in the isolated section. The first membranelle of a series may therefore be regarded as a pacemaker which determines the frequency of membranelles distal to it. Being separated from proximal membranelles the pacemaker can establish its own intrinsic rhythm, often different in different sections. Usually, its rate was slower than that of the membranelles on the gullet side, but in a few cases it was more rapid, possibly due to excitation through injury. In the intact feeding organelles, the pacemaker would presumably be some membranelle within the gullet. In this region, Sleigh (1957) found that the wave lengths and wave velocity are smaller than in the distal lengths of the membranellar band; but this discrepancy he resolved by the observation that the membranelles are also closer together in the gullet. Therefore the number of membranelles in one wave length is the same throughout the band and hence the number stimulated per second is the same regardless of their density. " The wave velocity thus depends on the number of cilia involved in the transmission, and not on the linear distance traveled by the metachronal wave ". This is further evidence that the cilia themselves are involved in transmission of the metachronal wave and not the basal fiber connecting the basal plates.

Chemical and physical treatments thus indicated that there is an intraciliary excitation which is separable from a second process, the conduction of the impulse from membranelle to membranelle. From these and the cutting experiments, Sleigh proposed the hypothesis diagramed in Fig. 68. Only a single cilium in each membranelle is shown for presumably the closely packed cilia of each membranelle work together. Each cilium would then be capable of spontaneous beating but at a slower frequency than when excited by interciliary transmission. Increasing or retarding frequency of beat would simply alter the rapidity of ciliary contraction or response to the internal state of excitation and therefore need not affect the rate of conduction of the impulse between the motor organelles. On the contrary, digitoxin, by decreasing the threshold of excitability, as it does in heart muscle, might increase the speed of excitation and therefore lead to a more rapid tripping off of the conducted impulse so that wave velocity would be in-

influence passed like a flash over the entire surface of the mass
(Tartar, 1954). Myonemes respond similarly, components of a
fusion mass contracting together almost from the moment of
grafting (Weisz, 1951a).

One approach to analyzing what the functions of fibrous
structures associated with the membranelles may be is provided
by the selective resorption of parts of bands during fusion of heads
in grafted stentors. In the specimen shown in Fig. 69 the resorbing
membranelles first lost their metachronal rhythm, beating irregularly in a local area. This is as if structures responsible for this

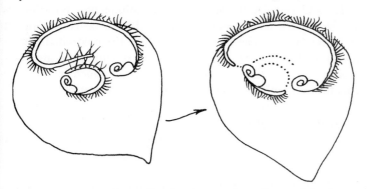

FIG. 69. Loss of coordination in membranelles anticipating
resorption of portions of the membranellar band. The ends of
the two peristomes which were resorbed in a doublet stentor to
fuse the frontal fields first showed independent beating of
membranelles.

type of coordination were the first to become dedifferentiated, for
the ectoplasm presumably retained its continuity.

Other responses of the membranelles to chemical treatments
have been observed (Tartar, 1957a). In solutions of 1% NaI the
membranelles remained continuously stopped, but in $CaCl_2$ they
kept beating vigorously until the organelles were destroyed.
Ethanol stimulated the membranelles to keep beating even while
the remainder of the cell was being destroyed, confirming the
earlier observation of Daniel (1909). This activity was in marked
contrast to the normal avoiding response in which the membranelles are stopped. In $MgCl_2$, at much higher concentrations than
used by Sleigh, the membranelles continually started and stopped

at a rate of about one change per second until the band itself was destroyed. $NiSO_4$ in very weak solution is an effective ciliary anæsthetic for protozoa (see Tartar, 1950); body cilia and membranelles in *Stentor* were stopped in weak solutions, but although not beating, the membranelles keep changing their orientation in the two positions shown in Fig. 67B and C. This reorientation in membranelles which were not beating was most striking to observe — like the batting of eyelashes — and it should also be mentioned that the body contractions of the stentor were in no demonstrable way affected by $NiSO_4$. Hence the unstriated basal lamellæ and associated fibers of the membranelles, homologous with the striated ciliary rootlets described in metazoa by Fawcett and Porter (1954), may be contractile (like the unstriated ribbon bundles of the clear stripes) and serve for orienting the membranelles in one direction or another, a function which in this case seems to be completely dissociable from ciliary beating.

2. Coordination of body cilia

Every part of the ciliated ectoplasm, without endoplasm or nucleus, is a self-contained coordinating system. This was demonstrated for *Stentor* and *Spirostomum* by Worley (1934) who found that in isolated patches the cilia could start and stop, reverse their effective stroke, and beat in metachronal rhythm. Treatment with ciliary anæsthetics such as potassium chloride resulted first in loss of the capacity to reverse, then of metachronal rhythm, and finally of ciliary beating itself. These three kinds of ciliary action are hence dissociable. Individual activity of a cilium and the two types of coordinated movement of cilia therefore are probably due to separate processes. Reversal of beating spread instantaneously like a signal passing over the surface, uninterrupted by incisions and therefore probably not mediated by conductile fibers. Metachronal waves are much slower. Hence Worley suggested that they are mediated by interciliary fibers, specialized structures whose effectiveness in integrating cilia may, paradoxically, be due to their slowing down interciliary impulses. In *Spirostomum*, the kineties of which closely resemble those of *Stentor* (Randall, 1956), Worley found that the metachronal beat could circumvent surface cuts, indicating the presence of transverse connections between rows of body cilia.

Reversal of beating of the body cilia in unattached stentors is immediately manifested in backward swimming in which the effective stroke of the cilia is directed forward instead of backward. Merton (1932, 1935) made an extensive study of the effects of various salts and other substances in compelling stentors to swim backward. The species used were *roeseli*, *coeruleus*, and *polymorphus*.

First it should be mentioned that distilled water alone produced backward swimming, with most of the animals disintegrating in two hours. Peters (1908) had early shown this injurious effect of pure water on *coeruleus*. He transferred the animals every 15 minutes to fresh distilled water and all then died within an hour, death occurring not by swelling of the whole cell but by the formation of internal vacuoles which increased in size and led to a blistering of the surface with final disruption. Death he attributed to washing out of the salts of the cell, but it may just as well have been due to other osmotic effects; for Jennings (1902) found that sugars killed by the subtraction of water and that there is no effect at first but only after a sudden contraction, following which the animals crumpled and decreased in volume.

Therefore Merton made up his solutions in tap water which had no effect on their behavior and was not immediately injurious. He found that monovalent cations induced reversal of ciliary beating while the bivalent cations of calcium and magnesium did not. Thus weak solutions of KCl produced a continuous backward swimming. Using their chlorides, the monovalent ions tested were in approximately decreasing order of effectiveness: $K > Rb > Cs > Na > NH_4$. Anions also had some effect on the response. Potassium compounds were compared, and the order of decreasing effect of the anions in promoting ciliary reversal was

$$CO_3 > SO_4 > Cl > I, NO_3, PO_4 > Br > Ac.$$

I later confirmed these results in regard to contrasting effects of monovalent and bivalent cations (Tartar, 1957a). In addition I found that LiCl, which only produced disintegration of stentors for Merton, also induced conspicuous backward swimming. And ammonium acetate in strength of 1%, a compound not tested by Merton, caused the most prolonged and continuous reversal of any of the compounds used.

Merton also tested hydrochloric acid, fatty acids, saponin, and certain alkalis, which produced only injury and no ciliary reversal. Urea and sugars also gave no reversal, and this I can confirm.

Merton regarded the induced backward movement as a specific effect of the monovalent cations on the cilium. That osmotic effects are not involved is obvious from the fact that the type of ion and not its concentration is crucial. Nor was he dealing with avoiding responses, because he found that stentors show the normal temporary backing up even when they encounter calcium chloride, but this compound does not compel the continuous backward movement which KCl does. Also, the reversal in KCl, for example, was not counteracted by adding an equivalent amount of $CaCl_2$. The bearing which these results may have for an analysis of ciliary reversal is yet to be clarified, but to be able to produce reversal, immediate and prolonged, is a beginning. At least we can conclude that the mechanism of body cilia is such that it can adapt to an abnormally continuous backward beating at increased intensity under the influence of reversing agents.

3. Ciliary anæsthesia

It has already been mentioned that the heavy metal salt $NiSO_4$ at very low concentration causes reversible paralysis of both body cilia and membranelles in *Stentor*, as I found following a suggestion of Gelei (Tartar, 1950). After inducing ciliary reversal, NaCl and KCl also produce partial anæsthesia of the cilia (Merton, 1935) and the potassium salt seems to be the more effective for this use.

Following early exploratory tests of Verworn, Ishikawa (1912) obtained reversible narcotization of the cilia in *Stentor coeruleus* with chloroform vapor. He brought a piece of filter paper soaked in chloroform near the drop containing a stentor in order to quiet the animal for cutting operations, but by his own account this is not to be recommended because necrotic conditions easily develop. At lowest concentrations the stentors showed an accelerated activity, but at higher strengths the cilia were slowed and the animals became semi-elongate. Wounds from cutting were slow in healing. With nearly lethal concentration, the animals remained quiet as if dead, though sometimes they could recover slowly, and it was also reported that they might shed their cilia or begin disintegrating, a small portion at a time.

Hofer (1890) recommended hydrochlorate of hydroxylamine (0·25%) neutralized with sodium carbonate for slowing the cilia and relaxing myonemes in *coeruleus*. Of several related compounds Mugard and Courtney (1955) found that only KH_2PO_4 was a sufficiently non-toxic immobilizer of all ciliates tested, including stentors.

Methyl cellulose, first introduced for quieting paramecia by Marsland (1943), remains the least noxious method for slowing cilia in stentors. Its use will be discussed in the chapter on techniques.

4. Anæsthesia of myonemes

Stentors, like *Spirostomum* and the stalked Vorticellids are capable of very strong and instantaneous contraction. In my experiments with stentors I have been impressed by the observation that contractility seems to be one of the last functions to disappear, and even grossly abnormal and necrotic specimens, no longer capable of swimming with their cilia or of regenerating, nevertheless continue to react to poking with the needle by rapid and vigorous contraction, almost up to the time of their final demise.

Attempts to anæsthetize the myonemes and abolish contraction have been pursued both for the purpose of fixing and staining animals in the fully extended state and to test whether stentors behave like a typical nerve–muscle preparation.

It will be recalled that Neresheimer (1903) found what he thought to be nerve-like fibers which he called " neurophanes " running to the myonemes, and later Dierks (1926a) described similar fibers (" neuroids ") running exterior to the myonemes and terminating in or sending branches to them. That these fibers with their putative function represent specialized organelles and not mere artifacts of fixation is still very questionable (see p. 55), yet they led Neresheimer to an extensive study of the effects of drugs on *Stentor coeruleus* which may have its merits apart from the conclusion he drew. Control animals were first placed in a small dish on a platform to which a graduated stick was fastened in a vertical position so that a weight on a pulley could be dropped from a measured height onto the platform, the vibration of which would then stimulate the animals to contract. The minimum distance of fall to excite contraction was then used as a basis for comparison of the reaction of stentors subjected to various drugs.

Morphine hydrochloride apparently produced the greatest insensitivity. This relaxation was counteracted in a typical manner by the antagonists atropine and picrotoxin. Strychnine produced mild contractions, as would be expected from its effect on higher animals. In curare the contraction was so energetic that both clear and pigmented stripes were said to be torn loose in a way which he did not describe in detail. The antagonist, physostigmin, counteracted this effect. Neresheimer states that these results confirmed earlier studies by Verworn on *Stentor, Spirostomum,* and *Carchesium.* If the myonemes are excitable only through neuroid fibers one might have expected complete paralysis on the basis of blockage of the neuro-muscular junction which curare produces in higher forms. Complete relaxation of specimens which could then be fixed in the extended position was achieved in *Spirostomum* but not in *Stentor.* Caffein seemed to increase the sensitivity, but in nicotine the stentors relaxed and became more insensitive.

A student of mine (N. G. Parisis, 1956, unpublished student report), tested the effects of curare and strychnine, separate and combined, on *Stentor coeruleus* and *Spirostomum ambiguum.* Both drugs stimulated mucoid secretion, as demonstrated by the observation that the animals could be moved by an advancing needle before the needle came near the cell. In neither substance alone was contractility lost. In a mixture of strychnine and curare, however, the ciliates lost their power of contraction completely and could even be cut in two without responding, though the cilia kept beating.

Neresheimer also tested one bromide (NaBr) which also made stentors so insensitive that they could be cut in two without contraction, but apparently the effect was not reversible and the animals did not survive the treatment. I have found that 1% solutions of the iodides of sodium or potassium have the same effect and their action is completely reversible (Tartar, 1957a). Outstretched animals could be cut in two without a single twitch in either half, and after returning to normal medium complete contractility was recovered within a day.

Although they might become very insensitive, Neresheimer found that his treated stentors always contracted when treated with common fixing agents. From this fact together with the general similarity between the response of stentors and nerve preparations to the drugs and antagonists which he tested, Neresheimer concluded that the effects were not on the myonemes themselves but on the "neurophanes" which were therefore of a neuroid character. Dierks was, of course, of the same opinion with regard to his "neuroids" and he found that coeruleus became insensitive to touch in KCl, while $CaCl_2$ increased contraction and was antagonistic to the action of potassium; for animals made insensitive in the potassium salt regained their irritability when calcium chloride was added. Relaxed stentors still contracted when fixed with Flemming's solution. But contraction of the cell in strongly coagulating solutions can scarcely be taken as demonstrating that the myonemes were not directly affected and the impression remains that much more sophisticated studies will be needed to demonstrate similarities and differences between the responses of stentors and typical nerve–muscle preparations.

Merton (1932, 1935) also attempted to treat stentors so that they could be fixed and stained in the extended form. Anticipating Dierks, he found that KCl gives a partial anæsthesia of the myonemes. In dilute Ringer's solution, stentors became outstretched but their irritability was increased. Metal salts of iron and copper were said to produce differential contractions of the cell and from his description it appears that the anterior end of the stentor contracted while the tail-pole remained extended. Copper sulphate produced a hardening of the cortex which therefore antagonized the contraction of the myonemes and left stentors in a semi-extended state. Fairly well extended preparations were made by relaxing stentors for 2 to 3 hours in Ringer's solution diluted 1:3, then applying weak copper acetate to harden the surface, following this treatment with fixation.

Dierks (1926b) confirmed that a 0·5% solution of KCl renders stentors insensitive to touch. Conversely, $CaCl_2$ increased contraction and was antagonistic to the action of potassium, animals regaining their irritability when calcium was added. A 0·04% solution of Na_2SO_4 paralyzed both cilia and myonemes, but stentors relaxed in this way or with KCl still contracted on fixing.

5. Comparison of osmotic effects to cooling

Following the speculations of Jacques Loeb, Greeley (1901) tested whether increasing the osmotic pressure of the medium surrounding *coeruleus* had the same effect as decreased temperature. Reducing the environmental temperature to 2 °C not only quieted the animals but produced a variety of pathological conditions, including the disappearance of the feeding organelles and the lateral striations — to mention two of the most interesting effects which deserve checking. On rewarming, the " rest of the cells " apparently survived a couple of weeks but in only a few cases did they regenerate. Cane sugar was said to give the same effects as cooling, though a typographical omission in the published account prevents our ever knowing the concentration employed. As we shall see later, sugar causes shedding of the membranellar band, but disappearance of the lateral stripes does not occur and they merely collapse with the cell. Full regeneration followed sugar treatments; therefore we presume that the treatment was mild enough to allow the animals to survive. Loeb's conjecture concerning the similarity between cooling and concentration of protoplasm by loss of water through osmosis was therefore considered to have been confirmed.

Increasing the temperature to 25–28 °C apparently accelerated division, as would be expected; yet we cannot give credence to Greeley's account that within 3 to 4 hours there were many successive divisions induced without marked decrease in size.

6. Acceleration of division

In addition to the strange account of accelerated division just mentioned, Peters (1904) claimed that dilute solutions of KCl also stimulate fission in *coeruleus*. The solution used was 0·01 molar or a bit stronger. NaCl solutions of comparable strength produced a suppression of division instead. From the results it appears that Peters probably did get an accelerated division. He was looking for a specific, immediate impulse since the experiments were run for only 6 hours. Many abnormalities were also encountered. Apparently the peristomal band was shed in some specimens (because regeneration occurred) although he did not say so explicitly. Unequal divisions and production of small blebs of cytoplasm were reported. For a division experiment Peter's procedure was odd, as he did not count the smaller individuals! But if anything this should mask the strength of the results produced, and hence we are merely left with the suggestion that possibly KCl may supply an impulse to division. The effect, if valid, was apparently not due to osmotic pressure, because lactose solutions of even higher osmotic tension were without effect.

7. Changes in state of the protoplasm

An incidental observation of Prowazek (1913) was that sodium taurocholicum causes the endoplasm of stentors to clump into balls and the nucleus, at first highly refractive then disappears.

Changes in the internal viscosity of stentors in relation to various ions was studied by Heilbrunn (1928). Centrifuging the animals in various salt solutions he observed the relative speed with which internal granules and particles passed through the endoplasm. Bivalent cations (calcium and magnesium) apparently decreased the viscosity of the interior, producing liquefaction. Monovalent ions (K, Na, NH_4, Li) increased the viscosity and caused coagulation. But later Heilbrunn (1943) admitted that calcium, on rapid entrance into the cell, could produce gellation instead of liquefaction. Precisely what was happening in these experiments is therefore not clear.

Heilbrunn also studied in *coeruleus* and in Arbacia eggs what he called the surface precipitation reaction, or the formation of films over crushed cells which prevents their explosive dissolution. Calcium appears to be necessary for this reaction, presumably a type of coagulation, for no film formation occurred when the calcium was removed with ammonium oxalate. (Schmitt, as quoted by Moore (1945) states that calcium has more affinity for water than protein polar groups and therefore desolvates these groups which then join with others to produce a more solid state.) Magnesium could not replace calcium in this reaction but strontium could. That cells do not supply their own calcium for this reaction he explained by conceiving that intracellular calcium is bound and not free.

Noting the difficulties of studying effects on the endoplasm by simple immersion of a cell, Chambers and Kao (1952) micro-injected solutions into the interior. Among other subjects was a " large variety " of *Stentor*, quite possibly *coeruleus*. They injected

CaCl$_2$ and SrCl$_2$ in the concentrations used by Heilbrunn and found that there was an endoplasmic clotting at the site of injection, hence agreeing with his addendum and general thesis that calcium has a clotting effect. It was especially interesting to me that the clot was moved to the surface and pinched off, as also in amœbas. Even when as much as two-thirds of the interior had been coagulated the clot was still ejected and the cortex apparently not violated.

Swimming of stentors was normal in solutions of CaCl$_2$ and SrCl$_2$, but if the ectoplasm was torn, the wound opened and there was a clotting of the exposed endoplasm, much as in Heilbrunn's surface precipitation reaction. Conversely, in NaCl and KCl tears were never repaired, the endoplasm flowing out of the cut without any sign of coagulation. The responses of *Stentor* protoplasm were therefore quite like those previously found by the senior author in *Amœba dubia*.

Chambers and Kao also injected phenol-red and bromcresol-purple into their unnamed *Stentor* and found that the cytoplasm had a pH of 6·8 while that of the macronucleus was at least 7·6. Correspondingly, Strom (1926), using very dilute mixtures of phosphates to obtain a varying pH without specific ionic effects, found that stentors are only slightly influenced by changes of pH from 6·5 to 8·0.

8. Tests for an antero-posterior metabolic gradient

In pursuing his theory of metabolic gradients in organisms, Child (1914) subjected *coeruleus* to a respiratory depressant, KCN. The animals were promptly disintegrated, starting from the frontal field and membranellar band and extending posteriorly over the lateral ectoplasm. In a few cases there was a secondary wave of disintegration beginning at the posterior end. The species *polymorphus* gave a similar response, though difficult to follow because of the unpigmented cortex. A number of other ciliates also showed graded disintegration of the cell. It was concluded that there is an antero-posterior gradient and that this is metabolic in character.

On another species ("probably *roeselii*") Child (1949) used a more subtle approach in studying the intracellular reoxidation of reduced Janus green and methylene blue. Oxidation changes the green dye to red. This color change passed in a wave from the anterior to the posterior pole followed by a wave of ectoplasmic disintegration in the same direction. The membranellar band, especially at the level of the basal bodies, showed the sharpest effect and therefore seemed to be a site of vigorous oxidation. Methylene blue gave essentially the same results and Child felt confirmed in his demonstration of a metabolic gradient in *Stentor*.

Confirmation also seemed to be evident in the work of Monod (1933) who studied the differential susceptibility of different parts of the cell in *Stentor* and other common ciliates to ultraviolet radiation. Again there was an antero-posterior gradient in disintegration of the ectoplasm.

Although Weisz (1948d) confirmed Child in regard to the gradient response of stentors to KCN and KMnO$_4$, he stood strongly against Child's interpretation. This was largely because he had found (Weisz, 1948a, c) that, other factors being the same, the rate of oral regeneration and subsequent growth of fragments was independent of the level of the body from which they were taken, though of course the shape of *Stentor* does not admit of much variation in this regard.

Holding that primordium formation and rate of growth are more indicative of metabolic state than is cellular disintegration, Weisz denied the whole concept of metabolic gradients as applying to *Stentor* and also questioned its applicability to other forms. He gave a new twist to these experiments by studying the disintegration of fragments of stentors in KCN. Anterior pieces disintegrated from the anterior end the same as whole animals. Posterior fragments began disintegrating not at their anterior ends but at the holdfast. And middle pieces started disintegrating first in the region of the contractile vacuole. Hence he viewed the *Stentor* cell as a heirarchy of structures which vary in their susceptibility to external agents, and this is a function not of any cellular gradient but of the organization of those structures, although it is stretching the point to say that the contractile vacuole is more highly organized than the lateral ectoplasm of middle fragments.

In answering Weisz, Child (1949) seems to be saying that *Stentor* is not a good form for studying this problem anyway because it does not have the long and cylindrical shape of worms and hydroids. But we shall shortly describe that there are a great variety of simple salts and other substances, not directly related to

R

respiration or metabolism, which produce shedding of the membranellar band in *Stentor* followed by a wave of disintegration passing over the ectoplasm towards the posterior pole. I am therefore inclined to agree with Weisz that the localized disintegrative action of various solutions is a function of the special state of organization of the different parts of the cell cortex.

9. Acquired tolerance to external agents

Pre-treatment of organisms with sub-lethal concentrations of killing agents generally increases subsequent tolerance of originally lethal concentrations of the same substances! This adaptation has also been demonstrated in *Stentor*. Davenport and Neal (1896) succinctly summarized their studies on *coeruleus*. "Stentors reared for two days in a culture solution containing 0·00005% mercuric chloride resist a killing solution of 0·001% $HgCl_2$ nearly four times as long as those reared in water. Similar results were obtained by use of quinine. " This was not due to the selection of resistant individuals but a genuine acclimatization, because no deaths occurred at the lower concentration and the same individuals were carried into the higher. Nor was this a general adaptation to increased osmotic pressure; for the concentrations used were very low, and NaCl solutions of the same osmotic pressure gave no increased tolerance to the killing agents. The increased immunity was acquired rapidly, measurable resistance developing after 1 or 2 hours exposure to the sub-lethal concentrations, gradually increasing thereafter until exposure of longer than 96 hours gave no further resistance. The stronger the acclimatizing solution the greater the resistance developed until the strength was such that the lethal effects were additive. Killing, by disintegration of the cortex of the cell, occurred about three times more rapidly at 23° than at 15 °C, indicating that death was caused by a chemical reaction.

Similar effects were studied in the response of *coeruleus* to alcohols and glycerine by Daniel (1909). Animals lived well for weeks in 1% ethanol, were destroyed by 6 hours in 2%, and died in 2 hours at 3%. At lethal concentrations the body cilia soon stopped beating but the membranelles remained active up to the time of death. Two different stocks showed notable differences in regard to acquired tolerance. In the first stock, 1% solutions stimulated the animal to great activity, accelerated division with production of many smaller cells, and gave no acquired immunity to higher concentrations. The resistance of this stock was already high but Daniel showed that this did not obscure a fundamental lack of acclimatization.

In the second stock, animals in 1% ethanol were also excited to increased activity but showed practically no increase in rate of division, and they acquired a marked immunity as a result of remaining in this weaker solution. For example, in 6% solutions they died in 162 seconds if not acclimated but lived for 301 seconds if pre-treated for 4 days in 1% ethanol.

If acclimated, 6% ethanol made the membranelles beat so vigorously that the whole cell shook. The acquired tolerance was a function of the strength of the acclimating solution and the length of time the animals were exposed to it, appreciable immunity being obtained by 4 hours; with no further increases after 4 days exposure to sub-lethal concentrations.

All stentors were killed in 8% ethanol. The membranellar band and frontal field were the last parts to become quiet and begin disintegration. Acquired tolerance for ethanol was not transferable and gave no increased immunity to methanol.

In 1 to 1/4th molar glycerine, pigment was not shed as in the alcohols. Stentors remained motionless and then suddenly contracted, whereupon the membranellar band was shed as a ribbon. If rescued from the solution, survivors could then regenerate a new set of feeding organelles. Otherwise the animals plasmolyzed, beginning at the posterior end. Ethanol immunity was not transferable to glycerine and indeed only made the animals more sensitive to the latter. Hence in general Daniel regarded his findings as demonstrating Ehrlich's principle that immunity is specific and non-transferable.

Daniel also found, as had Peters (1904), that stentors are not tolerant to excess alkali or acid, and this has also been my experience. Even very dilute solutions of hydrochloric acid produced rapid killing after the membranelles stopped beating and pigment was shed. Apparently sodium hydroxide does not penetrate the cell so rapidly, and stentors could live for a remarkably long time if the pellicle was not ruptured. The alkali caused a loss of membranelles as in glycerine and the shed pigment became a

" beautiful sea-green ". Body cilia beat as long as the ectoplasmic structure remained intact.

10. Shedding of pigment and pellicle

The pigment of stentors is largely located in ectoplasmic granules beneath the pellicle where it is often readily affected by external agents. The species which has been studied is *coeruleus*, observation of which indicates that pigment sloughing may even occur under natural conditions, as was first suggested by Schuberg (1890).

Loss of pigment occurs under three guises. A homogeneous blue-green halo may be ejected, suggesting that the pigment granules have been burst and their contents set free. The granules may be cast off as such and appear as tiny particles, which seems to be the case in natural sloughing. And finally, one or more layers of the pellicle may also be shed, and in this case the outer surface carries the granules with it where they remain in rows corresponding to the pigmented stripes. It is surprising that the pellicle can be sloughed without apparently interfering in any way with the cilia, for the outer coating of the cilium is in all ciliates continuous with the pellicle covering of the cell body. This also occurs even more clearly in *Blepharisma* treated with strychnine in which the animals swim out of the discarded pellicle (Nadler, 1929). As already suggested, pellicular shedding may have been elaborated as a method of case-making, both in certain species of *Stentor* and in *Folliculina*. In the latter, Andrews (1923) found that the forming sac at first shows lines of pigment granules corresponding to stripes on the body. An appearance very much like this can be induced in *coeruleus* which forms no lorica.

In methylene blue, Neresheimer (1903) produced a separation of the stentor ectoplasm, and it was in this way that he obtained the pieces which he stained to demonstrate " neurophanes ". Much later Weisz (1950a) obtained sloughing of pigment and pellicle in Janus green.

Prowazek (1904) found that brief immersion of *coeruleus* in $\frac{1}{2}\%$ NaCl caused a shedding of pigment as a homogeneous blue halo. The coloration was then regenerated in about a day after returning to normal medium. In the same year, Peters (1904) independently made the same observation and carried the study much further.

He found that pigment shedding was the immediate response of stentors transferred to certain solutions and that animals could even later divide in media which caused shedding. The colored slough he described as of gelatinous consistency, a homogeneous halo without granules. Such sloughing was produced in KCl, NaCl, KNO_3, Na_2SO_4, $(NH_4)_2SO_4$, Na_2HPO_4, NaOH, HCl, lactose, and chloroform but no shedding occurred in $CaCl_2$, $Ca(OH)_2$, $CaSO_4$, or $MgSO_4$. Hence monovalent cations which are the ones producing reversal of ciliary beating also elicit the sloughing response, but bivalent cations do not. The effect is obviously not osmotic since lactose and chloroform gave a similar result and $CaCl_2$ protected the animals against the shedding effects of Na_2SO_4, although the osmotic pressure was correspondingly increased. In chloroform and Na_2SO_4 some layers of the pellicle apparently were also shed as a " heavy coat ". Peters suggested that the pigment is a protein which is dissolved by certain salts.

We have just noted that Daniel (1909) obtained shedding of pigment in alcohols and NaOH but not in glycerine.

Peters' study was confirmed and extended in some of my own investigations (Tartar, 1957a). I also found that monovalent cations produced pigment shedding, while calcium and magnesium salts did not. The most vigorous shedding occurred in $NaHCO_3$, NH_4Cl, and LiCl. In strychnine there was a violent shattering

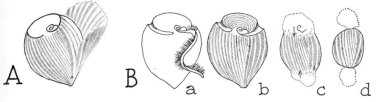

FIG. 70.

A. Shedding of pellicular layer and some pigment granules in *S. coeruleus* in 1% ammonium chloride.

B. Casting off the membranellar band in 2% urea. *a:* Band shed following fimbriation of membranelles, with last part to go being the gullet lining. *b:* Neat removal of peristome in proper treatment, with lateral and frontal stripe structures remaining unaffected. *c:* Extended treatment produces two fronts of disintegration, but if stopped (*d*) middle piece separates, survives, and regenerates. (After Tartar, 1957a.)

loose of the granules and the pellicle was shed in pieces, not as a hull, as in the amazing demonstration with *Blepharisma* by Nadler. Shedding of the pellicle was especially noticeable and clear-cut in NH_4Cl, ammonium acetate, LiCl, and egg albumen (Fig. 70A). Stentors apparently regenerate both pigment and pellicle when returned promptly to culture medium, for their later appearance was altogether normal. The concentrations employed were usually 1%, made up in the filtered lake water used for culturing. Attempts by repeated treatment with salts to obtain stentors which were completely devoid of surface pigment granules and could not recover them later were not successful. Granules located in the endoplasm (Weisz, 1949a) may have been mobilized (and multiplied) to take their place.

These shedding responses might therefore be useful in tracing the origin of the pigment granules during their rapid regeneration, as well as in testing the consequences for respiration of greatly reducing the number of cortical granules. And treatments causing a neat shedding of the pellicle should provide a means of studying the significance of this layer in permeability as well as in immunological reactions.

11. Shedding of the membranellar band

In addition to producing extrusion of pigment, Prowazek's (1904) $\frac{1}{2}$% solution of table salt caused the shedding of the membranellar band in *coeruleus*; Daniel (1909) obtained such cast-offs with glycerine. These reports were generally neglected until, independently, I found the same effect when stentors were subjected to 25% sea water (Tartar, 1957a). I then tested several chlorides, sulfates, acetates, sugars, urea, and albumen — usually in 1% solution. All produced sloughing of the membranellar band with one exception. This was ethanol in which, as in the studies of Daniel, the membranelles remained completely intact and beating as the last part of the cell to disintegrate. In all treatments which produced sloughing, the animals could later recover and regenerate the feeding organelles, with the single exception of $NiSO_4$ treatment. The typical response was for the stentors to swim about in agitation, backwards in the monovalent cations, then suddenly contracting as if the agents had succeeded in penetrating deeply. Following this contraction, the membranelles became fimbriated and usually the major portion of the band was cast off, including both membranelles and a basement ribbon (Fig. 70B). This effect was all or none; for although only part of the band might be shed, there was no case in which the band was simply injured while remaining in place. When the animals were left in these solutions, the wave of disintegration of the ectoplasm passed over the frontal field and proceeded posteriorly down the lateral surfaces, often being met by a corresponding wave originating in the holdfast and moving forward (B). Hence the appearance was just like that of the disintegration in KCN demonstrated by Child (1914). Again, there was an all or none effect, the ectoplasm becoming totally disintegrated or remaining intact with cilia beating. Even after half the ectoplasm was destroyed, disintegration stopped at once on return to normal medium and the remaining part could still survive and recover. The disintegrated ectoplasm as well as the underlying endoplasm was then pinched off to leave a viable mid-fragment (B).

It seems odd that the membranelles, with their deep-lying basal plates, should have been the first to go, but this was clearly the case. In fact, urea and sucrose treatments gave very neat shedding of the membranellar band if treatment was stopped promptly, without the frontal field or lateral ectoplasm being affected in any way. Sea water and most of the other treatments caused a lifting of the band first at its distal end. Specimens were often obtained in which the mouthparts remained intact, complete with their membranelles; but in Holtfreter's solution the membranelles lining the gullet and bordering the oral pouch were usually the first to go. Therefore it is possible by choosing the proper treatment to produce specimens in which the mouthparts alone are complete, and others in which only these parts have been subjected to deletions. This technique is also convenient for producing large numbers of animals in simultaneous regeneration (p. 353), or for inducing primordium formation in graft complexes without the need for cutting operations which might disturb a contrived arrangement of the lateral striping.

Oral primordia were also shed in salts, urea, and sugars. The more advanced its development, the more likely was the primordium to be shed. Sloughing usually began at the anterior end and proceeded posteriorly. At early stages, on the contrary, in which oral cilia had not yet grown out to their definitive length, the anlage was notably resistant and resembled in this regard the general ectoplasm from which it presumably arises. Stage 4 is the time when the primordium becomes susceptible to sloughing. It may be inferred that development involves the elaboration of a certain type of organization which is peculiarly sensitive to these external agents.

We do not know how this shedding of the membranellar band is brought about but we can at least exclude some possibilities. Osmotic pressure probably plays no part because even very weak solutions of Na_2CO_3 produce sloughing, and sugars do likewise even long before the cell begins to collapse. The action is not ionic because it is shown by neutral substances like sugars. There seems to be no relation to valency, for both NaCl and $CaCl_2$ produce like results. Hydrogen ion effects are ruled out by the efficacy of neutral substances. Nor does the result appear to be due to injury as such, since the most drastic operations with a glass needle do not produce it. The great variety of substances producing the effect itself poses a difficulty to analysis.

12. Morphogenetic effects

After encountering such striking and specific effects on the stentor cell of relatively simple compounds in lethal concentrations, I prepared sub-lethal solutions which obviously affected the animals but allowed their indefinite survival (Tartar, 1957a). When stentors which had shed their membranellar band in sucrose were not washed before replacing in normal medium regeneration was delayed from 1 to 2 days, doubtless because of the carry-over of some of the sugar. Otherwise the animals were entirely normal in their behavior. Hence sugar is in itself an effective inhibitor of primordium formation.

Diluted sea water also gave reversible inhibition of oral regeneration. Often there were graded effects, depending upon the concentration in the solution and the susceptibility of the individual. Sometimes regeneration was merely delayed. In other individuals or at different concentrations there was formation of a complete membranellar band but with inadequate development of the mouthparts, only a small pit being produced. A further influence was shown when the anlage was arrested in mid-development at

stage 4 and remained as such. All these effects are quite like those
obtained with acriflavin by Weisz (1955). Dilute sea water also
produced cases of aborted fission without separation of the daughter
cells, as well as ectoplasmic lesions which produced a sort of
self-mincing in which the ectoplasmic striping was broken up into
irregular patches (Fig. 71A).

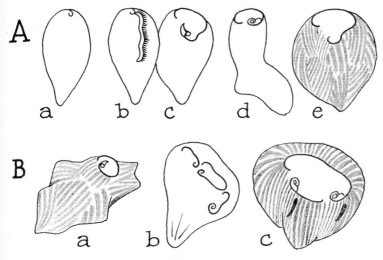

FIG. 71.

A. Effects of sub-lethal dilutions of sea water on *S. coeruleus*.
a: Reversible inhibition (or delay) of regeneration. *b:* Arrest
of primordium development at stage 4. *c:* Incomplete stomatogenesis. *d:* Incomplete division. *e:* Astomatous regeneration
and breaking of stripe pattern into disorganized patches.

B. Reactions to sub-lethal concentrations of lithium chloride
include the above, as well as (a) a more exaggerated self-mincing
of the stripe pattern with corresponding abnormality of cell-
shape, (b) stacking up of oral sets due to resorption failure in
repeated reorganizations, and (c) extraordinary increase in
breadth of the cell from hypertrophy of striping, leading to
spontaneous formation of self-reproducing doublets. (After
Tartar, 1957a.)

Lithium chloride in concentrations of 0·1 to 0·005% gave
reversible effects which were especially interesting (Fig. 71B).
Again, primordium formation could be reversibly inhibited for

1 to 4 days, with complete regeneration occurring on return to normal medium. Regeneration was sometimes merely delayed, astomatous, or blocked in development at stage 4, which is just the stage at which the primordium becomes susceptible to shedding. Abortive fissions were noted, as well as distortions of body striping. In successive reorganizations, LiCl prevented the resorption of the old organelles, with the result that there was a stacking-up of several sets of feeding organelles, as shown. Perhaps most provocative of all was that the stentors became very broad, as if multiplication of lateral striping had been stimulated much beyond the normal bounds, and in fact some of these animals spontaneously converted into doublets, as illustrated.

The only previous test of the effect of LiCl on ciliates to my knowledge was that of Fauré-Fremiet (with J. Ducornet, 1949) who found that this agent produced microstomatous forms in *Tetrahymena*. This he attributed to inhibition of the multiplication of cilia, yet it appears that, in *Stentor*, broadening of the cell is accompanied by increase of kineties and therefore considerable multiplication of cilia and related structures.

It is well known that lithium has special effects on developing eggs, producing in general a vegetalization or depressing a gradient whose maximum is at the animal pole (see Gustafson, 1954). The precise nature of this effect is not known. It may be that lithium alters the hydration of proteins, for it seems to produce a coarse-ness of the cytoplasm in general and to cause proteins to become fibrillar, coagulated, and stable. Raven (1949) states that lithium seems to affect especially the density of the cortical cytoplasm in the eggs of *Limnæa*. Since the major morphogenetic events in stentors are also located in the cortex of the cell, the effects may be comparable and one might even regard suppression of differen-tiation of the feeding organelles and concomitant broadening of the lateral ectoplasm as a parallel of " vegetalization ". At any rate it is most interesting that lithium has unique effects upon *Stentor*, as it does upon embryos.

13. Inhibition of growth by X-ray, and other effects

Kimball (1958) subjected *coeruleus* to X-rays and found that when irradiated animals were returned to culture medium fission was much delayed. Although the stentors fed and formed food vacuoles they grew slowly or even decreased in size. But they could form primordia in reorganizations apparently induced by the irradiation, or in regenerations following transection. The nuclei were likewise apparently unaffected. At least some digestion evidently occurred, because starvation controls decreased in size much more rapidly than the irradiated stentors. Therefore, Kimball concluded that X-rays inhibit growth by decreasing or blocking the net synthesis from feeding, though not preventing such synthesis as occurs in the building of primordia. Delayed fission would hence be due to the animal's failing to attain fission size or only slowly achieving the maximum volume, and not to incapacity to form primordia or undergo the nuclear changes which accompany division.

These effects were independent of the presence or absence of oxygen during irradiation. But anoxia combined with X-ray (irradiation in an atmosphere of nitrogen) resulted in deformities such as ridges, flanges, in-pocketings, and extra tails and sets of feeding organelles. It seems likely that these abnormalities resulted from breaks in the ectoplasm followed by improper healing; for the forms described resemble those obtained by disarranging the ectoplasmic pattern mechanically so that disjunctive areas no longer coordinate (see Figs. 65B and 66E). If so, it may be suggested that in these operations the separated areas join but fail to achieve intimate union because of misorientation, while in the radiation studies the orientation is at first correct, but intimate rejoining, say, of the fibrous structures of the clear stripes, is inhibited as an after-effect of irradiation. This in itself would be an interesting effect, though still leaving the question why outgrowth and joinings of fibers, which undoubtedly occurs during oral primordium development, is not also inhibited.

14. Effect of temperature on size

A statistical sudy of variation in dimensions with temperature (Zingher and Fisikow, 1931) showed that mean size of stentors increases with rising temperatures up to a certain limit. Natural collections accordingly showed a similar enlargement, and also an increased coefficient of variation, from winter to summer. Since the measurement curves were unimodal, apparently only one race of *coeruleus* occurred in the pond sampled. Nor was illumination a

CHAPTER XV

METABOLISM

1. Effects of starvation

Apart from eventual death, the most conspicuous response of protozoa to suspension of feeding is an often marked decrease in size of the individual. That is to say, the animal consumes some of its own substance before dying. Protozoa differ in the extent of reduction which is possible. Paramecia decrease little before they shrivel and die, but *Dileptus* (Visscher, 1923) and *Amœba* (Hartmann, 1928) can persist and dwindle to 1/100th, and *Didinium* (Mast, 1909) to 1/6th their original volume. *Bursaria truncatella* can diminish in length from 500 to 90 μ as the feeding organelles become proportionately smaller (Lund, 1917), and Dembowska (1938) showed that under starvation *Stylonychia* repeatedly reorganizes on a smaller scale until very tiny animals are produced. When great latitude in size is permitted, the protozoa do not simply become thin and emaciated like starving vertebrates; as with many invertebrates, including hydras and flat worms, they become proportionately reduced in most of their parts so that they may properly be called dwarfs. Minute forms are not only the result of individuals consuming their own substance but may possibly also involve so-called " hunger divisions ", or an initial persistence of the rhythm of fission in spite of decreasing size during the first days of starvation. The two factors are not easily separable when dealing with large samples difficult to count. Yet Maupas (1888) confirmed Gruber (1886) in reporting that large, well-fed *coeruleus*, when isolated, continued dividing 3 or 4 times, producing smaller than normal individuals. Division without attaining maximum size was indicated, though on Maupas' evidence the stentors must not have been totally without food since division products much larger than one-eighth, say, of the maximum volume were produced. In my experience, on the contrary, even large stentors very seldom divide after they are isolated into a large drop of coarse-filtered medium on a depression slide. The reality of hunger divisions in stentors therefore remains still in question.

Many have observed that in the largest stentors, *coeruleus* and *polymorphus*, dwarf forms appear under conditions of starvation (Maupas, 1888; Johnson, 1893; Popoff, 1909; Prowazek, 1904 and Schulze, 1951). Stolte (1922) observed both large and small forms in starving cultures. I have myself frequently noted a similar range in size which is not always correlated with cannibalism. Possibly the larger forms are animals which had recently divided, do not then divide further after food is withheld, and therefore would gradually diminish only through the utilization of their own substance. To complete this historical résumé Sosnowsky (1899), as reported by Sokoloff (1923), stated that division in stentor is stimulated by starvation, and that the macronuclear membrane disappears under these conditions. Ivanić (1927) contributed the equally improbable notion that, when feeding is stopped, stentors and other protozoa actually increase in size as they use up the remaining food but fail to divide.

Several visible changes besides decrease in cell volume occur during starvation. In *coeruleus* and perhaps in other pigmented stentors the coloration tends to disappear. This fading to nearly white is conspicuous in single animals long isolated on slides, but larger samples in a culture dish remain fairly green for a month or more though starved. Weisz (1949a) thought that the pigment granules are digested during starvation. Granular bands do seem eventually to disappear in isolated animals, but only as death approaches. But stentorin itself is certainly not easily assimilated in cannibals and the pigment may even be ejected as waste. Pigment changes are therefore enigmatic and require much more study. Stolte (1922) emphasized that starvation produces vacuolization of the endoplasm but this pathological state, again, is prominent only near the point of death. An important alteration which occurs only gradually is that the macronucleus becomes reduced. On the evidence it cannot be decided whether this is because the substance of the nucleus is drawn upon to maintain life or because the nucleus is adapting in size to the decreasing volume of cytoplasm, or both. That regulation of nuclear to cytoplasmic volume is more important than consuming the nucleus as a reserve is indicated by the often poor survival of hypernucleated stentors (p. 304).

It was Johnson (1893) who first noted that dwarf stentors have smaller and fewer macronuclear nodes than well-fed animals at any stage, and Prowazek (1904) provided further confirmatory observations. Allescher (1912) made a separate study of this phenomenon. First she found, naturally, that decrease in size of starving stentors was greatest at higher temperatures, at which metabolism would be expected to proceed at a higher pace; but rate of decrease also then fell off rapidly, as if definite limits to reduction in size were met. Cool and warm cultured animals eventually shrunk to the same small size. Apparently the nucleus decreased but little at lower temperatures, while in warm cultures under starvation decrease in the size and especially in the number of macronuclear nodes was conspicuous: of the order of from 20 to 5. In this reduction some of the nodes decreased in stainability as their substance was apparently transferred to adjacent beads of the nucleus. The reduction was therefore especially one of surface area. Her interpretation was that the nucleus as well as the cytoplasm was consumed during starvation and that this is possible in ciliates with widely dispersed macronuclei, such as *Stentor* and *Dileptus*, but not in forms with compact nuclei, like *Paramecium*. I have found, indeed, that *P. caudatum* forced to carry two macronuclei do eventually resorb *one* entirely, instead of diminishing *both* (Tartar, 1940). Perhaps it might with equal plausibility have been suggested that paramecia cannot decrease the nuclear surface further, while stentors with their nodulated nucleus can and do, in adaptation to decreasing size.

In a clone of *coeruleus* I made some observations on starvation dwarfs simply by isolating abundant samples in caster dishes and allowing them to stand for a month without added nutrients. The size of the ciliates decreased from a maximum diameter of $376\,\mu$ to a minimum value of $94\,\mu$. After two weeks of starvation the nuclear picture was varied, for the number of nodes ranged from 6 to 16 and large and small nodes were frequently found within the same individual. This indicates that the nucleus was still in process of adapting to decreasing size of the animals. Eventually the dwarfs contained only 5 or 6 nodes which were still large in proportion to the volume of the cell yet smaller than those of normal animals (Fig. 72). The dwarfs had tiny, proportionate feeding organelles and the number of lateral stripes was about half the normal, indicating the morphological adaptation to decrease in size. Johnson had found that such dwarfs undergo no irreversible changes and are capable of complete recovery, growing and dividing when later fed. I demonstrated that fragments of these tiny stentors were capable of normal oral regeneration.

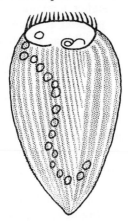

FIG. 72. Largest *S. coeruleus* compared to smallest individual in starvation culture. The larger had a contracted diameter of $376\,\mu$, 18 macronuclear nodes, and c. 110 pigment stripes. The smaller: $94\,\mu$, 5 nodes, and c. 56 stripes. Note that membranelles, colored stripes, and nodes are not proportionately smaller in the tiny stentor.

As expected, the fat and carbohydrate reserves (further discussed in the following section) are exhausted during periods of starvation (Zhinkin, 1930). According to Weisz (1949a) their utilization is so rapid that the endoplasm is cleared of these reserves within a day. My impression is that at least the carbohydrate stores, which are clearly visible as white granules in dark-field illumination are exhausted much more slowly. Moreover, when survival of anterior halves with little if any such reserves was compared with that of posterior halves bearing abundant reserves no conspicuous advantage from the stored material could be demonstrated. This may have been due to the abnormal conditions apparently involved in isolating animals into small drops on slides, for some specimens even died before the carbohydrate stores were exhausted (Tartar, 1959a).

All these findings merely confirm that stentors, like other organisms, are able to continue living for some time by consuming nutrient reserves or their own vital substance during periods of starvation. More precise studies of starving cells might dissociate factors most dependent for their maintenance on continuous inflow of new materials, or starving protozoa may prove particularly sensitive and discriminatory in their response to specific additives such as certain amino acids, in contrast to well-fed cells. At present, one is above all impressed by the adaptive morphological changes whereby starving ciliates become not merely shrunken but re-formed on a smaller scale, as tiny but perfectly formed dwarfs are produced.

2. Storage and utilization of nutrient reserves

Visible reserves in *Stentor* take the form of glycogenoid granules and fat droplets. The first can be demonstrated by dark-field illumination or Lugol's iodine stain and the second by Sudan III. These reserves were the subject of an extensive field and laboratory study of Zhinkin (1930) on *polymorphus*, with incidental observations on *coeruleus*.

Carbohydrate reserves are present in the form of granules which are concentrated toward the posterior pole. Clearly revealed by Tyndall effect using side illumination against a dark background, one can observe the precise location of these granules in living *coeruleus* (Tartar, 1959a). In animals which have been cleared of food vacuoles by withholding food organisms, these reserves are seen to occupy a subcortical band, forward from the posterior pole and discontinuous in the oral meridian (Fig. 73). This is the regular and preferred location, though overstepped if the carbohydrates are especially abundant. Soluble in hot water and staining red with iodine, Zhinkin identified the granules as glycogen. Weisz thought them sufficiently different to merit the name paraglycogen. Fat stores are present in the form of tiny droplets throughout the endoplasm.

Zhinkin followed stentors through an annual cycle. The most conspicuous changes were that, with decreasing temperature in the autumn, the carbohydrate reserves increased; but when the ponds

S

were covered with ice and developed an oxygen deficiency these reserves disappeared as the abundance of fat droplets increased. This alternation of reserve stuffs suggested correlations with temperature and oxygen tension, as well as the possibility that the carbohydrate was converted into fats. Zingher (1933) in fact maintained that both starches and proteins are convertible into fats by ciliates.

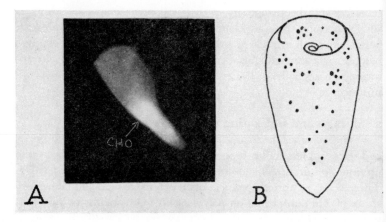

FIG.73. Nutritional reserves in *S. coeruleus*.

A. Photo showing location of glycogenoid carbohydrate granules (cf. Fig. 17A).

B. Random distribution of fat droplets revealed by Sudan III staining. (After Zingher, 1933.)

In laboratory tests, Zhinkin found maximum increase in number and size of glycogenoid granules at 3–5 °C, while the primary condition for fat accumulation was lack of oxygen. In general it appears from his data that, naturally, an accumulation of nutrient reserves requires a temperature which is not so low that metabolism is sharply curtailed nor so high that increased activity in cell multiplication utilizes the food directly and may even draw upon reserves already present. Weisz found that fat stores were not used in regeneration, and Zingher considered them necessary to a normal condition of the cytoplasm. My impression from long observation of stentors in culture is that well-fed animals always have abundant carbyhodrate reserves and probably fat stores as well. Only with considerable trouble could *coeruleus* be divested of its glycogenoid granules (Tartar, 1959a). The seasonal cycle which Zhinkin seems to have well documented may therefore be the consequence of a delicate and changing equilibrium between rates of feeding and cell growth.

3. Respiration

The oxygen requirements of *Stentor* have been little studied. Stolte (1922) remarked that decreased oxygen produced vacuolization of the endoplasm. In a Russian ecological study which I have not seen, Zhinkin and Obraztsov (1930) observed that *polymorphus* and *coeruleus* are found in ponds only where there is abundant oxygen: under ice, only where bottom springs provided enough of the dissolved gas. Sampling of an Iowa pond showed stentors to be abundant only near the bottom under nearly anærobic conditions according to Sprugel (1951), a result most paradoxical since the same animals lived well when transferred to jars in the laboratory. Oxidation–reduction studied by means of color indicators in protozoa, presumably including *Stentor*, was pursued by Roskin and Semenov (1933) in a study which was not available to me. It has been observed (Whiteley, personal communication) that in some races of *coeruleus* the animals remained near the bottom while in other clones they always collected near the surface, suggesting that there may be racial differences in oxygen requirement.

Using the Cartesian diver technique, Whiteley (1956) discovered a marked and unique increase in respiratory rate in halves of starved *coeruleus* containing all the macronucleus and hence having abnormally high ratios of nucleus to cytoplasm. During the first day the rate of respiration showed increases of as much as 175%. This acceleration was correlated solely with the nucleo-cytoplasmic ratio and was repeated after a second removal of cytoplasm. Appropriate controls demonstrated that neither cutting nor regeneration were responsible for the increase. Enucleates showed a low and gradually decreasing rate of respiration; that of whole animals, high and also only decreasing. In the critical macronucleate halves the accelerated respiration temporarily approached the values shown by whole cells. The whole macronucleus therefore tends to form the respiratory system of a whole, even in a diminished amount of cytoplasm.

Yet it is interesting that when de Terra (1959) forced all the macronucleus into one daughter cell during division and so produced *coeruleus* with twice the normal macronuclear complement, the uptake and incorporation of radiophosphorus was not different from that of normal cells.

As relating to energy metabolism, sites of acid phosphatase in *coeruleus* were determined by Weisz (1949b). Positive tests were obtained around macronuclear nodes and other bodies in the endoplasm as well as at the basal granules of membranelles and body cilia. Enzyme activity decreased during starvation but not during periods of morphogenesis, and appeared in oral primordia only after cilia were present and active. Therefore, acid phosphatase is probably involved in the action but not in the development of cilia.

4. Digestion

In *Folliculina* and *Stentor* the transit of the food vacuoles is not in a definite track provided by cyclosis of the endoplasm, as in *Paramecium*, but each is individually handled, according to Andrews (1955). Schwartz (1935) described the normal digestion of *Colpidium* by *coeruleus*, which required about 20 hours and included dissolution of the nucleus of the prey. In feeding enucleates, however, the food vacuoles from the start contained excess fluid and at no time was digestion normal or complete. It will also be recalled that Schwartz found indication that even a substantial reduction in number of macronuclear nodes resulted in abnormal metabolism with inadequate digestion.

Meissner (1888) reported that stentors (apparently *polymorphus*) take up and digest starch grains. This was confirmed by Zingher (1933) who also noted increased fat droplets following the starch meal, suggesting that carbohydrates are converted into fats; yet *coeruleus* predominantly rejected starch grains in the feeding studies of Schæffer (see p. 11). Contrary to Meissner, Zingher found that *coeruleus* ingests the fat droplets of milk, which he thought were assimilated directly because rapid cell multiplication followed. In rich cultures with little oxygen, digestion was inhibited and stentors became stuffed with undigested food vacuoles, according to Stolte (1922), a condition which could be corrected by supplying oxygen through algæ added to the medium. His interpretation was that oxygen is necessary for the elaboration and activity of digestive enzymes.

5. Symbiosis with green algæ

As in many other ciliates and in simpler metazoa, certain stentors may bear spheroid, grass-green cells of *Chlorella* living within them. These species include *polymorphus*, *igneus* (Balbiani, 1893), *amethystinus*, and *niger* (Maier, 1903). The algæ reside in the endoplasm (Johnson, 1893), where they are scattered at random. That the relationship is symbiotic is shown by the demonstrations that the stentors in question can live without the algæ, that the algæ do not disintegrate on death of the stentor (Balbiani, 1893) and may even continue life as free-living cells, and that both stentors and algæ receive advantages from their association.

The first experiments on symbiosis in *Stentor* were made by Prowazek (1904). He reported that chlorellæ can multiply within dead and crushed *polymorphus*, indicating that the algæ in stentors can probably be grown in " tissue culture " like those of *Paramecium bursaria* (Loefer, 1936). Having obtained artificial symbiosis by infecting *Stylonychia* and *Euplotes* with free-living *Chlorella*, Prowazek tried unsuccessfully to obtain the same with *Stentor coeruleus*. Failure occurred in spite of the fact that the *coeruleus* digested the chlorellæ only partially and ejected the remainder. Even the enucleated stentors would not accept chlorellæ intimately into their cytoplasm, ingesting the algæ but retaining them, undigested, within food vacuoles. Prowazek concluded that the cytoplasm of *coeruleus* is unfavorable for *Chlorella* and he therefore doubted Kessler's (1882) report that symbiosis can be established between this *Stentor* and the chlorellæ from a freshwater sponge. Certain experiments of mine were confirmatory (Tartar, 1953). In interspecific grafts (a convenient method for introducing symbionts) any substantial admixture of *coeruleus* cytoplasm with *polymorphus* resulted in the ejection of symbionts natural to the latter species. In Prowazek's observations neither enucleated *polymorphus* nor enucleated *coeruleus* with ingested chlorellæ survived longer than controls without algæ.

The most comprehensive study of symbiosis in *polymorphus* has been that of Hämmerling (1946) and Schulze (1951) who began their work together but published separately. Their findings will be reviewed together, noting points of difference in interpretation or observation. In the cultures of *polymorphus*, the stentors collected appropriately at the lighted sides of aquaria, yet too intense an illumination was detrimental. Hämmerling remarked that the stentors divided only at night or in the dark. This observation may be important in providing a means for obtaining simultaneous fission of animals in well-fed cultures.

Stentors were not easily divested of their symbionts. When grown in the dark, chlorellæ decreased greatly in abundance but a few algæ were always retained, mostly toward the posterior pole. Persisting symbionts in these pale ciliates might therefore have been removed by cutting and culturing a number of anterior fragments. Instead, the method employed by Pringsheim (l.c.) for *Paramecium bursaria* was used: pale stentors previously grown in the dark were cultured with abundant food (free-living algæ) at high temperature of 30°C. Under these conditions for rapid division, some stentors would outpace the chlorellæ and emerge entirely white. Three classes of animals from the same stock could therefore be compared: green forms with abundant chlorellæ, pale stentors grown in the dark but always retaining some algæ, and white animals completely devoid of symbionts.

The presence of actively metabolizing chlorellæ promoted the survival of starving stentors. This was demonstrated by " feeding " the symbionts while starving their hosts. Light and the mineral nutrients in soil extract or Benecke's solution provided conditions for metabolism and growth of the chlorellæ, as proved by the fact that symbionts did increase and pale animals became green when only these factors were supplied. Conditions for starvation of the stentors were established by withholding the free-living algæ which they had been eating and digesting, and by repeated transfers to remove bacteria. Controls were afforded by comparing white with green stentors and survival in darkness as well as in the light.

When kept in the light, green stentors survived twice as long as white animals without symbionts, and pale stentors with few but increasing chlorellæ were in between. The capacity of the stentors to undergo occasional fissions following starvation was in the same order, green ones dividing the most. In the dark these differences disappeared and maximum survival times were the same. Hence photosynthesizing chlorellæ did confer an advantage in survival of their starving hosts. Schulze further noted, however, that in the dark the first individual to die was always a white one, for minimal survival times were in the order: white, pale and green. This result seems enigmatic since one would expect the catabolism of stentor and symbiont to be additive. But according to Hämmerling, stentors receive some advantage from their symbionts even in the dark.

What is the nature of the aid to survival provided by *Chlorella*? First, this succor was not complete, because stentors with thriving chlorellæ did eventually die. Therefore the ciliates did not become autotrophic, or capable of living indefinitely through their symbionts on light and mineral nutrients alone, as is possible in the more complete symbiosis found in *Paramecium bursaria* (Pringsheim, 1928). Schulze showed this deficiency to be the same in *igneus* as in *polymorphus*. At first Hämmerling said that starving stentors simply digest their symbionts, so that animals with abundant chlorellæ should live longer on these food reserves; but he later softened this conclusion. And Schulze found that the hosts only partially and never completely digest their symbionts. Moreover, any minor aid from partial digestion should be compensated by multiplication of the chlorellæ at the expense of their hosts. Digestion of the algæ was therefore probably not the basis of longer survival. Hämmerling observed that pale animals with very few chlorellæ nevertheless lived much longer in the dark than white animals, though of course not as long as green ones, indicating that the algæ were supplying some minor factor important to survival. The possibility that *polymorphus* has lost the capacity for the synthesis of one or more vitamins was suggested by Schulze's finding that his white stentors could not live indefinitely unless fed on green, free-living algæ. This species of *Stentor* may therefore have become dependent on plants for certain vitamins.

As stated by Hämmerling the general conclusion from the tests was that the presence of chlorellæ enables stentors better to endure a period of starvation. That such is the only advantage conferred by the symbionts was further indicated by studies of the division rate of well-fed stentors. He found that the fission rate was only slightly higher if chlorellæ were present and Schulze said that the multiplication rate was, if anything, slower. Evidently the symbiosis is of no particular advantage to stentors under optimal conditions. In any event, rapid division led to decrease in symbionts as the host outpaced the chlorellæ.

Interesting experiments on the artificial development of symbiosis and exchange of chlorellæ were also performed. Animals without symbionts were put in an appropriate culture medium to which was added a brei of crushed cells containing chlorellæ. White ciliates would then ingest the liberated symbionts, which

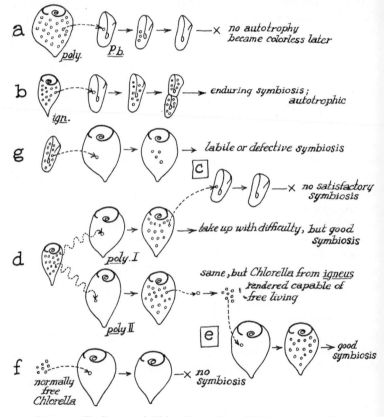

FIG. 74. Exchange of Chlorellæ and establishment of artificial symbiosis between *Stentor polymorphus*, *S. igneus*, and *Paramecium bursaria*, diagramming data of Schulze, 1951. Letters correspond to descriptive paragraphs in text, p. 271.

were first encapsulated in food vacuoles but not digested and later freed into the endoplasm. By this means normal symbiosis could be reestablished in either *Stentor polymorphus* or *Paramecium bursaria* provided with their own type of chlorellæ. The procedure itself was therefore adequate.

Exchanges of symbionts made by Schulze, in part confirmed by Hämmerling, are diagrammed in Fig. 74 and may be summarized in the following propositions:

(a) Colorless *P. bursaria* readily acquired *Chlorella* from *S. polymorphus* but did not become autotrophic as with their own chlorellæ. Enduring symbiosis was not established, for the ciliates later became white. This was confirmed by Hämmerling.

(b) In contrast, the paramecia established a true symbiosis and became capable of autotrophic nutrition when chlorellæ of *S. igneus* were substituted for their own.

(c) However, if chlorellæ from a stock of *igneus* had previously resided for 7 months in *polymorphus*, they then gave no satisfactory symbiosis when introduced into white *P. bursaria*. The host can therefore alter the symbiont, and in this case the pyrenoid of the *igneus* chlorellæ was lost.

(d) As the preceding implies, colorless *polymorphus* could establish an enduring symbiosis with chlorellæ from *igneus*, in spite of the fact that the algæ were not readily taken up and the hosts remained paler than *polymorphus* with their own chlorellæ. Using certain stocks of both species of *Stentor*, chlorellæ from the *igneus* were said to be rendered capable of free-living existence after passage through the *polymorphus*, again indicating an effect of host on partner.

(e) These independent algæ could then quickly establish a good symbiosis when taken up by colorless *polymorphus*.

(f) But when normally free-living *Chlorella* were offered to white *polymorphus* no symbiosis developed.

(g) Colorless *polymorphus* established with chlorellæ from *P. bursaria* what Schulze called a labile partnership. Only with difficulty was a symbiosis established, and this relationship persisted only if bright light and soil extract were provided, but Hämmerling succeeded in maintaining a green culture for one year. Notable was the fact that the chlorellæ did not render the stentors autotrophic as they do the paramecium.

From these experiments it is clear that symbiosis with chlorellæ is a precise relationship involving a delicate equilibrium between specific host and specific symbiont. Morphological differences noted by Schulze certainly indicate that the chlorellæ normally found in *polymorphus*, *igneus*, and *P. bursaria* are distinct types. Successful symbiosis was not related to the readiness with which the ciliates took up chlorellæ, for in some cases colorless animals rapidly became green but not symbiotic, and vice versa. A first requirement is that the chlorellæ be not digested, though taken into food vacuoles, and later infiltrated intimately into the cytoplasm. It is not known how digestion is prevented, since the hosts seemed to be able partially to digest symbionts when starved, and they could also fully digest free-living chlorellæ. The second requirement is that a harmonious equilibrium be established between multiplication of host and symbiont such that the one does not outpace the other in reproduction.

According to Hämmerling (1946), Öhler (1922) and Pringsheim (1928) have found that *P. bursaria* can take up different types of algæ, but free-living forms are not capable of substituting for the natural symbionts. Apparently this is also the case with *S. polymorphus*, for I have found animals containing both *Chlorella* and

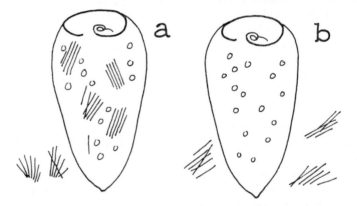

FIG. 75. Facultative multiple symbiosis. *a: Stentor polymorphus* with both *Chlorella* and a needle-like algæ free in endoplasm. The needle forms were same as those growing in the culture. *b:* On isolating onto slides, the needle algæ were shed — apparently alive — but not the *Chlorella*.

bundles of a needle-shaped alga intimately within the endoplasm; but on isolation the latter were always eventually ejected (Fig. 75). The transient residents were apparently picked up from those free-living in the culture jar.

6. Parasites of stentor

A natural transition leads from symbionts to parasites, though their effects on the metabolism of stentors have not been explored. For the following account I have relied in part upon Kirby's (1941a, b) excellent reviews.

Unidentified undulating filaments occurring in bundles within vacuoles in the cytoplasm of stentors were observed by Müller (1856) and his students, two of whom considered these inhabitants probably parasitic (Claparéde and Lachmann, 1857). Balbiani (1893) observed *S. polymorphus* with bloated nuclei in which the macronucleus was parasitized and largely disintegrated by "Holospora". The host was otherwise normal but its ultimate fate was not determined. *Sphærophrya stentoris* Maupas is an unstalked suctorian which is both free-living and parasitic on species of *Stentor*. In its parasitic phase this organism lives in the cytoplasm and is without tentacles or cilia. Kalmus (1928) reported it in *S. roeseli*. Hetherington (1932b) reported a cytoplasmic invasion by bacilli in *S. coeruleus*. The infection caused the animals to become pale, but they could be "cured" by repeated transfers to fresh medium.

In *S. coeruleus* and *Spirostomum ambiguum*, Howland (1928) found an euglenoid with metabolic movements which appeared commensal or endoparasitic. This she identified as *Astasia captive* Beauchamp. The intruder restricted itself to the subpellicular cortex. It was previously reported as an endoparasite in a rhabdocœle in France. Recently an apparently different species of *Astasia* has been described as a facultative parasite in *S. coeruleus* by Schönfeld (1959). When well-fed stentors were presented with this organism, grown separately in cultures, the stentors ate few and digested those without ill effects. Starved animals gorged themselves on the astasias, which were not digested but were liberated from the food vacuoles and wandered about in the endoplasm. The stentors eventually degenerated and died, a preceding vacuolization possibly resulting from enlargement of the emptied food vacuoles. Filtered *Astasia* culture fluid also killed the stentors when transferred into it.

Somewhat resembling Schönfeld's account, a student (William Lewis, 1959) has recently observed that *coeruleus* may ingest and form food vacuoles of the flagellate *Rhabdomonas incurva* but the prey passes through the stentors, emerging by defecation in a living and active state. This could be the beginning of parasitism, since at least many of the flagellates enter the stentor but are protected against digestion.

We may choose this place to mention a report that stentors are possibly toxic to other organisms. Otterstrøm and Larsen (1946) very doubtfully attributed kills of fingerling fish in hatchery ponds to *wild* (but not to cultured) *Stentor polymorphus* producing toxins only when *irritated*.

7. Abnormal stentors

Here we shall describe certain abnormalities in *coeruleus* relating to the pigment granules which sometimes arise without operational interference in cultures or stentor samples. Whether these aberrant forms are due primarily to disturbance of metabolism or involve other factors and even racial differences as well we do not know. Very little is yet known about the abnormal animals themselves or their origin, but they offer promising lines for further study.

(a) DEPIGMENTED STENTORS

In starving samples of *coeruleus* and even rarely in normal cultures one finds stentors which are nearly devoid of pigment granules and appear colorless. Stolte (1922) thought that the amount of pigmentation is a function of metabolism and decreases with decreasing oxygen tension, but the presence of both green and white forms in the same culture or sample implies that external conditions are not wholly determinative. Colorless *coeruleus* were seen by Schuberg (1890), Johnson (1893), and Gelei (1927). Johnson concluded that the pigment granules had been excreted or ejected, because green clots were found in the sample dish or attached near the base of the stentors. In my observation white *coeruleus* retain a very few pigment granules in bands which then appear not granular but trabecular, indicating that the granular bands do have some intrinsic structure. Hetherington (1932b) said that pale stentors were often infected by a great number of bacilli and that normal ones showed none. A pathological cause seems unnecessary, however, because every time I isolated one of these stentors the normal coloration was eventually regenerated. Why an occasional stentor should pass through this depigmented stage remains a mystery and problem. A suggestive parallel is found in the chimera studies, in which a small graft of *polymorphus* causes the depigmentation of a *coeruleus* host.

(b) OVER-PIGMENTED STENTORS

Sometimes one finds stentors which are very dark in color, appearing deep red by reflected light. Such animals may appear in the same culture in which depigmented stentors are found and have also been observed to be capable of oral reorganization and to recover the normal pigmentation. Generally these "reds" were smaller and thinner than normal stentors, and lacking in food vacuoles, but the nucleus appeared normal. The pigmentation of the granular stripes is in these specimens supplemented by an overload of pigment granules in the endoplasm. Though some recover, others become exceedingly abnormal and are characterized

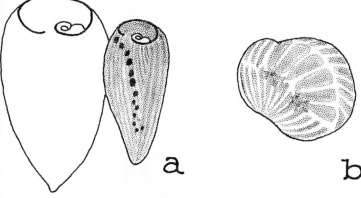

FIG. 76. Over-pigmented phase of *S. coeruleus*.
A. Such specimens are smaller than the average (to the left) probably by undernourishment because they show no food vacuoles, and the coloration is very dark blue-green.
B. Later stage, showing disorganization, some extraordinarily broad pigment stripes, and abundant pigment granules inside. Alternatively such animals may return to normal.

by extraordinarily wide pigment stripes in some areas of the ectoplasm, which again suggests that an oversupply of granules is present and crowding to expand the stripes (Fig. 76).

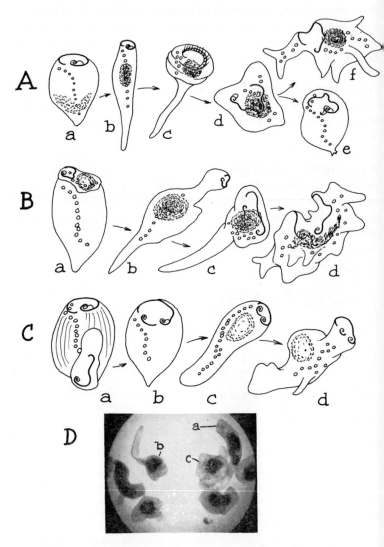

FIG. 77. Autonomously developing amorphous *S. coeruleus*.

(c) Amorphous stentors

These bizarre specimens first appeared in crowded samples in small dishes which were kept for two weeks or more without added nutrient (Tartar, 1959f). They have also sometimes developed in animals isolated on slides. The usual course of changes leading to gross abnormalities is shown in Fig. 77A. The animals are first noticed as longer and narrower than usual. Then appears a central mass of compact pigment granules which later becomes sharply delimited from the surrounding cytoplasm. The form is increasingly long and snake-like. Eventually much of the cytoplasm is concentrated at the anterior end in a bouton, while a long tail dangles behind resulting in a characteristic tadpole or vorticellid

---

A. Course of development. *a:* Possible initial stage in which internal pigment granules accumulate among the carbohydrate reserves. *b:* Narrow " snake " form with sharply bounded pigment mass but normal-appearing macronucleus. *c:* Bulbous "tadpole" form with long tail and transverse stripe arrangement anteriorly. *d:* Increasing abnormality of shape and defective stomatogenesis though nuclear nodes appear normal. *e:* Recovery of one such specimen, with pigmented core lost, normal feeding organelles and nearly normal shape. *f:* Usual course toward completely amorphous condition showing projecting processes and followed by death.

B. Transmission of abnormality to normal stentor. *a:* Amorphous stentor grafted in place of head of a normal, in ratio of about 1:8 by volume. *b:* Gross abnormality developed throughout by next day. *c:* "Tadpole" stage, with new reorganization peristome but no mouthparts. *d:* Amorphous by day 4 of the experiment, pigmented core now rather diffuse. Specimen later recovered somewhat but died on the slide.

C. Similar abnormality produced by grafting normal *polymorphus* to normal *coeruleus*. *a:* Enucleated *polymorphus* without symbionts grafted to *coeruleus* in proportions by volume of 1:4. *b:* Reorganized as a doublet with good integration of shape, but almost all of the cerulean pigment lost by influence of the graft. *c:* Elongated form with large core of unpigmented granules. Nuclear nodes appear normal. *d:* Development of amorphous condition. Time-span shown: 7 days.

D. Photograph of amorphous *coeruleus* in various stages of development: *a:* elongated cell; *b:* bulbous form; *c:* complete loss of normal form.

shape. Finally, the animals become completely amorphous, showing incomplete feeding organelles and finger-like processes extending out from the mass in all directions.

In these abnormal forms the nucleus appears quite normal. There are several indications that the nucleus is not involved. Pigmented cores have also appeared in enucleated stentors; but these generally did not live long enough, apparently, to develop the amorphous shape. When nuclei from abnormals were substituted in normal stentors no abnormality resulted; but when abnormal cytoplasm was added by grafting to normals, the whole fusion mass usually became and remained aberrant. Whole normal cells were grafted to abnormal whole cells. In about half the cases normals resulted; in the remainder, a normal stentor, even when predominant in volume, was converted into an abnormal, and this might even occur overnight. (Fig. 77B).

Amorphous animals could also be simulated by *coeruleus* to which a minor piece of colorless *polymorphus* was grafted. Sometimes the central mass was of colored pigment granules, in other cases the mass was colorless but granular (Fig. 77C). In the latter, the mass may have been composed of depigmented *coeruleus* granules or possibly of the non-pigmented ectoplasmic granules typical of *polymorphus*.

In some instances it was demonstrated that tadpole-shaped abnormals could recover if transferred onto a slide with fresh medium, but the introduction of normal animals into fluid dishes in which abnormals had appeared did not result in their becoming promptly abnormal. Therefore changes in the medium do not seem to induce this condition. Racial differences may be more important. Three races of *coeruleus* produced abnormal stentors when starved, but five did not.

The development of such amorphous forms is much in contrast to the usually amazing capacity of stentors to return to normal after the most drastic operations and disturbances. A connection with cancer or abnormal growth is suggested, first, by the stentor — as an organism — "going wild", and second — as a cell — transforming, among its normal fellows, into a pathological type.

Treatments which prevent or hinder primordium formation may do so by disrupting the basis of protein synthesis, and these

have already been summarized in the section on blockage of
regeneration (p. 132).

Speaking generally, metabolism studies on *Stentor* may be
fruitful in two directions. Demonstration of metabolic similarities
between these and other animals would prove the appropriateness
of using the special advantages of *Stentor* in pursuing problems of
"universal biochemistry". In addition, stentors may reveal or
provide initial discoveries of features of metabolism hitherto
unknown.

T

CHAPTER XVI

BEHAVIOR AND FUNCTIONS
OF THE NUCLEUS

STENTORS have two kinds of nuclei, yet the nuclear story can be simplified because the role of the micronuclei may be stated briefly. On some signal from the cytoplasm during fission they divide and reproduce themselves by typical ciliate endomitosis. This also occurs during the related cycles of reorganization and regeneration, in which the cytoplasm is similarly activated to oral primordium formation. Although multiplication in these two processes may be meaningless, that during fission obviously assures the continued presence of micronuclei, available for their single known function, namely, to produce a new macronucleus after sexual reproduction or conjugation. In this, their performance is indeed complex and will be described in the following chapter.

But for the vegetative life of stentors the micronuclei are demonstrably without significance. In a few ciliates bearing a single, non-vesiculate, "massive type" micronucleus the situation may be otherwise. By massive type is meant that the micronucleus is relatively large and appears on staining to have a consistency much like that of the macronucleus. Thus in *Uronychia transfuga* (Calkins, 1911a), *Euplotes patella* (Taylor and Farber, 1924; Reynolds, 1932), and in *Paramecium caudatum* and *bursaria* (Schwartz, 1934, 1947; Tartar, 1940), excision of the single micronucleus is immediately felt and manifests itself in defective regeneration or reduced rate of fission, though later adjustments may correct these deficiencies. But in *Stentor coeruleus* which has numerous vesiculate micronuclei, a careful study by Schwartz (1934, 1935) has shown that the micronuclei may be entirely removed without any appreciable effect on the macronucleated cell; and conversely, that, as in *Bursaria* according to Schmähl (1926), in the absence of the macronucleus micronuclei which are present are not only unable to carry on the life of the cell but are incapable, without the stimulation accompanying the process of conjugation, of regenerating the macronucleus. This result is fortunate indeed, permitting us to neglect the micronuclei which cannot be seen in the living animal and would be most difficult to work with. Schwartz's demonstration of the ineffectiveness of the micronuclei must have been confirmed many times in the study of emacronucleate stentors; for although most of the adhering micronuclei are no doubt removed with the macronucleus, a few scattered ones probably remain, yet these specimens never regenerate nor long survive. In what follows we shall therefore be concerned only with the macronucleus, designating it as such or simply by the word nucleus.

1. Location of the macronucleus

In small species of *Stentor*, such as *igneus* and *multiformis*, the nucleus is a single ovoid mass near the center of the cell; but in forms like *coeruleus* and *polymorphus*, which are about a hundred times larger, the nucleus consists of many parts or nodes in linear sequence within a common nuclear membrane. In between, there is *roeseli* with an elongated, nodulated nucleus and *niger* which is about the same size but has the compact nucleus. It may be significant that nodulation after division is delayed in *roeseli* (Johnson, 1893) so that for a considerable time the nucleus has a rod shape, which might be considered a transition form. The species *niger* is conspicuously slow and lackadaisical in its swimming movements. Phylogenetically this suggests that the former is on the way to developing a moniliform nucleus out of one which is rod shaped and arose by elongation of the compact form, as well as that the latter is pushing the cell size as far as it can go on a compact nucleus whose surface area of interaction with the cytoplasm is minimal with reference to the volume of nuclear material. The chain nucleus of a form like *coeruleus* of course passes through rod and spheroid phases during division and other times when there is oral primordium formation. These changes in form led Johnson to the conjecture that ontogeny is here repeating a phylogeny in which the compact form of the nucleus can be assumed to be the most primitive.

We shall confine our discussion to the well-studied chain nucleus of *coeruleus*, but this description will serve fairly well for all species with moniliform nuclei. There is apparently a standard pattern for the distribution of nuclear material in all large species. The essential point is that with remarkable constancy the macronucleus tends toward a definite arrangement with reference to the topography of the cell and that if this pattern is not fulfilled or if artificially disturbed the nodes can and do move in such a way that they tend to recover the normal arrangement.

The typical disposition of the nuclear beads is shown in Fig. 78A. With the possible exception of a few of the posterior nodes the nucleus is usually entirely subcortical in its location. This is no doubt why it can remain fixed in position; because it adheres to the inside of the ectoplasm. We do not say attached, because one has to allow for the movement of the nucleus during clumping and in the correction of disarrangements. Generally, the longest part of the nucleus is a row of nodes extending almost directly posteriorly under the surface near the meridian which connects the mouth with the posterior pole and considerably to the right of the primordium site. From this row, beads extend around the anterior end of the cell to the right for some distance, while at the other end the row bends back on itself and terminates in several beads which seem to be rather indefinite in their location though they tend to place themselves on the opposite or left side. I think this arrangement is what one would expect if he had to work with a nucleus of minimal length for the sake of economy, to fasten it inside the cell so that it would not "fall to the bottom", have every point in the cytoplasm as close as possible to some nuclear material, and place the nucleus as near as manageable to the most active regions (the membranellar band, the mouthparts, the primordium site, and the holdfast), while keeping it out of the way of the migrating primordium, i.e., to assure that the ectoplasm under which it lies will not undergo major shifts of position. The actual deployment fulfills these assumed requirements.

Having made these statements, we now have to qualify them by saying that the nucleus is not always in the same position, as well as that its precise location is evidently not essential to the economy of the cell. The first of these qualifications is documented in Fig. 78B, which shows a number of the atypical arrangements which have been found in stentors fished out of regular cultures in which the majority of individuals showed a more normal

listribution of the macronucleus. Several of these forms have
already been described by Stolte (1922). He associated chains
having noticeably recurved ends with interdivisional addition of
new nodes; and he observed that in stentors with double, parallel

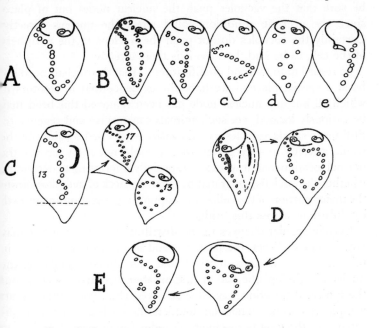

FIG. 78. Location of the macronucleus in *S. coeruleus*.

A. Normal location, with post-oral row, right anterior wing,
and recurved terminal chain.

B. Atypical macronuclear arrangements appearing autonomously, including (a) secondary row, (b) forked chain, (c)
coiling and posterior shift, (d) scattered nodes (whether connected was not determined), and (e) "situs inversus" in animals
of reversed asymmetry.

C. Divider with 13 nodes and posterior end excised produced
proter with 17 small nodes in normal location and opisthe with
13 in a ring, later becoming distributed normally.

D. Doublet produced by engrafting an extra primordium
site (without nucleus) in time develops double macronuclear
chain, each deployed normally with respect to the stripe pattern.

E. When such a doublet reverts to single form the macronuclear chain becomes single correspondingly.

nuclear chains this condition is corrected after clumping and renodulation in division. Stolte also made much of divergence from the normal picture with regard to the nucleus which occurs in highly vacuolated stentors. But in pathological material one cannot be sure that the vacuoles push the nuclear nodes out of place since the necrotic condition could affect the nucleus directly. Certainly the vacuoles do not push the nucleus to the periphery of the cell, as he said, because it is there already.

In regard to the second qualification — that the nucleus need not be at a special place — we have the evidence that in stentors in which all but one nuclear node has been removed this bead may be variously located, yet such animals can survive and regenerate. Still more satisfactory tests could easily be devised by shifting the whole nucleus in such a way that it could not soon recover the normal location, and it would be especially interesting to determine whether the nucleus, separated by a narrow neck of cytoplasm from the major portion of the cell, could support regeneration and growth by diffusions across this bridge.

Certain regular changes in the distribution of the nucleus may now be noted. When the posterior end of *coeruleus* was cut off in mid-fission it was consistently found that after renodulation the nucleus in the opisthe had at first an abnormal arrangement, but the typical disposition was later achieved (Fig. 78c). When graft complexes become persisting doublets the nuclear chain is duplicated even though the specimen started with but one (D), and when doublets transform back into singles they soon achieve a normal, single chain (E). In Fig. 59c we have a stentor developing a secondary tail-pole which later became furnished with an extension of the nuclear chain.

Similar deviations in the location of the nucleus in abnormal forms have been observed in the related genus *Condylostoma* (Yagiu, 1951, 1952). The simplest explanation of these cases would be that the stripe pattern guides the location of the macronuclear nodes. And the best substantiation thereof is that in cases of reversed asymmetry, with the same cell shape as in normal animals, the macronucleus assumes a reversed location (see Fig. 49).

2. Clumping of the nucleus

Typically, all nodes of the moniliform nucleus lie within a single nuclear membrane, doubtless facilitating their coalescence into one mass during oral redifferentiation and especially in division. When fully deployed the strand connecting individual nodes may be exceedingly tenuous (Fig. 79), yet rarely do terminal nodes break off and not participate in coalescence during fission. Opinions differ regarding whether separated nodes or sections of the nucleus can rejoin their fellows. Stolte (1922) observed that broken nuclear chains in vacuolated dividers condense separately, and I too have found occasionally a double fusion mass; but he stated categorically that permanent reunion was not possible because the nuclei were within separate membranes. This supposed behavior is, however, contrary to common experience with hypotrichs, such as *Oxytricha*, in which widely separated macronuclei, for which there is no evidence of a common boundary, nevertheless fuse at every division. Much earlier, Prowazek (1904) had reported that transected nuclear chains "regenerated" separately, producing two rows of beads; but whether the nuclear volume was doubled he did not tell us. It is probable that the normal nucleo-cytoplasmic ratio was not upset.

Weisz (1949a) reported that broken nuclear chains can rejoin. I severed the nuclear strand in *coeruleus* into five or more pieces and its distribution was then for a while disturbed, but the animals later became normal to all appearances, with the nodes closely approximated in a single uniform row in the usual location

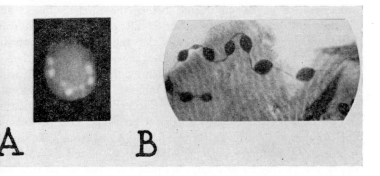

FIG. 79. Photographs of *S. coeruleus* showing macronucleus as seen (A) in living stentor against dark field and (B) after feulgen staining to reveal internodal connections.

(unpublished). Such nuclei have not yet been examined after staining; all we can say is that either separated nodes fall into perfect alignment or they are able to rejoin and become enclosed again in the common membrane. The latter seems more probable.

Coalescence begins at both terminals and progresses toward the mid-nodes, as Weisz (1950b) and others have noted. How is this accomplished? Stolte suggested fusion by swelling of the nodes, but I think what he observed was simply the coalescence of the individual nodes into larger ones; and there certainly does not appear to be an increase in the total volume of the nucleus during condensation as his suggestion would imply. More probably, internodal connections swell while the nuclear membrane contracts and decreases greatly in area.

There remains to be conjectured why the chain nucleus should clump at all. In both *Loxodes* (Balbiani, 1893) and in *Dileptus* (Jones, 1951) there is a distributed nucleus consisting of many separate macronuclei and these do not fuse during division and regeneration. Coalescence therefore seems not absolutely necessary in the life of ciliates, though it may bring advantages. That no nuclear changes occur until the oral primordium is nearly completely developed, as Balbiani (1893) first emphasized, does not suggest that either coalescence or moving all parts of the nucleus close to the primordium is necessary to its development. Hence Balbiani did not share Gruber's idea that clumping is to give a single, central guidance to morphogenetic events, because these processes are nearly completed before the nucleus fuses; and besides, the macronuclear chain is all one nucleus anyway. Balbiani's suggestion was therefore that the nucleus concentrates in order to have the greatest effect; but the action of the nucleus is more likely to be promoted by increasing rather than by decreasing its surface. As already mentioned, Johnson held that coalescence of the nuclear chain is an instance of Haeckel's law of recapitulation and hence is performed for "historical" reasons. That the macronucleus clumps in order to insure equal division through the simple splitting of a compact mass has also been suggested (Sonneborn, 1947), but in *Stentor* at least, clumping does not insure this end (see p. 71). Many hypotrichs like *Euplotes* produce reorganization bands at every division and somehow transform or rework the macronucleus; yet in *Stentor* no one has found evidence of any such change in the fine structure of the nucleus during clumping and renodulation. According to certain of Weisz's findings (see below), coalescence of the macronucleus would be necessary for homogenization after individual nodes at its extremities had become diverse, but this diversity could not be confirmed. It may be that the nucleus in stentors coalesces into a single mass in order to make possible its complete renodulation (Tartar, 1957b); for in division the nucleus produces at one stroke about twice the number of the original nodes which are now half-sized. This could explain why coalescence is often not complete in regeneration and reorganization: because the nucleus will generally return to about the same size and number of nodes.

3. Nodulation

Following fusion into a compact mass the macronucleus extends to a long and conspicuous rod or sausage shape which is then renodulated, again, generally from both ends towards the middle. An exception is *roeseli*, in which node formation proceeds only from the anterior end.

As Johnson described it, nodulation seems to involve the aggregation of chromatic substance into serial packets separated by clear nuclear material where constriction then occurs; and he also remarked that the new nodes are usually "beautifully symmetrical and alike in size". Rarely there is produced a forked nucleus or nuclear chain with a side branch (Fig. 78B), of which Johnson illustrated one case in *coeruleus*, also noting that Stein (1867) showed a similar case in *polymorphus*. The same have been observed in *Condylostoma* (Yagiu, 1952) and in *Spirostomum ambiguum* (Bishop, 1927). These may be ectopic rejoinings of separated parts of the nucleus with the main strand.

Even after the period of renodulation, the number of nodes can undergo small changes, reduction through fusion of adjacent nodes, or increase either by the splitting of one node into two or by the interpolation of new nodes between existing ones (Fig. 80A). It is not uncommon to find dumbbell-shaped nodes or one or more tiny nodes lying between the larger. Prowazek (1904) first described a step-wise increase in nodal number, and his account was generally corroborated by Schwartz (1935). According to the earlier investigator a node may either split in two or part of its substance may travel along the tube-like internodal connections, stopping between two nodes and growing into a new one. Weisz (1949a) stated that extra nodes are thus interpolated whenever the strand between two nodes measures approximately 2 nodal diameters or more. Yet it should be emphasized that major nuclear increases occur only following primordium formation in division, regeneration, and reorganization.

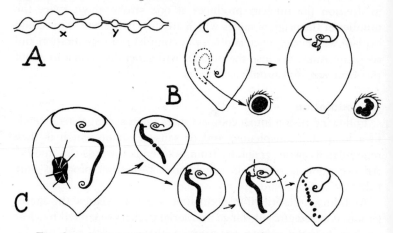

FIG. 80. Aspects of macronuclear nodulation in *S. coeruleus*.

A. Diagram of two means by which single nodes appear to be added: (*x*) by division and (*y*) by interpolation between nodes.

B. When the clumped macronucleus of a stage–6 regenerator is excised with a small amount of cytoplasm, the primordium completes stomatogenesis and the nucleus attempts to renodulate though isolated and confined.

C. When coalesced nucleus of a divider is sliced into several times, the macronucleus is divided but fails to renodulate, doing so only much later after regeneration is induced by excision of mouthparts without injury to the nucleus.

I have found that when the clumped nucleus of a divider is isolated into a small volume of cytoplasm it nevertheless attempts to renodulate in spite of the confinement (Fig. 80B). This suggests that the impulse to nodulation is intrinsic with the nucleus itself since the nuclear environment was so completely altered. Individual nodes are very tough and resistant to cutting but the clumped nucleus can easily be slashed through with a glass needle. In the few cases in which this has been done in dividers, subsequent nodulation was inhibited (unpublished). The nucleus extended as a rod but remained as such without any further change until regeneration was induced by excising the mouthparts, whereupon the normal nucleus was recovered (Fig. 80c). Therefore, although nodulation may be intrinsic, the stimulus for it is given by the cytoplasm during the last stages of oral redifferentiation.

As previously discussed in the chapter on division, daughter cells have about the same number of nodes as the parent (see Fig. 78c). Therefore coalescence of the macronucleus may be necessary for its rapid renodulation into twice the number of nodes of about half the size of the originals during fission.

4. Equivalence of macronuclear nodes

Nuclear fusions and clumping were also simply explained as a means for recovering uniformity in parts which have become diverse. In substantiation of this presupposition, Weisz (1949c) claimed that an intranuclear difference does regularly develop during divisional and reorganizational cycles in *coeruleus*, posterior nodes (but not posterior cytoplasm) becoming increasingly incapable of supporting regeneration or even of maintaining oral and caudal organelles as they approach the time of coalescence. Fusion was then said to restore normal potency throughout the renodulated macronucleus. Development and obliteration of differences seemed to be correlated with degree of polymerization of nuclear DNA as tested by methyl green staining (Weisz, 1950b), though the reliability of this determination was later questioned (1954).

A similar development of intranuclear heterogeneity was proposed for *Blepharisma* (Weisz, 1949), but in this case the mid-portion of the macronucleus which no longer supported regeneration was destined for extrusion and dissolution anyway. The general conception is brought further into question by Weisz's interpretation that proximity to organelles is the basis for maintenance of potency in adjacent nodes; for the mouthparts in *Blepharisma* are near the level of the mid-nodes which should therefore retain their full capacities; and in *Stentor*, the posterior nodes should support maintenance and regeneration of the holdfast, contrary to Weisz's own account. Since even enucleate fragments can regenerate the foot (Tartar, 1956c), it is indicated that the conditions in Weisz's experiments were not optimal. Further-more, Suzuki (1957) could find no evidence for differences in the potentiality of parts of the nucleus in *Blepharisma* at any stage.

Above all, I was unable by similar experiments to confirm that a regular and recurring difference develops between the serial nodes of the nucleus (Tartar, 1957b). I tested five different races of *coeruleus* and observed not only oral regeneration but also recon-stitution of the nuclear chain from a single node and the capacity of fragments to reproduce indefinitely in clones. For comparison I studied *Condylostomum magnum*, which is a very long ciliate with mouthparts far to one end and a uniform chain nucleus running the length of the body. If posterior nodes regularly become depotentiated, the same should be manifested in this form even more than in *Stentor*. It was found that even the single, terminal posterior node in many cases or at least the last four could support complete oral regeneration at any stage (Fig. 81). In stentors (where this was tested) pre-fissional and pre-reorganiza-tional fragments with only such nodes could give rise to viable lines with normal chain nuclei.

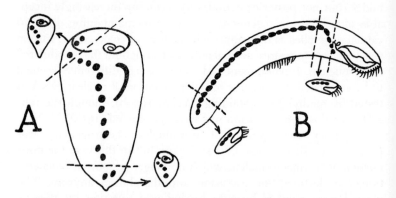

FIG. 81. Equivalence of macronuclear nodes in (A) *Stentor coeruleus* and (B) *Condylostoma magnum*. Tiny fragments of early dividers, carrying only a few of the most anterior or posterior nodes, are capable of regeneration and more.

Evidently intranuclear differentiation is neither necessary for nor the consequence of cytoplasmic differentiation in ciliates. We can therefore return with confidence to the old dictum that any portion of the macronucleus is sufficient for regeneration and survival, implying that this nucleus is highly polyploid, with representation of the complete genome throughout. The development of *inter*nuclear differences as in mating type determination in certain ciliates is of course a demonstrated fact. Had regular intranuclear differences been confirmed, we would have been provided with another and most excellent means for analyzing nuclear functions. Our disappointment is however mitigated by the consequence that we are now apparently free to continue experiments on ciliates without having to take into consideration an additional factor of varying capacities within the macronucleus.

5. Shape, size and number of nuclear nodes

When he removed all but a single node of the macronucleus from *coeruleus*, Prowazek (1904) found that the remaining bead became much elongated and spindle shaped. Schwartz (1935) observed the same, as well as that the remaining node may become much flattened like a ribbon. Cases from my own observation are shown in Figs. 82A and 86C. These increases in the nodal surface are as if to compensate somewhat for the great diminution in nuclear volume.

Starting from a single node, the nuclear chain is regenerated during episodes of primordium formation. Two reorganizations seem to be required to recover the typical nodal number from a single bead. This number is quite variable and in *coeruleus* is between 6 and 20, with a mode around 15. K. M. Møller (unpublished) has a race with a mode of 10–11 nodes and suspects that the average number may prove to be a racial characteristic. When de Terra (1959) implanted into enucleate *coeruleus* 2 macronuclear nodes labeled with adenine–C^{14} she found that the regenerated nuclear chain was labeled throughout, confirming the cytological picture that this regenerative growth is not accomplished by simple addition of new nodes. Instead, the implanted nodes increased greatly in size, coalesced, and renodulated into many nuclear beads from a common pool of macronuclear material.

Although the nucleus readily adapts by increase in size, the occasions when it should decrease give an entirely different impression. It appears difficult for the cell to take down or diminish a too-large macronucleus. Starving stentors with decreasing cytoplasmic volume (Allescher, 1912), or animals regenerated from fragments with proportionately too much nucleus, tend at first and for a long time merely to decrease the surface of the nucleus by fusion of nodes (Fig. 82B). Nor did Hartmann (1928) observe decrease in size of the nucleus in successive excisions of amœba cytoplasm. Yet indubitable decrease in nuclear volume eventually occurs in hypernucleated *Stentor* fragments, as Prowazek (1904) first reported. Stentors therefore certainly tend by nuclear increase or decrease toward a nucleo-cytoplasmic ratio of limited range.

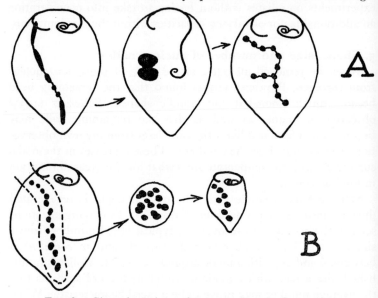

FIG. 82. Size adaptations of macronucleus in *S. coeruleus*.
A. Stentor with only 6 nodes, half of which are much attenuated, as if to compensate with added surface and to make a typically disposed nuclear chain. Mouth was excised and after coalescence during regeneration 12 nodes were formed, normal in shape, but in forked arrangement in this case.
B. Nucleate portion with 14 nodes is excised, regenerates proportionate feeding organelles and reduces the number but not the size of the nodes.

Size of nuclear beads in the row is generally quite uniform, with the exception of interpolated nodes which are, at least initially, very small. Daughter cells have approximately the same number of nodes as mature animals but the nodes are at first small and all presumably increase in size during the interdivisional period. However, I have seen cultures of *coeruleus* which consistently produced animals with non-uniform macronuclear chains, some nodes being too large and others abnormally small. The lines eventually succumbed.

There is some evidence that the size and number of the nodes may vary with the conditions under which stentors are grown. At 25 °C Prowazek (1904) found that *coeruleus* had fewer nodes (average of 8) than at 15°C (12). Following the earlier work of Allescher (1912), Stolte (1922) pursued this matter quite thoroughly, though with what we would now call a primitive control of culture conditions. For instance, to subject stentors to reduced oxygen he simply grew them in tall cylinders. His results indicated that cell size, macronuclear volume, and nodal size are complex variables which probably both interact and are subject to environmental influence. The results were summarized in a table from which Fig. 83 was derived. Rich food, abundant oxygen, and high temperature were correlated with a large number of smaller nodes, and vice versa.

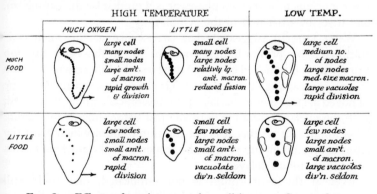

	HIGH TEMPERATURE		LOW TEMP.
	MUCH OXYGEN	LITTLE OXYGEN	
MUCH FOOD	large cell many nodes small nodes large amt. of macron. rapid growth & division	small cell many nodes large nodes relativly lg. amt. macron. reduced fission	large cell medium no. of nodes large nodes med. size macron. large vacuoles rapid division
LITTLE FOOD	large cell few nodes small nodes small amt. of macron. rapid division	small cell few nodes large nodes small amt. of macron. vacuolate div'n. seldom	large cell few nodes large nodes small amt. of macron. large vacuoles div'n. seldom

FIG. 83. Effects of environmental conditions on *S. coeruleus*, according to and adapted from a table of Stolte's, 1922.

6. Control of nuclear behavior

Balbiani (1893) first emphasized that the macronucleus of *Stentor* does not begin its major performance of coalescence until the oral primordium is well developed (stage 5) and capable of completing itself even in the absence of the nucleus. This chronology suggests that clumping of the nucleus has nothing to do with primordium formation; and in reference to fission (Johnson (1893)) it indicates that the cytostome leads the nucleus — rather than the reverse, as in the case of mitosis in cleaving eggs and dividing tissue cells. We can readily suppose that the primordium can go through its entire development in regeneration and reorganization without the act of nuclear clumping, and indeed this occurs in experimental animals in which only one bead is left. Again, since the products of artificially divided (transected) stentors behave normally there seems to be no obvious reason why a dividing stentor could not simply pinch the nuclear chain in two where it originally lies. Perhaps we may put it this way, that if the macronucleus is to clump, this has to occur before the cell divides, if one daughter is not to be left without a nucleus.

Questions concerning control of nuclear behavior include the following: What "tells" the nucleus when to fuse? Is the macronucleus capable of autonomous division, or is it merely pinched in two by the division furrow? Does the rod-shaped nucleus have to be "told" to renodulate? Less anthropomorphically, does the macronucleus time its own phases or is it guided by the cytoplasm, and if so, by what part of the cytoplasm?

Weisz (1951b) suggested that coalescence of the nucleus is stimulated by primordium formation, for if the early division primordium is removed or caused to be resorbed there is no division and no compacting of the nucleus. Yet the division anlagen may be removed at stage 4 or even stage 3 and fission can still be completed, with the nucleus clumping normally just before furrow formation. This implies either that it is not the primordium which gives the stimulus for clumping or that the response of the nucleus to this stimulus is much delayed.

Even if the primordium is not implicated, one could still maintain as Weisz (1954) said, that "Evidently, nuclear kinetics depend on direct stimulus from the ectoplasm". It has already been suggested that during primordium formation the cytoplasm, and perhaps especially or exclusively the ectoplasm, is in a state of activation. The ripening state of activation, or particularly when this stage is changing over to that of inhibition at stage 5 or 6, could therefore provide the stimulus or the means for coalescence of nuclear nodes. This would explain Weisz's (1956) observation that mid-division stentors grafted to non-dividers induce a coalescence of the nuclei of both partners. Originally evolved for the proper timing of nuclear clumping in division, this relationship between cytoplasmic and nuclear states would also be effective in producing a usually superfluous clumping during reorganization and regeneration because the state of activation always accompanies primordium formation. On this hypothesis the nucleus would fail to clump in dividers from which early-stage primordia were excised or caused to resorb, not because the primordium is missing as a stimulus to coalescence, but because the cytoplasm again came under the inhibitive dominance of the intact feeding organelles and the state of activation was abolished.

How, then, is the nucleus guided in elongating and renodulating? Does it divide autonomously? These problems have engaged the attention of Noël de Terra (1959) whose preliminary findings she kindly communicated. Apparently the cytoplasm gives the cue for elongation of the clumped nucleus, for if the compacted nucleus of a divider was transferred to an interphase stentor no elongation occurred. But if the condensed nucleus was transferred to a cell with nucleus in the same condition, then the two nuclei elongated together synchronously. Supportive are experiments already described, indicating that if the nucleus is prevented from renodulating at the close of division because of injuries suffered during its compacted stage, then it remains as a rod in the interphase cell and does not nodulate until the animal passes through another episode of activation or redifferentiation (see Fig. 80c).

De Terra is also finding evidence that the macronucleus in *Stentor* is generally incapable of autonomous division and therefore has to be pinched in two at the rod stage by the division furrow, though autonomous division of macronuclear anlagen occurs during conjugation. This correlates with the cytological picture when separation of daughter cells is prevented by injury to late dividers, the compacted nucleus elongating and renodulating as a single chain instead of two. When she caused stentors to divide very unequally, the macronucleus was also unequally and proportionately distributed to the daughter products, quite as if the furrow cuts through the rod nucleus wherever it happens to strike. Likewise, when the clumped nucleus of a reorganizer, not normally

coalesced, and the nodes in the right-hand fragment without the primordium nevertheless fused simultaneously with those of the other fragment which carried the developing anlagen. Similarly, if stage–6 dividers were cut in the same way so that the clumped nucleus remained in the fragment without the primordium, the nucleus then extended and renodulated on time (Fig. 84). Such observations suggest that the nucleus is guided in its behavior by something which characterizes the whole cell rather than by stimuli emanating exclusively from the primordium.

7. Necessity of the nucleus for oral redifferentiation

No experiment demonstrates more dramatically the fundamental duality of the cell than the failure of *Stentor* and other ciliates to regenerate or survive without the nucleus. The nucleus cannot regenerate a cytoplasm around it and is indeed so dependent upon its cytoplasmic environment that naked nuclei soon degenerate and cannot viably be returned to the cell. Likewise cytoplasm alone can never produce a nucleus. Specifically in regard to *Stentor*, our starting point in the study of nucleo-cytoplasmic interactions is that oral regeneration or the formation and development of a primordium is a cooperative effort of nucleus and cytoplasm and does not occur in the absence of some portion of the macronucleus.

Yet the nucleus does not make the primordium in the sense of a handicraft but remains visibly unchanged while the anlage is elaborated at some distance from it. Hence there should be some intermediate step through which the nucleus contributes to the support of primordium formation in the cytoplasm. This intermediary would be truly essential to redifferentiation; the presence of the nucleus only indirectly as its source. Such a relationship is evident in the amazing case of the unicellular plant *Acetabularia* (see Hämmerling, 1953) in which both growth and the elaboration of specific organelles continues long after enucleation, in a way that can best be explained by supposing that the nuclear contribution is a durable substance which persists, quantitatively, in the cytoplasm until exhausted.

If the action of the nucleus is indirect and mediated through products which it contributes to the cytoplasm, there should also be some evidence of this lag-effect in *Stentor*. Using *coeruleus* as the test organism, I have found (unpublished) that the oral primordium can generally continue one or two stages further in its development after enucleation. Stage-2 primordia could continue to stage 4, and stage-4 anlagen to stage 6, etc. After going one or two steps further, early primordia through stage 4 were then resorbed. In incipient regenerators, enucleated, the primordium could put in its initial appearance and then disappear, i.e., development was possible from stage 0 to stage 1. Animals with stage-6 anlagen, or even at stage 5 when there is still no sign of a gullet and oral pouch, were able to complete oral differentiation and move the new structures into their definitive position (see Fig. 80B). These performances are explainable on the assumptions, first, that there is a nuclear contribution to cytoplasmic differentiation which does persist for a short while or is present in small quantity at any one time; and second, that by stage 5 the anlage has completed most of its synthesis of new material in the form of oral cilia, etc., and needs only to invaginate and shift the parts already formed to complete the elaboration of the feeding organelles.

Formation of the fission furrow after enucleation of mid-stage dividers demonstrates its independence from the presence of the nucleus.

The experiments on stentors with late-stage anlagen clearly confirm many earlier observations on the completion of regeneration and division of stentors in the absence of the nucleus, beginning with Gruber (1883, 1885a, b). He was much impressed by the continued normal behavior of enucleated *Actinophrys*, a heliozoan, and of *Stentor*. For the former, he claimed "regeneration" (however this may be manifest in a rhizopod) in the absence of the nucleus, but requiring cytoplasmic chromatin of nuclear origin. In *S. coeruleus* he found that cells, after removal of the compacted macronucleus, could complete division with separation of daughters and full development of the primordium in the opisthe. He therefore supposed that enucleated stentors might regenerate "under conditions not yet devised". This remark is not very different from Morgan's (1901a) conjecture that, if the nuclear contribution could be supplied in some other way, then the presence of the nucleus as such should not be necessary for regeneration in stentors. I therefore feel that Gruber has been somewhat maligned in reviews of this subject as saying that the nucleus is not necessary for regeneration and having to correct this assertion later. Both Gruber and Morgan were pointing to the high probability that the action of the nucleus is indirect and that what is crucial is not the physical presence of the nucleus but of something it produces.

Prowazek (1904) made more of a case for regeneration in *Stentor* without the nucleus, though he too regarded nuclear derivatives as indispensable. That enucleated dividing stentors can complete fission and oral differentiation of the posterior daughters, he also observed. In addition, he reported that elevated temperatures in "warm cultures" could supply the conditions for regeneration without the nucleus. Yet he cited only one case and he did not claim that the oral differentiation was complete. Ishikawa (1912) thought he confirmed this result in *Stentor* "in some cases". Sokoloff (1924) made similar experiments on *Bursaria truncatella* in warm culture and reported that eight out of thirty enucleated animals regenerated the feeding organelles and were able to ingest normally; but Schmähl (1926) denied this, though he did not say specifically that he tried high temperatures. Returning to Prowazek's studies, his strongest statement was that if stentors are cut and recut so that they are repeatedly compelled to regenerate, then in a few cases (3) oral regeneration could occur in enucleate pieces, and he did not say that the regeneration was incomplete. Regeneration in the absence of the nucleus, whether in warm cultures or by repeated cutting, he explained as due to the presence of chromidia, substituting for the nucleus. Before we smile at this, we should remember that just as the Feulgen staining anticipated the modern DNA doctrine, so the old chromidial hypothesis is a sort of pre-vision of the RNA story which is developing today; and Prowazek's exploratory study may contain the germ of new techniques.

8. Reconstitution of shape in relation to the nucleus

Though stentors cannot redifferentiate oral structures without the nucleus or its products, may they not at least recover their normal form after injuries? Cutting operations usually have two effects: the symmetrical, conical shape of a stentor is distorted, and the lateral striping if not the membranellar band is disturbed and misaligned. Cutting also produces a wound, with exposure of the endoplasm, and we can assert categorically that all investigators have found that healing is prompt and to all appearances as good in enucleates as in nucleated stentors.

In regard to shape recovery, Balbiani (1891c) had observed that enucleate aboral longitudinal halves which folded on themselves retained the abnormal shape; nucleates recovered. From less drastic distortions, Prowazek (1904, 1913) and Schwartz (1935) reported that enucleates are capable of rather extensive reconstitution of the normal axis and conical form. This was my experience also (Tartar, 1956c) and can be explained as merely the shifting in position of parts already present without requiring new syntheses. Schwartz observed little or no realignment of the striping of the ectoplasm, however, and made the point that, since these adjustments are gradual, the enucleated cell dies before they can be completed. I have found that separate or separated membra-

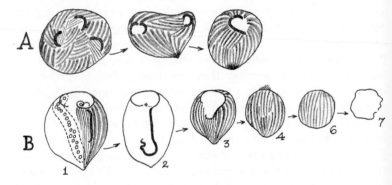

FIG.85. Activities during survival of enucleated (minus macronucleus) *S. coeruleus*.

A. Mass of 2 enucleate stentors minced and mouthparts removed. Sections of membranellar bands come together and join and there is considerable mending and alignment of stripe areas. Specimen lived 5 days.

B. Stage–4 reorganizer enucleated. By day 2 of the experiment the anlage had lengthened but there was no stomatogenesis and original mouthparts were resorbed. By day 3 specimen was about half original volume, indicating utilization of its substance during starvation. Considerable fading of coloration occurs. On day 4 lateral striping is present but only a few membranellar cilia remain. Day 6: glistening sphere without body or oral cilia but with vestiges of striping, found dead on day 7.

nellar bands can unite, oral parts may migrate together, and that there is a fair amount of reorienting and mending of stripe patches in minced stentors in the absence of the nucleus (Fig. 85A). Yet we still need clear-cut tests and a precise definition of capabilities for shape and form reconstitution in enucleated stentors.

9. Functioning and re-formation of vacuole and holdfast in enucleates

Balbiani (1889) found that the contractile vacuole of *Stentor* functions without the presence of the nucleus. Its rate of pulsation is even normal (Prowazek, 1904), as is the case in *Amœba* (Comandon and de Fonbrune, 1939b). A new contractile vacuole appeared in enucleated posterior pieces of *igneus* (Balbiani, 1893) and this was confirmed in *coeruleus* by Stevens (1903), Schwartz (1935) and Tartar (1956c). The same has been known for *Amœba* since the work of Hofer (1890). As Balbiani remarked, the new vacuole probably does not involve structural synthesis and may arise merely by the enlargement of some feeding canal of the existing contractile vacuole system. This is the more probable since Schwartz observed new pulsating vacuoles in enucleated stentors 3 minutes after the older ones had been removed.

In enucleated stentors the old holdfast is quite capable of functioning in reattachment (Stevens, 1903). It can also be re-formed in the absence of the nucleus, as attested by firm reattachment by a holdfast of *coeruleus* from which both tail-pole and nucleus have been removed (Tartar, 1956c). This regeneration is understandable on the basis that little if any synthesis is involved, only a modification of existing parts.

10. Behavior of enucleates

First let us note that Schwartz (1935) observed vigorous cyclosis of the endoplasm which continued nearly up to the point of death in enucleated *coeruleus*. In regard to the "external" behavior, investigators were impressed from the start by the sustained activity and normal swimming behavior of enucleated ciliates. Similarly, it is well known that amœbas can continue forming pseudopods in the absence of the nucleus. But in *Stentor* the vigorous beating of thousands of body cilia and numerous huge membranelles can continue for about one week and is dramatic evidence of the extent of energy metabolism which continues in the absence of the nucleus. Very likely this is to be explained by the presence of mitochondria or specialized ectoplasmic granules as relatively independent centers of oxidative phosphorylation.

Normal avoiding responses and searching behavior seem to be shown by enucleates; therefore, to repeat an *aperçu* of doubtful brilliance, the nucleus is not a brain. As the proof of the pudding is in the eating, so a test of effective behavior lies in the feeding. Prowazek (1904) found that enucleated *coeruleus* could ingest chlorellæ and Schwartz (1935) showed that some would take up Colpidia. Hence the general impression, which corresponds to my own observations, is oddly indecisive: enucleated stentors with intact feeding organelles can ingest food but, like enucleated amœbas (Brachet, 1955), usually do not. As a rule enucleates feed little and soon become transparent as they void the food vacuoles which were present in them originally; for, though incapable of further digestion, they are quite capable of normal defecation (Balbiani, 1889; Prowazek, 1904; and Schwartz, 1935). I have found that the presence of but one macronuclear node was sufficient to cause stentors to gorge themselves in the presence of abundant food.

11. Digestion in enucleates

Using vital dyes as indicators, Balbiani (1893) found that food vacuoles do not become acidic in enucleates as they do in normal stentors, and in this he confirmed the work of Hofer in 1890 on amœbas. Schwartz (1935) followed the fate of Colpidia which were ingested by some of his enucleate *coeruleus*. Digestion was never complete. From the start the food vacuoles were abnormally swollen. Staining showed no dissolution of the ingested ciliates, as occurred in controls. In one case I noticed that a motionless rotifer in a food vacuole within an enucleated stentor remained without apparent change for 4 days, although rotifers are normal food of stentors. Hence it is very probable that the macronucleus is necessary for digestion and hence for growth of the cell.

Though apparently incapable of digestion, enucleated *coeruleus* were able to utilize or cause the disappearance of their granular carbohydrate reserves, though possibly at a slower rate than in normal starving animals (Tartar, 1956c). This corresponds to Brachet's (1955) results with *Amœba*.*

Allied to the problem of digestion is the matter of autolysis or "self-digestion" or the capacity of enucleated ciliates to dedifferentiate and resorb existing ectoplasmic structures. As is too often disturbingly the case, some say they do and others say they don't. In *Frontonia*, Balbiani (1889) observed the disappearance of trichocysts and much of the ciliation in enucleates and he thought this might be an autodigestion of proteins. Schmähl (1926) said that membranelles are resorbed in enucleated *Bursaria;* but he remarked that Dembowska found no resorption of parts in *Stylonychia* after enucleation. Specifically in regard to *Stentor coeruleus*, we have already noted that early primordia are resorbed when the nucleus is removed, but the situation is quite different in respect to already formed structures.

Weisz (1949c) claimed that enucleation produces prompt dedifferentiation of existing feeding organelles and holdfast within 24 hours. He therefore believed that the nucleus is necessary not only for the production of new parts but equally for the maintenance of structures already formed. My experience has been to the contrary (Tartar, 1953). I obtained no impression that the feeding organelles soon disappear upon withdrawal of nuclear "support". Most frequently animals died with these organelles intact or, at most, a bit vague. Only when survival of enucleates was most protracted did extensive dedifferentiation finally occur (Fig. 85B), but since dedifferentiation was then so tardy it was probably the result rather of general necrosis. In the present context it is significant that in the experiments in which the heads, only, of stentors were excised, proportionality of parts, which undoubtedly involved resorption of considerable part of the

---

*Regarding transport mechanisms in the cell, de Terra (1960) found in *S. coeruleus* that during the later stages of division, after the macronucleus has condensed, uptake of phosphate as tested by radio-active phosphorus 32 is greatly reduced. This reduction occurred both in nucleate and enucleated animals. Return to high uptake after division was found only in cells with the macronucleus. Hence by inference this nucleus is chemically inactive during late fission (which therefore does not require the nucleus for completion), or at least the macronucleus is required for restoration of high phosphate uptake characteristic of the interdivisional period.

original membranellar band, occurred only if nuclear beads were present (Tartar, 1959d).

12. Survival of enucleates

Gruber, Balbiani, Prowazek, and Schwartz reported survival times of from 32 hours to 3 days. Demonstrating his main theme, Schwartz (1935) found that survival of *coeruleus* in which the macronucleus has been removed was not aided or extended by the presence of 1 to 16 micronuclei, again proving the indifferent character of these tiny nuclei with respect to vegetative functions. His enucleates lived for a much shorter period than starved controls which remained alive for a week. Therefore he concluded that death was not due to starvation but to some disturbance of the entire metabolism in the absence of the macronucleus.

I have found that the tiniest blebs of ciliated cytoplasm separated off in abnormal division of *coeruleus* can live for a little more than 5 hours. Larger enucleated fragments lived for about 3 to 4 days, and the largest enucleates generally lived for 4 days when isolated in depression slides, though some survived for 6. It is not uncommon to find enucleated stentors living as long as starved controls (Tartar, 1956c). One wonders, then, whether enucleates may not die merely from exhaustion of reserves rather than disturbed metabolism.

13. Consequences of excess nucleus

Stentor fragments and fusion complexes with an unusually high proportion of macronuclear material in relation to the cytoplasmic volume can be produced by cutting all the nucleus into one small fragment, forcing all the nucleus at division into one daughter cell, or grafting together sectors of several cells bearing most of their nuclei. Effects of this artificial alteration of the nucleo–cytoplasmic ratio in favor of the nucleus can be followed because, though neat studies of nuclear volume would be difficult and are lacking, there is no evidence or impression that excess nuclear material is quickly and adaptively resorbed in any way comparable to the speed with which the macronuclear chain is regenerated after all but a few nodes are removed. This statement corresponds closely to the observations of Schwartz (1935).

Both Prowazek (1904) and Causin (1931) noted that *coeruleus* fragments with too much nucleus had difficulty in regenerating and surviving and soon died, while Sokoloff (1924) found that *Bursaria* fragments of the same sort did not regenerate. Weisz (1948a), on the contrary, denied that excess nucleus was injurious.

The staunchest advocate of the importance of the nucleo-cytoplasmic ratio in protozoa was Popoff (1909). But we have to doubt, as an expression of over-exuberance for this idea, the report that he produced dwarf lines of *coeruleus* from small fragments of normal ratio, and note that his hopes for producing giant races of stentors by the same principle were not fulfilled. In fact, Burnside (1929) clearly demonstrated that *Stentor* fragments grow back to the normal size before they divide, and this was fully confirmed by Weisz (1948c). Yet Popoff made a summary statement which is probably valid: namely, that too much nucleus is not as injurious as too little but is not without its effect. This remark is in part substantiated in the following section. In the present connection, my experience has been that hypernucleate fragments of *coeruleus* often die prematurely or are notably tardy in regeneration (Tartar, 1959g) but this matter needs much more study (Fig. 86A). Comandon and de Fonbrune (1939b) found that uninucleate species of *Amœba* carrying 3 nuclei by transplantation did not divide though followed 2 months, but binucleates could divide.

14. Consequences of reduced nucleus

All but one macronuclear node can be removed from stentors and the nucleo–cytoplasmic ratio can be still further shifted in favor of the cytoplasm by grafting such an animal to one or more completely enucleated stentors. A combination of excisions and graftings therefore makes it possible in *Stentor* to produce truly extraordinary shifts in the relative volumes of cytoplasm and nucleus; and there is time to test the consequences because compensatory growth of the nucleus occurs only later during periods of oral primordium formation (Fig. 86c).

These methods were not available to earlier workers whose cut fragments yielded disturbance of the normal nucleo–plasmic ratio in narrower range and gave no effect. Balbiani, for example, said repeatedly (1889, 1891c, 1893) in reference to *Stentor* and other ciliates that the relative size of the nucleus is indifferent for the formative processes of regeneration. This was also the conclusion of Weisz (1948a, 1954). I have found, however (Tartar, 1953, 1959g), that in whole cells with only one node, appearance of the regeneration primordium is very much delayed, substantiating an early remark of Popoff (1909) regarding slowness of regeneration in animals with a decreased nucleo–cytoplasmic ratio. In grafts of two animals carrying only one node the delay was greater; primordium formation occurred only after two days, with development

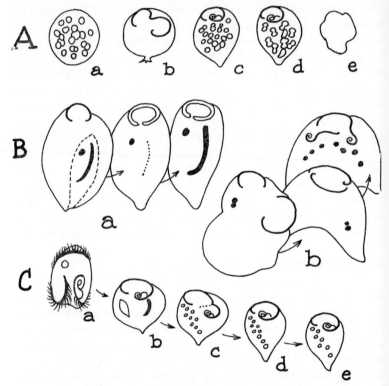

FIG. 86. Effects of marked shifts in the nucleo–cytoplasmic ratio.

A. Indication of disturbance in hypernucleates. *a:* Fragment containing all the macronucleus (20 nodes) of a *coeruleus* did not regenerate until one day later and then astomatously (*b*). *c:* By day 3, successful re-regeneration had occurred and specimen still had 17 to 20 nodes. *d:* Next day there were 10 oval or doublish nodes indicating fusion and reduction of surface. *e:* Specimen became sickly and died on day 5, a day earlier than demise of the enucleate cell remainder.

of the anlage proceeding slowly. In any case the single node was able to support regeneration eventually, for increases in the nucleus occurred only afterward (Fig. 86B). Occasionally no regeneration occurred at all, although the single macronuclear node persisted intact until death of the specimen. Therefore extreme reductions show that the nucleo–cytoplasmic ratio does have an important effect at least on the time required for oral regeneration.

An interesting question is posed by what happens to the single node which enables it to support primordium formation even in a large mass of cytoplasm. For if all but one nuclear bead is removed from a stentor in process of regeneration, I found that early primordia were then resorbed, though later anlagen could run their course of development with the support of the single remaining node (unpublished). In a stentor with 15 nodes each may carry only 1/15th of the burden of supporting primordium formation and development. For one node to do so, especially within a large mass of cytoplasm, may require an adaptation in which the output of this single node becomes greatly accelerated.

There is some evidence that in stentors with greatly reduced nuclear complement the general metabolism of the cell may be upset until this disparity is redressed. The first hint of such effects

---

B. Delayed primordium formation in hypernucleates. *a:* When a sector with stage–2 regeneration anlage and one macro-nuclear node was grafted to non-differentiating stentor minus nucleus and mouthparts the primordium was promptly resorbed and no regeneration occurred until 3 days later. No nuclear increase occurs until after anlage passes through stage 6. *b:* A fusion mass of 2 stentors *coeruleus* with mouthparts and all but 2 nodes excised did not regenerate until two days later, the 2 nodes increasing to 7 only as the anlagen completed development.

C. Regeneration of the macronuclear chain and reconstitution of proportionate parts. *a:* One macronuclear node in head folded on itself. *b:* Shape regenerated and feeding organelles reduced to proportionate size without primordium formation, single node now spindle form (to increase its active surface area?); reorganization primordium (to make possible nuclear increase?). *c:* After reorganization the specimen has 9 small nodes. *d:* Membranellar band and frontal field, again made relatively too large through reorganization, are adaptively decreased in size. *e:* Before its demise, the animal had 7 nodes (adaptation to decreasing size in starvation on the slide?).

is to be found in the work of Popoff (1909) who concluded from his observations of *coeruleus* that stentors with too little nucleus are sickly and in many respects like enucleates. Schwartz (1935) was even stronger in his statement that digestion and even "the entire metabolism" is greatly disturbed through removal of most of the macronucleus.

Although the old concept of nucleo–cytoplasmic ratio may not have fulfilled the original hopes that were invested in it, it is likely that the extreme variations in this ratio which can be produced in *Stentor* will have an important bearing in newer studies of respiration, synthesis, and enzyme production in single cells.

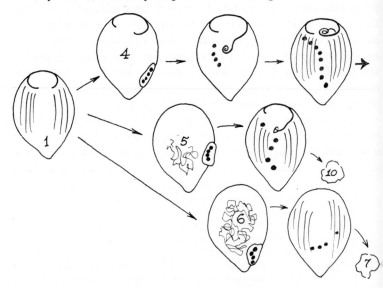

FIG. 87. Critical time for recovery after renucleation.

Macronucleus was excised from specimens on morning of day 1. If renucleated on day 4 complete regeneration of feeding organelles and of nuclear chain occurred, with continued survival. Renucleated on day 5, pale and murky stentor becomes healthier, regenerates faded pigmentation, and forms primordium which does not produce mouthparts. Specimen was dead on day 10. Renucleation on day 6, the faded, murky specimen became healthier in appearance and darker in color but died the next day without forming an oral anlage. Fifth day therefore seems to be transition period for recoverability of the cytoplasm.

15. Delayed renucleation

Since Verworn (1892), it has been found in *Amœba* and its relatives that the naked nucleus undergoes immediate degeneration in the absence of its normal cytoplasmic environment and is not viable when reimplanted (Comandon and de Fonbrune, 1939b; Lorch and Danielli, 1953). So it is with *Stentor* and with embryonic cells (Briggs and King, 1955). Cytoplasm in the absence of the nucleus shows a very much slower deterioration. This raises the question: Beyond what period of time is the cytoplasm irreversibly deteriorated so that it can no longer recover after reimplantation of a fresh nucleus? We would like to be able to analyse what goes wrong in enucleated cells and what the nucleus contributes to the maintenance of the cytoplasm. This approach might be especially fruitful if renucleations were made at a time when certain cytoplasmic functions were recoverable and others not.

Amœbas can recover normal activity and even divide if renucleated 2 days after enucleation (Comandon and de Fonbrune, 1939b; Lorch and Danielli, 1953); but the French workers found that practically no recovery occurred when renucleation was delayed to the sixth day. I have a few experiments of this type on *Stentor coeruleus* (unpublished). Animals renucleated on days 3 and 4 of the experiment, or 2 and 3 days following enucleation, could recover completely, regenerate the mouthparts, show increase in the number of nuclear nodes following regeneration, and divide. Very likely they would have developed into clones if the difficulties of culturing had been surmounted. A specimen renucleated on day 6 promptly corrected its faded coloration and necrotic turbidity of the endoplasm, but was not able to regenerate. Another, renucleated on day 5 recovered and regenerated incompletely, for although the new membranellar band was normal the mouthparts consisted only of a short tube (Fig. 87). This animal survived 5 more days on the slide. Apropos of the remarks above, the specimen lost its contractility completely and could be cut into without showing the slightest twich, as if the myonemes had suffered irreversible damage or loss of response. Evidently the fifth day without the nucleus is critical for *Stentor* cytoplasm and we should have more experiments covering this period.

All the evidence from *Stentor* points to the generally accepted conclusion that the nucleus acts upon the cytoplasm through the intermediation of chemical substances produced in the nucleus and transmitted to the cytoplasm. Weisz (1949a) has even found quite direct evidence for this transmission: fixed specimens which were undergoing primordium development showed macronuclear vesicles apparently breaking through the nuclear membrane to void their contents into the endoplasm. With due allowance for lag effects, the presence of a portion of the macronucleus is necessary for oral regeneration, digestion and synthesis, and survival of the cell. Energy metabolism continues unabated for a while in enucleates, to judge by their vigorous activity, but in the course of several days ciliary beating becomes progressively slower, either through the impairment of this metabolism or by failure to replace utilized substrates. The ease with which stentors carrying much more or less of the normal proportion of nuclear material can be prepared offers unusual opportunities for a quantitative study of the action of the nucleus on the cytoplasm. Eventually such studies may teach us why and how a fairly constant ratio between nucleus and cytoplasm is maintained.

Conversely, the *Stentor* macronucleus is clearly affected in many ways by the cytoplasm, in addition to the obvious fact that cytoplasmic environment supplies the basis for the growth and integrity of the nucleus. The location of the macronucleus is determined by the stripe pattern or geometry of the ectoplasm. Cytoplasmic events evidently guide the macronucleus in its complex behavior during coalescence and renodulation. Such control of the nucleus by the cytoplasm is at least as extensive as has been demonstrated in any other cell and in *Stentor* is capable of being investigated by micrurgical operations.

CHAPTER XVII

TOWARD A GENETICS OF STENTOR

THE collaborative functions of nucleus and cytoplasm can further be studied by artificial exchange of nuclei and cytoplasms between different individuals and even different species of *Stentor*. Potentially, natural exchange of traceable genetic material between members of the same species through conjugation would complement such investigations. The circumstance common to both approaches is that now we deal with qualitative alterations in either the cytoplasmic or nuclear component, or both.

1. Interspecific chimeras and nuclear transplantations

New possibilities for experimentation appeared when it was found that different species of *Stentor* could be fused together by their cytoplasms in enduring unions, and that when foreign nuclei are transplanted they are neither immediately ejected nor destroyed but also persist, with the expectation of revealing interactions between species–different nuclei and cytoplasms. Many combinations are possible. The macronucleus can be removed and replaced by that of a different species. Alien cytoplasm can be grafted so that the host nucleus now operates within a mixture of cytoplasms, or nuclei alone can be added so that now a mixed nuclear complement works with cytoplasm almost entirely of one type. And finally, relative amounts of the two types of nuclei and cytoplasms can be mixed together in any desired combination. The parts of three species could also be joined in similar permutations, but we need first to work out the simpler combinations. In comparison with the possibilities, the work which has so far been done (Tartar, 1953, 1956c) may be regarded as only exploratory. In fact, further development of these studies was postponed until conditions governing the states of activation and inhibition during primordium formation, as well as the effects of altering the nuclear–cytoplasmic ratio, and other points could be explored; for all these factors have

V

to be considered in arriving at any reliable interpretation of the effects resulting from species differences in cytoplasm and nuclei.

What may be called the capacity of foreign macronuclear nodes to support oral primordium formation and development in enucleated *coeruleus* from which the oral region was also removed has received a preliminary survey. We have to say preliminary, because nuclear transfers are not easy and the number of cases with certain combinations is still few. That there should be many is indicated both by the circumstance that one cannot always be sure that the last macronuclear node of the *coeruleus* has been removed, as well as the experience of Lorch and Danielli (1950) with interspecific transfers in *Amœba* in which many tests gave negative results though a small percentage could produce effective combinations. Hence the positive result is more significant in showing what an alien combination *can* do; but the negative result, in which no primordium formation occurs, may be merely the result of other factors such as poor viability or insufficient number of cases to include possible rare instances in which the combination would work.

In the first place, controls showed that nuclei could viably be transferred from one individual to another among similar stocks of *coeruleus* leading to their subsequent complete regeneration. The next closest combination was between typical *coeruleus* and an organism I called *Stentor* "X" (Tartar, 1956c). The latter was a small, blue-green stentor like *coeruleus* but only about 1/8th its volume, with far fewer stripes, usually opaque cytoplasm, and tiny nuclear nodes. This organism was at least a distinctly different variety of *coeruleus*, or possibly even a different though closely associated species. Transfers could be made in both directions and it was found that the nucleus of either could support regeneration in the cytoplasm of the other (Fig. 88). This may be called the expected result, because we can assume that the nature of nuclear support of regeneration is the same in all species and varieties of *Stentor*. Size of the feeding organelles was always appropriate for the host cytosome. Yet the chimeras did not survive as long as controls and soon died. This is the reason it is thought that the two were distant varieties, if not separate species. The appearance was, therefore, that a successful interaction between nuclei and cytoplasm of different type was later and gradually overwhelmed

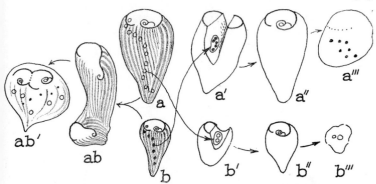

FIG. 88. Interactions between *S. coeruleus* and *Stentor X*, which was either a closely related species or a dwarf race.

a: S. coeruleus. b: Stentor X, of about ⅛ volume of former, fewer stripes, and smaller macronuclear nodes. *a'*: X–nuclei implanted into enucleated *coeruleus* gives complete regeneration (*a''*) but mouthparts resorption and death soon follow (*a'''*).

b–b''': Similarly for the reciprocal cross. Feeding organelles are in proportion to size of the cytosome in which they are formed.

ab: Graft of the 2 forms undergoes simultaneous reorganization and integrates the two shapes into a doublet (*ab'*) but the specimen then died. (After Tartar, 1956c.)

by some subtle and possibly immunological difference which resulted in eventual malfunctioning. The general picture suggested is that nucleus and cytoplasm no doubt have respective roles in the act of cytodifferentiation which are the same in all species, but that the specific adaptation of the one to the other is developed to such a degree that sooner or later a disharmony will almost always emerge to nullify whatever compatibilities were at first realized.

Initially it appeared that *polymorphus* macronucleus could not support regeneration in *coeruleus* cytoplasm (Tartar, 1953), but further tests (1956c) showed that primordium formation at least is possible (Fig. 89A). Typically, an anlage was produced which progressed to stage 4 and then was resorbed. Hence there was some effective interaction, but not as much as in the first combination described. In regard to other combinations, it was found that neither *roeseli* nor *niger* nucleus supported regeneration in *coeruleus*, but there was one positive result with *introversus* nucleus which after 5 days finally led to satisfactory oral differentiation in

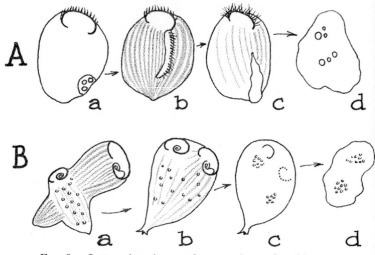

FIG. 89. Interactions in *coeruleus* × *polymorphus* chimeras.

A. *a:* Three *polymorphus* macronuclear nodes implanted into an enucleated *coeruleus* with mouthparts excised. *b:* Wide primordium forming in *coeruleus* cytoplasm under influence of *polymorphus* nucleus, 12 hours later. *c:* Anlage not developing, exudate in primordium site, and original *coeruleus* membranelles fimbriated. *d:* Specimen died after 3 days and showed 6 nodes, indicating nuclear increase in alien cytoplasm.

B. Mutual integration of shape. *a:* Polymorphus grafted at right angles to *coeruleus*. *b:* Harmonization of shapes and spread of chlorellæ throughout. *c:* Oral structures dedifferentiated, *coeruleus* pigment lost, chlorellæ clumped. *d:* Prompt death of species combination. (After Tartar, 1953, 1956c.)

coeruleus cytoplasm. If pigmentation is a sign of taxonomic related-ness, the blue-green color of both *introversus* and *coeruleus* suggests that these species are more closely related than others, and this could be the basis for effective interaction between their parts. The species *multiformis* is also blue-green and in fact appears like a miniature of *coeruleus*, with but a single macronuclear node. These animals are so small that a whole cell had to be implanted in the enucleated *coeruleus*. In 4 cases no regeneration occurred, but we have to remember that regeneration on one node is greatly retarded so that in this combination the chimeras may have run into difficulties of another sort before they were able to express their regeneration possibilities. Nevertheless, this combination should be attractive for further studies because of the great difference in size together with general similarities in other respects.

Nucleated cells and cell parts were grafted to obtain mixtures of widely varying proportions of *coeruleus* and of a *polymorphus* strain which was grass-green with abundant symbiotic *Chlorella*. The general result was that successful oral redifferentiation occurred only when there was a preponderance of one species of nucleus in a preponderance of its own type of cytoplasm. The more nearly the two types of cells approached equality the less successful was oral reorganization, and instead existing feeding organelles were promptly resorbed. When both species were represented in the cytoplasm but with the nucleus from *polymorphus* only, some oral differentiation occurred and the indications are therefore that there is a conflict between the nuclear components such that *polymorphus* nucleus is more effective when acting on a mixture alone.

In spite of incompatibilities in regard to oral differentiation, mixtures of *coeruleus* and *polymorphus* in any proportion showed very good shape reconstitution as manifested by the realignment of cells and cell parts to form a single, conical stentor shape (Fig. 89B), and was better than that of enucleated grafts of either species. This suggests that reorientation of the cortical pattern is either a more generalized function in which species differences are not prominent or makes less precise demands on nucleo–cytoplasmic interaction. Were the cytoplasm less specific than the nucleus, as appears, this would substantiate present-day conceptions (Monné, 1948).

In these quantitatively varying combinations of *coeruleus* and *polymorphus* it was also found that any considerable admixture of *coeruleus* cytoplasm resulted in the ejection of chlorellæ from the fusion mass, and it should be added that uniform distribution of the symbionts throughout showed there was complete mixture of the endoplasm. Hence *coeruleus* cytoplasm appears to be antithetical to the entertainment of the symbionts. Correspondingly, admixture of *polymorphus* cytoplasm resulted in depigmentation of *coeruleus*.

Similar results in regard to pigmentation have been found in recent tests in which nucleated *coeruleus* was fused with a smaller portion of white *polymorphus* which had been grown in the dark and contained few if any chlorellæ (unpublished). Even when the portion of *polymorphus* was relatively small there occurred an aggregation of the pigment granules of *coeruleus* into splotches which later disappeared so that the fusion complex became entirely colorless and very much resembled in general appearance the white *polymorphus* stock. These combinations could regenerate, reorganize and even divide. They also showed several interesting abnormalities (Fig. 90A). In some cases the form of the cell became abnormally elongated and occasionally this also led to a complete

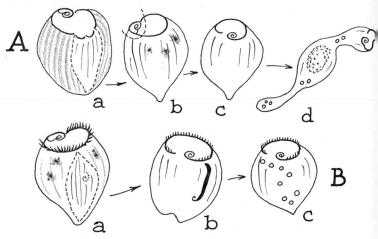

FIG. 90. Abnormalities from grafting a small *polymorphus* to a large *coeruleus.*

A. Abnormal form with granular core. *a:* Half a *polymorphus* engrafted, with cytoplasm and nucleus. *b:* Aggregations of *coeruleus* pigment as graft causes loss of pigmentation; mouthparts excised. *c:* Regeneration of colorless chimera resulting. *d:* Snake-like form with mass of colorless granules and irregular distribution of nuclear nodes.

B. Bleaching and failure to form membranelles. *a:* Feeding organelles of grafted *polymorphus* resorbed, *coeruleus* fading, with splotches of pigment granules. *b:* Chimera now colorless, with half-length adoral cilia which start and stop together but show no metachronal beating nor organization into membranelles. *c:* Reorganized animal may have longer peristomal cilia but still no membranelles. Eight large nuclear nodes are seen. Specimen died on day 7 in isolation on slide.

disruption of the normal form, resembling the "amorphous phenotype" (see p. 276). The nuclear picture also became abnormal, with nuclear nodes of greatly varying size, atypically located within the cell.

One special case should be mentioned in detail for the interesting possibilities suggested. Addition of the *polymorphus* component caused the major *coeruleus* part to dedifferentiate its original feeding organelles, and when regeneration occurred the oral cilia were at first only half the normal size and never did they group into membranelles. These cilia started and stopped together but there was no metachronal rhythm as when membranelles are present (Fig. 90B). An oral differentiation was obtained which was, however, very different from the normal.

In these chimeras, the complex appeared at first as if stricken by the shock of incompatibility, and regeneration was often at first abortive or incomplete; but the specimens then recovered and generally showed good oral redifferentiation, yet with the abnormalities described often appearing later. One may expect, therefore, that from small additions of one species of *Stentor* to another, after the manner of transduction, and with greater skill in keeping the specimens alive, very interesting results will emerge.

Referring again to the combination of *coeruleus* and *niger*, it was found that the *coeruleus* cell was greatly affected by the addition of a relatively small piece of *niger* cytoplasm (Fig. 91). In only one case was the host able to regenerate and maintain good feeding organelles, for in other tests regeneration was incomplete or not even begun (Tartar, 1956c). These two species are apparently so distantly related that even a small admixture of *niger* greatly affects the behavior of *coeruleus*, including the condition of the macronucleus. Conversely, *coeruleus* caused depigmentation of the *niger* graft.

The studies of Hämmerling have shown that in the unicellular and uninucleate plant, *Acetabularia*, the cytoplasm is relatively passive and can elaborate cell structures with the support of any species of nucleus of this genus which was tested, and the form is that of the species contributing the nucleus or the nuclear products. For in combinations containing two types of nuclei the form was more like that of the species contributing the most nuclei. If the nuclear contributions were balanced the structures produced were

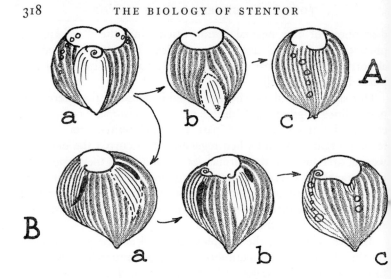

FIG. 91. Effects of *niger* graft on *coeruleus*.

A. Regeneration blocked, no bleaching of *coeruleus* — the usual result. *a:* Enucleate *niger* grafted and mouthparts of *coeruleus* excised. *b:* Yellow *niger* pigment disappears but not the *coeruleus* coloration. *c:* In spite of regression of *niger* graft no primordium formation occurs and macronucleus becomes of 5 large nodes.

B. Unusual response to same type of graft. *a:* Regeneration occurs, with a secondary primordium forming in suture between fine *niger* stripes and broad striping of host. *b:* Only the host anlage has complete stomatogenesis. *c:* re-regeneration follows with still less development of the primordium associated with *niger* graft. Host nucleus abnormal, with few and unequal nodes, two of which migrated to lie underneath the graft. (After Tartar, 1956c.)

in character halfway between those of the two species. In some combinations differentiation occurred but the cooperation of the two nuclei was defective and abnormal structures resulted, as in the case without membranelles in *Stentor*.

On the whole this behavior is quite different from the situation in *Stentor*, although the comparison is limited by the fact that all stentors produce the same form of oral differentiation. In *Stentor* the cytoplasms seem to be much more specific and nuclei are effective in alien cytoplasm only when the taxonomic relationship may be considered close. Another difference is that in acetabularias both growth and differentiation can occur for some time in the absence of any nucleus, whereas in stentors whatever the nucleus contributes to the cytoplasm for growth and morphogenesis is not stored or is exceedingly short-lived.

Following methods devised by Comandon and de Fonbrune (1939b), Danielli and his co-workers have made exchanges of nuclei between *Amœba proteus* and *discoides* (Lorch and Danielli, 1950, 1953; Danielli *et al.*, 1955; reviewed to date in Danielli, 1959). In either transfer the enucleated cell of one species recovered its capacity for normal pseudopodial locomotion and its survival was promoted after receiving a nucleus from the other. For the most part these chimeras, as in my experience with stentors, did not survive; but in one instance at least the implantation of a *proteus* nucleus into *discoides* cytoplasm did produce a clone which was kept in mass culture for over 8 years. Back transfers showed that both nucleus and cytoplasm became altered in the alien combination, but the *proteus* nucleus never became functionally or morphologically identical to that of *discoides*, nor did the *discoides* cytoplasm become the same as that of *proteus*.

The persisting influence of both the nucleus and the cytoplasm was also evident in such characteristics of the chimeras as nuclear size, form of the pseudopodia, growth rate, and response to antiserum, which in general fell between those expressed by the two species in pure form. These results led Danielli (1958) to emphasize the irreducible importance of the cytoplasm, because it was never completely made over into the type of the nuclear species, and to suggest the reasonable hypothesis that the nucleus of the cell determines the specific types of macromolecules which are synthesized, while the cytoplasm controls the way in which they are organized into functional units. This conception is certainly indicated by studies of ciliates and especially of *Stentor*. Failure of regeneration and growth in the absence of the nucleus indicates this organelle to be essential for synthesis. But the cytoplasm, and especially the ectoplasmic pattern, is obviously intimately concerned with guiding nuclear behavior and determining the location, extent, and direction of asymmetry of the developing feeding organelles.

2. Racial differences

In the best known species, *coeruleus*, definable differences between various stocks and clones may turn out to be inherited racial differences because they have appeared and persisted in strains cultured by uniform methods. Since we still lack the means for inducing conjugation at will in stentors, the most fruitful approach would be by nuclear exchanges to test whether these traits are determined by the nucleus or the cytoplasm. In one instance this has been done, but for the most part we can at present merely describe possible strain differences which might be analyzed in this way.

State of the endoplasm. Separate clones of *coeruleus* may differ in regard to the transparency of the endoplasm, a difference which manifests itself very clearly in the ease with which macronuclear nodes can be made out in enucleation experiments. The two extremes of this condition are shown in my stock from Urbana, Illinois, in which the cytoplasm is consistently transparent so that the nucleus is clearly visible except in over-fed animals, and another from Stella, Washington, in which the endoplasm is notably opaque, except when the animals have been completely starved, and this stock has also remained consistently so characterized for 4 years.

Size. If the *Stentor* "X" mentioned in the preceding section was indeed a race of *coeruleus*, then we had a dwarf variety in which the cells never attained a volume larger than about 1/8th that of most stocks of this species. Other stocks of *coeruleus* seem to show much less striking differences in the maximum size attained, but careful measurements might reveal consistent size differences such as have already been found in other genera of ciliates, notably Paramecium.

"Astomatous". A stock of *coeruleus* obtained from Woods Hole Biological Supply in 1950 was unique in producing some individuals temporarily without mouthparts (Tartar, 1957b). After growing these organisms in the laboratory for 4 years it was noticed that in certain subcultures about 1% of the stentors were poorly fed because they lacked ingestive organelles. In division, reorganization, and regeneration the oral primordium developed without its posterior end invaginating and forming a gullet, and the oral pouch was generally missing. The membranellar band itself

appeared altogether normal, and it seemed to be of the usual length, including the part which descends into the gullet, because this band curved into a long spiral (Fig. 92). If this appearance is correctly interpreted, then normal length of the row of membranelles is not used as a sign that successful oral differentiation has been completed; for regeneration or reorganization then followed,

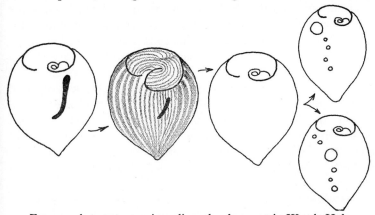

FIG. 92. Astomatous primordium development in Woods Hole race of *S. coeruleus*. Normal animal reorganizes, producing peristomal anlage of normal length which fails to invaginate to form mouthparts. Following regeneration now produces complete mouthparts. Animal feeds and divides, forming daughters with complete feeding organelles but each having one unusually large macronuclear node.

with the production in the same individual, usually on the first try, of good mouthparts. The animals could then feed, explaining why the abnormality did not result in its own extinction but persisted in the subcultures for about a year, after which only normal animals have been found. Astomatous stentors appeared normal in other respects except for a variability in size of the macronuclear nodes, and analysis of this trait is the more difficult because the same individual could manifest both the complete and incomplete development of the feeding organelles. Isolated normals could pass through the mouthless phase while astomatous individuals later became normal. Anterior and posterior fragments did not differ significantly in the frequency with which they regenerated incompletely. Until this abnormality reappears and can be studied further, we can only note that since the mouthparts are induced by the ectoplasm of the posterior pole, this induction or its gradient basis is apparently highly labile in certain stocks.

Fluorescence. That fluorescence is characteristic of certain races of *coeruleus* was discovered by Møller (see p. 48), these animals when killed appearing red in ultraviolet radiation.* Other races lack the trait, although they look the same in visible light because the major component of the pigment is the same in all *coeruleus* and is not fluorescent. Whiteley and Møller (unpublished) neatly demonstrated fluorescence to be a trait under control of the nucleus. When animals of a fluorescent race were enucleated, the fluorescence soon disappeared; or if the macronucleus of fluorescents was replaced by the nucleus of a non-fluorescent race the fluorescence still disappeared. Therefore the manifestation and maintenance of this trait seems to depend upon the presence of a certain type of nucleus and may be regarded as a genetic characterization of great interest in itself and also potentially valuable in tagging cells of different origin.

Cannibalism? In the discussion of feeding reactions in stentors, reference has already been made to the work of Gelei (1925) on cannibalism in *coeruleus*. One of the main points of this study was that the proclivity for eating one's fellows is a racial character. This conclusion was based on the observation that some samples from a culture, containing a natural collection of stentors which was not a clone, showed cannibalism and others did not. Daughters of cannibals cannibalized each other. Even when not densely concentrated, and regardless of whether they were well-fed or not, cannibals seemed actively to pursue their fellows, while in other samples the stentors simply turned away on encountering each other. On dubious grounds Ivanić (1927) questioned that cannibalism is a racial character in protozoa, including *Stentor*. More to the point is my observation of cannibalism in all 9 stocks or clones of *coeruleus* which I have under cultivation, strongly indicating that cannibalism is common to all representatives of this species regardless of origin.

Other possible racial differences have been indicated in respect of the following characteristics: Requirement, or not, for high

*Lately (1960) Møller reports that some races of *S. coeruleus* exhibit all degrees of fluorescence.

oxygen tension (see p. 265). Presence of 3, or of 2 rows of cilia in the membranelles (p. 30). Acclimatization, or not, to alcohols (p. 248). Suitability, or not, of certain culture media, like Benecke's solution for *polymorphus* (p. 268). Negative, or indifferent, response to light, as shown by *coeruleus* (p. 22). Presence, or absence of visible nucleoli; for de Terra (1959) remarked a race of *coeruleus* without nucleoli, but Schwartz (1935) demonstrated their presence in his strain. And average number of macronuclear nodes (Møller, unpublished).

3. Conjugation

Sexual reproduction by temporary fusion of partner animals with cross-fertilization and complete renewal of the nuclear apparatus occurs in *Stentor* as in other ciliates. Breeding experiments towards an analysis of inheritance and the roles of nucleus and cytoplasm in the development of racial differences, which may well include mating types, should therefore eventually be possible in this genus. Yet conjugation is rarely observed and seems to be quite adventitious in its appearance, for the means have yet to be discovered by which stentors can be induced to conjugate as we desire. There is available, nevertheless, a comprehensive cytological study of sexual reproduction in *Stentor* which has been generally neglected in reviews of this subject.

The general occurrence of conjugation in the genus *Stentor* is attested by the observation of pairs in *niger* (Stein, 1867), *coeruleus* (Moxon, 1869; Balbiani, 1891c), *igneus* (Johnson, 1893), *polymorphus* (Mulsow, 1913) and in *roeseli* (Balbiani). I also observed fusion pairs in a colorless race of *polymorphus* in which symbiotic chlorellæ were almost completely lacking. In seven stocks of *coeruleus*, conjugation in five was observed at least once during a period of 10 years. Schwartz (1935) remarked that he found no evidence of autogamy in his extensive studies of *coeruleus*; and I, too, have never seen any indication of nuclear renewal in unpaired animals.

Exploratory studies of conjugation were included within the compass of those works by Balbiani and Johnson to which we have so often referred. Finding that the old macronucleus could be distinguished by its no longer being clear and refractive in living animals, Balbiani (1891c, 1893) studied the behavior of fragments in relation thereto. Pieces of exconjugants did not resorb the old portions of the macronucleus if new nuclear anlagen were not present in them. New macronuclei could support regeneration from the start, but after the first stages of disintegration the old nucleus could not. These conclusions are in line with what is found in other ciliates, and I also have noted that *coeruleus* which had begun conjugation were unable to regenerate excised oral parts.

That the proper conditions for conjugation seldom occur was noted in the first extensive study by Hamburger (1908), who remarked that *Stentor* cultures may be carried on for years without noticing pair-formation. When conjugation does occur only about 1 to 10% of the animals are involved so that no mass " epidemics " occur, as in *Paramecium*. She also found that many isolated single animals from cultures in which conjugation was occurring did not themselves subsequently pair. Her study was therefore of only 55 conjugants, the products of which did not live sufficiently long to reveal the complete nuclear transformations. Later, Mulsow obtained material from mixed pond samples which were rich in fauna and flora. They were left unfed in the laboratory and after a week apparently abundant conjugation of *coeruleus* and *polymorphus* present occurred. The experience was repeatable on fresh samples. Bad conditions may have developed in the jars because all the stentors died following the period of conjugation. Possibly a putrid condition developed although he did not say so. At the same time *Paramecium* and *Frontonia* present in the samples also conjugated, which would indicate that methods employed for paramecia might be applicable to stentors. However, I have made mixtures of 5 stocks of *coeruleus* in the hope of providing mating type diversity, and subjected them to feeding and starvation routines to which paramecia are usually responsive, but this first attempt to induce conjugation was entirely unsuccessful.

Mulsow's (1913) study included over 2,000 conjugating pairs of *coeruleus* and a smaller but substantial number of *polymorphus* conjugants, incidentally confirming many of the points made by his predecessors. He was able to keep his exconjugant animals considerably beyond the period required for completion of all transformations. Sectioned material was studied, for he found that squashed preparations and total amounts were not satisfactory. I have tried to express Mulsow's account of the course of conjugation in these two species in the diagrams and legends of Fig. 93 and 94 and therefore will touch only the main points in the following paragraphs.

S. coeruleus: The *size* of conjugating animals is always smaller than the maximum, as Hamburger had also noted, and Johnson observed that conjugants were without food vacuoles apparently from the start. Sometimes the partners are of different sizes but they are not necessarily so and hence there was no indication of "gamete" differentiation. All this accords with my own observation. *Attachment* is by the anterior rim so that the partners rest at an angle to one another and swim together with their axes parallel. In the conjugants I have observed there was always a special place of attachment: a patch immediately below the membranellar band and to the left of the mouth. In location this point corresponds to Hamburger's figure though she said that attachment was by the membranellar bands. That this locus of joining is not invariable, however, is shown by the fact that Mulsow often found three animals together in conjugation, all undergoing nuclear changes simultaneously. He also found that the degree of union is variable, from a small bridge to quite complete fusion of the two lateral surfaces, and that this does not depend on the stage of conjugation. Hence there may be endoplasmic fusion, but the migratory nucleus always penetrates through a separating, pigmented membrane toward the anterior end. The *duration* of the union is about 30 hours, which is not unusual, and nuclear renewal is not completed until 10 days after separation.

The *old macronucleus* first breaks up into separate nodes which then lose their orderly arrangement in a chain as well as their adherence to the inside of the ectoplasm. Johnson had observed that the nodes carry cytoplasmic (attachment?) threads as they break loose from their former locations and are carried about in the cell by a cyclosis of the endoplasm, which is unusually rapid in conjugation. At this time, Hamburger said that the nodes lose their amorphous character and show a honeycomb structure. The original macronucleus so remains until its parts begin disappearing as soon as the new macronuclear anlagen have attained considerable size.

After breakup of the macronucleus into separate nodes, the

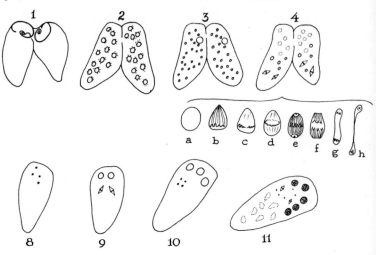

FIG. 93. Conjugation in *S. coeruleus*, largely following the
account of Mulsow, 1913.

1. Stentors attach by areas just below membranellar bands,
maintaining a separating partition or fusing to some degree.

2. Old macronuclear nodes break apart, become spherical, and
may show honeycomb structure. (These organelles are omitted
from subsequent drawings up to stage 11.) The 50–70 micronuclei are near the macronuclear nodes.

3. Micronuclei separate freely in the cytoplasm, all enlarging
and stain less intensely.

4. Up to 10 micronuclei in both cells degenerate. Others
divide mitotically but not simultaneously, giving about 60 nuclei
in each. These are probably not maturation but "multiplicative"
divisions. Stages in mitosis are shown below:

a: homogeneous, swollen micronucleus.

b: parachute stage, with chromatin at one end, single
spindle pole at the other.

c: chromatin pulling toward equator (by traction fibers?).
Degeneration may occur after this phase.

d: equatorial ring of chromatin.

e: development of second spindle pole, spindle fibers
pointing toward centrioles.

f: polar cones flatten as nucleus becomes cylindrical; no
fibers found between chromosomes, approximately 80
in number.

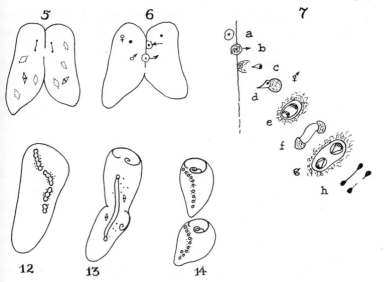

g: anaphase separation.

h: chromosomes reach poles as granules, and spindle body disappears.

5. Nuclei near the partition may be the sexual nuclei, considerably reduced in size from reduction of chromosomes to 20 by maturation division. Further division figures and degenerating mitoses elsewhere.

6. Exchange of migratory pronuclei.

7. Fertilization and first 2 divisions of the amphinucleus.

   a: male pronucleus becomes surrounded by halo of cytoplasm.

   b: halo carried with it as it penetrates partition into the partner cell.

   c: nucleus with chromatin massed forward breaks free from halo.

   d: union of male pronucleus with female, which is larger and more loosely formed.

   e: fertilization spindle figure, always surrounded by a thickened cytoplasmic halo.

   f: termination of this first division.

   g: beginning of second division, with parachute-form nuclei.

   h: division produces 4 similar products.

8. Partners, each with four new nuclei, now separate.

W

many *micronuclei* depart from their location on or near the macro-nuclear surface and become freed in the endoplasm. All become greatly enlarged and hence less strongly staining. Then occur a series of non-simultaneous mitotic divisions, but increase in the number of micronuclei is overbalanced by the fact that many degenerate even after they have begun the first stages of mitosis. As these divisions proceed, the remaining micronuclei become smaller and fewer in number until there is only one sexual nucleus in each partner. Presumably the penultimate division is the first maturation division and division of the last remaining micronucleus is the second maturation division with reduction in number of chromosomes in the migrating and stationary pronuclei formed.

The *migrating pronucleus* then becomes surrounded by a halo of homogeneous, darkly-staining cytoplasm. Nucleus and halo both break through the separation membrane to move across to the partner cell so that there is always a small exchange of cytoplasm. At early stages it appears that this cytoplasm is pulling the nucleus along, later the reverse. Once across, the migratory pronucleus breaks loose from its halo and unites with the partner stationary pronucleus of different appearance. The fertilization nucleus then becomes itself surrounded by a thickened halo and undergoes two post-fertilization divisions giving rise to four simpler nuclei.

Separation of the animals occurs about this time. Two of the

9. Two nuclei form macronuclear anlagen and two produce mitotic spindles but without showing chromosomes and will form 4 micronuclei.

10. Day after separation 1 to 10 macronuclear anlagen, depending on combinations of fusion and amitotic increase. Four micronuclei.

11. Two–four days after separation. Anlagen with chromatin net resembling chromosomes, and nucleoli appear. Old macro-nuclear nodes resorb as soon as anlagen attain same size. Micro-nuclear increase by mitosis with clearly defined chromosomes.

12. Constriction of anlagen into nodes and their attaching together. They are not sorted out between daughter cells. Micronuclei have final size and location but are not yet of definitive number.

13. First fission 10 days after separation of conjugants, with the usual vegetative division of nuclei producing 2 normal vegetative stentors (14).

nuclei remain heavily chromatic and will form macronuclear anlagen, while the other two undergo mitosis, but without showing clear chromosomes, and produce four equal micronuclei. The number of macronuclear anlagen then changes by combined fusions and amitoses so that there may be 1 to 10 masses.

Two to four days after separation the appearance is as follows: macronuclear anlagen enlarge and show at first a chromatin network resembling chromosomes, and nucleoli appear. The nodes of the old macronucleus then begin absorbing. By mitotic division, with appearance of definable chromosomes, the micronuclei increase in number. Eight days after separation the macronuclear anlagen separately constrict into nodes or chains of beads which then attach together to form the definitive macronuclear chain along which the micronuclei, now of their final size and number, find their location. There is hence no sorting out of anlagen between daughter cells, and when the first division occurs 10 days after separation this is the fission of an animal which has in itself regained the completely normal nuclear picture. Two variations in macronuclear development were described but these may have been pathological.

S. polymorphus: Conjugation in this species is of course quite similar. Multiplicative divisions of the micronuclei and concomitant degenerations occur as in *coeruleus*. Cross-fertilization was established, but the amphinucleus divides three times to produce 8 products before nuclear differentiation begins. Normally 6 of these form macronuclear anlagen by increasing in size and producing from the karyosome a spireme, later breaking into segments or chromosomes which seem to be in the diploid number and split in two longitudinally, like chromosomes, before they are reduced to chromatin granules. The anlagen then nodulate and join to form the definitive macronucleus. The two remaining products of the amphinucleus form the micronuclei by repeated mitotic divisions, during which the nuclei decrease in size. Because the number of macronuclear and micronuclear anlagen may vary, it seems likely that the 8 products of the third division of the amphinucleus are still equivalent, and that differentiation is not predeterminedand might even be guided by their location in the cell, as is the case in other ciliates.

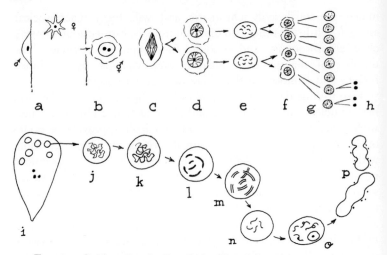

FIG. 94. Conjugation in *S. polymorphus*, following the account of Mulsow, 1913. (Early stages are like those numbered 1 to 6 in *coeruleus*, Fig. 93.)

- *a:* Both migratory and stationary pronuclei surrounded by halos of cytoplasm excluding chlorellæ, that of the female nucleus being stellate. Immediately preceding maturation divisions apparently reduced the chromosomes from 56 to 28 and from 28 to 14, the latter by seemingly transverse division. Male pronucleus flattens as a disc against the partition.
- *b:* Male nucleus breaks through and unites with partner's stationary pronucleus.
- *c:* First mitotic division of the amphinucleus.
- *d:* Products retain cytoplasmic halos and have karyosomes with achromatic fibers connecting to nuclear membranes.
- *e:* Second division, halos disappeared and 56 pear-shaped chromosomes, producing —
- *f:* Four nuclei with karyosomes.
- *g:* Third division, simultaneous, yielding 8 nuclei, 6 of which usually form macronuclear anlagen and have karyosomes, and usually 2, becoming granular, form the new micronuclei.
- *h:* Division and reduction in size of progenitors of micronuclei.
- *i:* Separation of partners, each usually with 6 macronuclear anlagen and 4 micronuclei.
- *j:* Karyosome of macronuclear anlage forms chromatic spireme.

In the *polymorphus* studied by Mulsow, the micronuclei showed larger and fewer chromosomes than his *coeruleus*. The latter seemed to have about 80 in the vegetative stage, while the comparable number in *polymorphus* was close to 56. Therefore, in *polymorphus*, Mulsow could demonstrate reduction of chromosomes during maturation divisions as he could not in *coeruleus*. During maturation the micronucleus is not homogeneous but has a central chromatic body and it is surrounded by a halo of clear cytoplasm without symbiotic chlorellæ. The number of chromosomes seemed to be at first halved to about 28 and then, when the final division of the last remaining micronucleus into the two pronuclei occurred, the chromosomes appeared to be further reduced to 14. Such double reduction would be entirely anomalous, as Mulsow noted, and would even call into question whether the bodies observed were in fact true chromosomes. I suppose that this paradox can be resolved on the basis that in ciliates chromosomes are sometimes dumbbell-shaped and only apparently double. If the chromosome number in *coeruleus* is reduced from 80 to 20, as Mulsow indicates, one wonders why he did not also consider this a case of apparent double reduction.

Conjugation accomplishes at least, and probably mainly, a recombination of chromosomes with their varying genetic determinants, both by the selection of one set of chromosomes from two for the pronucleus of one animal, and the combination of these with a pronucleus from a different individual. This is accomplished through the micronuclei which alone seem to retain the capacity to form typical chromosomes, but any recombinant difference resulting has to be transmitted to the macronucleus which alone

---

k: Anlage enlarges.
l: Spireme fragments into pieces — like chromosomes — of different length but equal thickness.
m: These chromosomes split longitudinally into 56 pairs.
n: Some chromosomes disappear (?).
o: Chromatic bodies now with nucleoli, "plastin" body with chromatic center develops and later disappears.
p: Anlagen nodulate and attach; micronuclei multipled by mitosis. Normal vegetative stentor produced before first fission following separation of conjugants.

CHAPTER XVIII

SPECIES OF STENTOR

BRIEF histories of our knowledge of the kinds of stentor are included in Kent's *Manual of the Infusoria* (1881) and in Johnson's monumental study of the genus (1893). The first recorded observations of the group were made by Abraham Trembley of *Hydra* fame. In a letter to the Royal Society of London (1744) he described "funnel-like polypes" of green, blue, and white types which would correspond to the present species called *polymorphus*, *coeruleus*, and *roeseli* or *muelleri*. Feeding, with both rejection and retention of particles he noted. Division was correctly described as being oblique and this was confirmed somewhat later with much surprise by Packard (1937). The present *S. roeseli* was included in Linnaeus' *Systema Naturæ*, tenth edition of 1767, under the name of *Hydra stentorea*. Stentors were later clearly differentiated from hydras and the first use of the generic title *Stentor* for this group was made by Oken in his *Lehrbuch der Naturgeschichte*, 1815.

Oken's genus was not taxonomically accurate, for it included vorticellids and rotifers and did not consistently use the binomial nomenclature. Nevertheless, to retain a well-known name, the genus *Stentor* Oken 1815 was recently validated at the instigation of Kirby (1956), whose account of the generic term is here summarized. It is well that this was done because at one time the name had been suggested for a group of howler monkeys. *S. muelleri* was chosen as the type species since it was the first species adequately described and figured, by Ehrenberg in 1831.

Descriptions of the more common and better known species *coeruleus* and *polymorphus* have already acquainted the reader with the general morphology of this genus. The most outstanding features in common are the trumpet shape from which the group derives its name, conspicuous contractility throughout the length of the body, longitudinal rows of cilia throughout, attachment by a holdfast at the pointed end, and at the other end a wholly frontal disposition of the feeding organelles, which spiral clockwise as seen from above, and consist most obviously of an almost complete circle of membranelles terminating in a mouth but with no undulating membrane. The implication of variable morphology in the names *polymorphus* and *multiformis* is misleading and erroneous.

The most complete and recent treatment of the taxonomy of stentors is to be found in the great work of Kahl (1935) on the classification of ciliates. Since his writing, one species has been

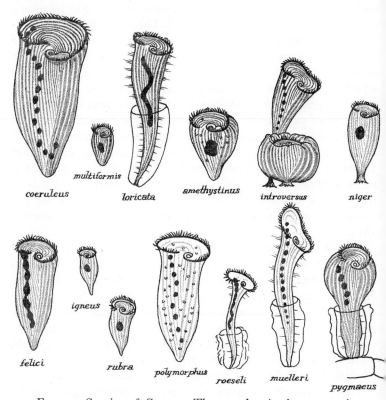

FIG. 95. Species of *Stentor*. The *coeruleus* is about 500 μ in length and others are approximately in scale. *S. pygmæus* after Swarczewsky, 1929; *rubra* and *loricata* after Bary, 1950; *felici* after Villeneuve–Brachon, 1940; and *amethystinus* after Kahl, 1935. *S. introversus* (contracted and expanded; after Tartar, 1958a) and others were drawn from life.

transferred to a different genus and a few new ones have been added. Stentors are perhaps most easily confused with unstalked vorticellids, but the latter have ciliary rows which are transverse rather than longitudinal and the oral band spirals in the opposite direction.

A key to the species and guide to synonomy was provided by Kahl. Drawing on the available literature and mindful that I have not seen every one of the species, I shall attempt to give a brief but distinguishing description of each, illustrated by the frontispiece and Fig. 95. For all its variability, size is still a useful criterion. Approximate average diameters of *contracted* animals are given, because the degree of extension is variable and samples to be examined are generally not in repose. New species have been described from a single specimen but this is certainly to be frowned upon, because stentors can easily be injured when pipetted with filamentous algæ and may retain abnormal or incompleted shapes for some time. Moreover, in the method of cell fusion by grafting we now have a new means for testing species differences. When diverse forms are combined in about equal proportions they appear as if stricken and do not produce viable clones as do fusion complexes of like species.

The following species have blue to greenish or violet pigment granules:

S. coeruleus Ehrenberg 1830. This is the large, cerulean blue species, largest (350μ) of all the stentors, with a moniliform macronucleus.

S. loricata Bary 1950. The only large, self-pigmented green stentor which builds a case or lorica. The macronucleus is vermiform. So far reported only from a stream in New Zealand.

S. multiformis Müller 1786. This is a tiny (95μ) blue-green stentor with an oval macronucleus. (A few further comments are apropos. When swimming, these stentors often appear plump, with rounded posterior ends. They have few — approximately 25 — pigment stripes which are therefore relatively large. Kahl states that typically there is but one micronucleus. I have found some collections with symbiotic chlorellæ. This species is reported from brackish or salt water, but I have repeatedly found animals corresponding to its description in fresh water. The fresh water form may be a different species, as Penard (1922) first suggested, and as such may deserve his designation, *S. gallinulus*. Further study is required.)

S. amethystinus Leidy 1880. A medium-sized stentor distinguished by its violet-blue color and the fact that it does not stretch out but remains habitually pyriform or conical. Macronucleus is oval — hence the only medium sized blue stentor with a compact nucleus. Symbiotic chlorellæ are present and with the pigmentation often produce a dark colored animal.

S. introversus Tartar 1958. A medium-sized (280μ) blue-green stentor distinguished by a retractable head. When withdrawn the feeding organelles and frontal field are surrounded by a lip of folded lateral body ectoplasm. Endoplasm is brown, combining with the pigment to give an olive-green color by transmitted light. Moniliform macronucleus. The holdfast is relatively large.

The following species are yellow in color:

S. niger (Müller) Ehrenberg 1838. A medium-sized (200μ), yellow to brownish stentor with an oval macronucleus. (Maier (1903) states that this species has myonemes which are weaker (narrower?) and that therefore the structure of the kineties is more easily studied. These animals do appear delicate as they wheel slowly through the water.)

S. felici Villeneuve-Brachon 1940. A medium-sized yellow stentor with moniliform macronucleus. (According to its author the yellow color of this species is not due to the granules but resides in the cytoplasm. I think this is to be questioned, since in all other self-pigmented species the granules are pigmented, and she remarked that the color is deepest in the granular stripes. *S. niger* at first appears to be colored throughout the ectoplasm but it is the granules which are yellow.)

The following species are small and pink in color:

S. igneus Ehrenberg 1838. This is a tiny (100μ) pink to nearly colorless stentor with an oval macronucleus. It may have chlorellæ (Balbiani, 1893; Johnson, 1893), but all those I have seen were without symbionts. According to Johnson there is no oral pouch. As in other tiny stentors, the pigment stripes are few and relatively broad.

S. rubra Bary 1950. A small, pink stentor like *igneus* but distinguished by a rim-like margin on the frontal disc exterior to the membranellar band. (One wonders if this is merely a variety of *igneus*.)

The following species have no pigmented granules and appear white by reflected light, except when containing symbiotic chlorellæ:

S. polymorphus (Müller, 1773) Ehrenberg. A large (250μ) not self-pigmented stentor without a case, usually grass-green with symbiotic Chlorella. (My observations confirm Johnson's, that this species is probably never entirely free of chlorellæ unless special steps were taken to remove them.)

S. roeseli Ehrenberg 1835. This is a small (140μ) colorless stentor which lives in a case. Usually, but not always, the posterior nodes of the moniliform macronucleus run together as a rod, or are more spindle-shaped than the anterior nodes. (In both this and the following species — *muelleri* — the stretched animal shows a much attenuated stalk right up to the well-expanded frontal disc, hence the shape of an uncoiled trombone; and both show conspicuous "bristles" or quiet and extended lateral body cilia near the anterior end.)

S. muelleri (Bory St. Vincent, 1824) Ehrenberg 1838. A medium-sized (250μ) stentor without pigment granules which produces a thick lorica. The cytoplasm is rather brownish in color. The frontal field generally rests at an angle to the cell axis, hence cala-like in shape. With uniform chain macronucleus.

A stentor with dark pigment of undetermined color because described only from preserved specimens:

S. pygmæus Swarczewsky 1929. A medium-sized pigmented stentor with an abbreviated, chitinoid case found attached to certain crustacea (gamarids) in the deeps of the Baikal Sea. (Apparently the case is used chiefly for attachment because most of the animal does not withdraw into it. There is a short, moniliform macronucleus with 4 to 6 nodes.)

This list includes species recognized by Kahl, as well as the new species *loricata*, *rubra*, *Felici*, and *introversus*, described since his publication. He also allowed the species *Stentor globator* Stokes, 1885, though questioning its validity. Since *globator* is very similar to *multiformis* (*gallinulus?*) and was described from a single specimen, I do not think there are adequate grounds for admitting this species. Two marine species unique in having a notched membraneller band, the so-called *S. auriculata* Kent, 1881, with a compact macronucleus, and *S. auriculatus* Kahl, 1935 (*auricula* Gruber, 1884), with a multinodal macronucleus, are probably variations of the same species (see Andrews, 1948a). They have been shown to be not stentors at all but to belong to the genus *Condylostoma*, because they have an undulating membrane and creep along the bottom as well as attaching by the posterior end (Fauré-Fremiet, 1936). Also with notched oral band is a non-pigmented ciliate found in numbers on a branch of Fucus by Silén (1948) who proposed the name *Stentor acrobaticus*. This interesting organism, attaching by the posterior end or clinging by 2 folds of the lateral body wall, glides along cross-striated filaments apparently of its own making. Two compact macronuclei were stained. This is a doubtful species because its contractility was not notable as in stentors and neither feeding organelles nor lateral striping were described.

Hence there are about 13 known species of *Stentor*. This number includes quite recent discoveries, suggesting that still more species are to be found. I have myself seen two or three additional forms which do not correspond to present descriptions, but I would not give them names until more abundant collections are available.

CHAPTER XIX

TECHNIQUES

THE unique combination of qualifications of *Stentor* mentioned at the beginning and displayed throughout this review, may well have intrigued the reader with the opportunities provided by this animal for an integration of multiple approaches to a study of the life and structure of the cell. He will also have become aware of the evident gaps in our knowledge, and the need for pursuing provocative suggestions or following hints in the literature to demonstrated conclusions, as well as the value of confirming and thus securing as a sound foundation many points not yet well established. Above all, the special promise of the Stentor studies should be carried to the level of theory on which new explanations and general principles emerge; and for this task all the many past investigations may be regarded as establishing only the beginnings. It remains to connect the potential student of *Stentor* with this organism through an account of methods, which are themselves doubtless capable of much further refinement and expansion.

1. Collecting

Stentors are most likely to be found in large, permanent ponds or lakes, but they also live in streams; and the outflows of sewage plants are not to be neglected. The collector may equip himself with a set of cream cans of two-quart capacity and a kitchen strainer fastened to a long handle. Keeping in mind that stentors are usually attached, one gathers with minimum disturbance samples of submerged and floating vegetation such as duckweed, *Spyrogyra* mats, and dead cattail leaves which are placed in the container. More vegetation is then scooped up with the strainer and gently wrung out into the can until it is nearly filled. Attached and loosened stentors are likely to be gathered in this way, with sufficient natural medium to start a culture. Location of each sample as a possible source should be noted on the container because one can return to a source year after year and find the same species of *Stentor*.

Returning to the laboratory, the lids are removed from the cans to expose them to the air. They are left to stand for half a day but no longer. In this time the stentors will swim to the top. If allowed to stand longer an injurious putrefaction may set in, or worms and water fleas may take their toll, for stentors do not appear to be a dominant form like paramecia or hypotrichs, and persisting cultures are usually not obtained by simply letting the samples stand. After a few hours, stentors, if present, will be found near the surface where they are gathered by pipetting along the miniscus and agitating the floating vegetation and debris. A scraping action with the tip of the pipette when water is being sucked up will serve to loosen stentors which have become attached. This material is

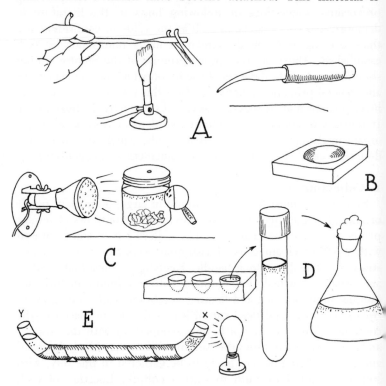

FIG. 96. Equipment for culturing stentors.

transferred to a caster dish or other shallow container and examined for stentors under low powers of a stereomicroscope. If stentors are found, the whole sample container may then be rotated for gentle agitation and more samples poured out. A portion of the original sample is then passed through filter paper of medium porosity which will remove all large forms and pass only minute organisms on which stentors can feed, and this natural medium can then serve for the starting of cultures.

If stentors cannot be collected in the field they may be obtained in mixed culture from several biological supply companies.

The next step is to select stentors out of the sample dishes, leaving competitors and predators behind. For this purpose micropipettes are necessary and the ones I use are made from narrow, polyethylene, catheter tubing obtainable from surgical supply companies. This and other items of culture technique are illustrated in Fig. 96. The tubing is softened by placing it across the narrow flame of a wing-top gas burner and pulled out to a fine point. The degree of heating is critical. If too cool the tubing breaks when pulled and if too hot it collapses. One can expect to spoil a dozen pipettes before one gets the knack. When good tubes are drawn they

---

A. To the right: micropipette (actual size) with polyethylene tip, rubber tubing "bulb", and glass rod plug; as well as fine wire (bent) used when cleaning. To left: drawing out polyethylene catheter tubing over wing-top burner for pipette tips.

B. Glass block cell containing 1 ml in which all specimens are clearly visible.

C. Culture in jar with hole punched in cap, examined briefly with spotlight and magnifying glass to follow development of a culture.

D. Development of clones. Single stentor first introduced into one cell of deep depression slide; transferred to test tube when multiplied to about 25 animals; transferred again from hundreds in the test-tube to a cotton-plugged Ehrlenmeyer flask. Filtered culture medium plus culture of food organisms used throughout.

E. Migration tube for obtaining clean stentors. Main body of half-inch diameter tube is covered with black plastic electrician's tape and filled with clean water. Concentrated *S. coeruleus* introduced at (x) will migrate away from lighted end and are recovered, clean, at other end (y).

are cut off to proper length and diameter with scissors and a piece
of thick-walled rubber tubing, plugged with glass rod, slipped on as
a bulb which will not be over-responsive to pressure of the fingers.
These pipettes are unbreakable and can be used for years if cleaned
out occasionally by passing a twirling fine wire through the points.

Sample dishes are now searched and individual stentors picked
up and transferred to glass block cells, one for each species if
desired. About 50 stentors of a kind should be isolated, if available,
and the isolation dish should then be surveyed, this time to
pipette out any contaminating organisms that may have been
carried over with the stentors. Block cells or their equivalent are
recommended because in them no organism escapes from view.

Enemies of *Stentor* and reports of their predation include the
following: the heliozoan *Actinosphærium eichhornii* (Cienkowski,
1865); the water plant *Utrichularia* which captures and kills stentors
in its unique bladders (Hegner, 1926); rhabdocœle worms
(Prowazek, 1904; Gelei 1925); oligochæte worms like *Chætogaster
diaphanus* (Lankester, 1873); the giant ciliate *Bursaria truncatella*
(Lund, 1914); and the smaller ciliate, *Dileptus*, with its proboscidial
stinging trichocysts. I have observed that the little scavenger
ciliate, *Coleps*, devours injured stentors; and nematodes, water
fleas, and hypotrichous ciliates are to be excluded as predators or
otherwise undesirable.

2. Culturing

I shall now describe my method of setting up cultures, though
this is not the only nor possibly the best procedure. A half-pint,
wide-mouthed peanut butter jar is filled to a depth of about one
inch with the filtered pond water. A large pinch of absorbent cotton
is then pulled apart to form a loose mesh and dropped in. The
cotton is regarded as a purified substitute for pond vegetation.
The isolated stentors are then washed into the jar with a squirt of
filtered pond water. One drop of skimmed milk, one or two boiled
wheat or rice grains, or fragment of a rabbit-food pellet is then
added as a source of nutrients, producing a population of bacteria
and tiny flagellates and other food organisms from the original
pond water which passed through the filter paper. In this way as
many seeding stentors as obtainable are returned to the same water
from which they came. Only about 100 ml of starting culture is

set up in order that the stentors may themselves possibly regulate the medium to their liking; and very little nutrient is at first added, in proportion to the few stentors present.

Progress of the starting culture can then easily be followed by placing the jar briefly in front of a bright spotlight and examining with a magnifying glass. At the end of a week, if the stentors are multiplying, more nutrient is added, at first only a drop or two of skimmed milk, but only if the water has become clear. If turbid with uneaten flagellates and bacteria, the jar is let stand another week before nutrifying. Since milk is a complex mixture forming a nearly perfect food, it serves as a good basic nutrient and ionic medium for stentors and a variety of other protozoa, including of course the food organisms (Tartar, 1950).

As the stentors increase in number, more lake or other natural water which has been passed through a Millipore filter to remove all protozoa and their cysts is introduced from a stock jar, with a little more cotton. Eventually the culture jar will be filled to the top and can be nutrified once a week with 5 or 6 drops of skimmed milk. (Cream content would form a film on top and exclude the air.) From the beginning the jar is covered with its original cap, in the center of which is punched one hole with a large nail or ice pick, the cap preventing contamination and evaporation and the hole allowing gaseous exchange.

Such cultures will remain in thriving condition for many months. If removal of detrimental cohabitants was unsatisfactory, or if hypotrichs, nematodes, etc., should later infest the culture, one has to begin again, treating the culture as if it were a pond sample and isolating stentors as before. A cardinal precaution is never to over-nutrify the culture so that a distinctly putrid condition arises. In the course of months the stentors may diminish in abundance in spite of the regular additions of milk. When this occurs it is assumed that the water should be changed. Since the stentors are mostly attached to the sides and the cotton fibers, the whole jar can be gently emptied, or the cotton can be retained, and then immediately filled with filtered water. In the meantime the stentors have remained attached to the sides and are protected by a fluid film. In spite of some loss there will probably still be enough animals to handle the large amount of new water. One may want to add less milk now until the animals become plentiful. A continued source of food organisms will of course have been retained in the film adhering to the emptied jar. It is well to have three or four jars of the same stock. These can be developed by splitting the contents of one jar between two and refilling both to the top with filtered lake water, adding more cotton as needed.

These procedures may not appear elegant but they have served to maintain healthy stock animals in more than sufficient abundance for my micrurgical operations continuously for 8 years, during which not one of 10 stocks has died out. The same method has been used successfully for growing *coeruleus, polymorphus, roeseli,* and *introversus.* For the last named, skimmed milk must be added very sparingly and never when clouds of uneaten colorless flagellates are still present. In my experience, the cultivation of other species like *niger* and *multiformis* is attended with great difficulties and probably calls for exploring distinctly different methods.

Temperature at which the stentors are grown is another important factor. Schwartz found that stentors do better at lower temperature than at higher (10° vs. 22°C). I have found that in winter the culture room must be thermostatically controlled to avoid wide changes in temperature.

Genetically more uniform material is assured by developing clones or cultures derived from a single individual. This is best done after a good culture of the wild stock is obtained, for one can then use filtered water from the culture itself as a starting medium and be sure of its optimal nature. First one should develop a separate culture of food organisms, either by nutrifying coarse-filtered *Stentor* culture fluid with skimmed milk or by growing any of the food organisms soon to be listed. Into a deep depression slide holding about 1 ml is isolated one stentor in a small drop, checking at once that only a single animal is present. Then are added 5 drops of the filtered parent culture and 5 drops of food organisms. The slide is placed in a moist chamber and more food organisms can be added as needed. One should of course start with several such isolations to assure that at least one will be successful. Further addition of food culture may be necessary. When about 25 stentors have developed, the contents of the slide are transferred to a 25 ml test-tube with aluminium cap into which have previously been added, at the bottom, 10 ml of food organisms and, on the top, the same amount of filtered parent culture medium. When the stentors become abundant, the test tube can be emptied into a culture jar which is carried forward as described.

Alternatively, the test tube with its clone of stentors can be emptied into an Ehrlenmeyer flask, plugged with cotton and fed by repeated additions of food organisms, sub-culturing when the flask becomes filled. Growing the food organisms separately prevents over-nutrification and is therefore recommended for developing clones as well as for producing very abundant and clean cultures for biochemical studies.

To obtain concentrated animals one can gently shake the flask cultures to loosen stentors attached to the sides and pour the contents into graduate cylinders; for at first the oxygen will be uniform throughout and the stentors (at least *coeruleus*) will rapidly sink to the bottom in mass and the overlying fluid can be decanted. If it is now desired to free these animals from most of the food organisms one may take advantage of the speed with which most races of *coeruleus* swim away from the light—or perhaps the reverse in the case of green *polymorphus* and *niger*. Whiteley introduces the concentrated animals at the lighted end of a large, horizontal, covered tube with both ends bent upward and filled with Millipore filtered medium (Fig. 96E). Stentors soon migrate to the lighted end, leaving the slower bacteria and food organisms behind, and are promptly removed for study.

Other methods which have successfully been employed for the cultivation of stentors will now be reviewed. First we have to consider the basic fluid medium. Distilled water is not used because it is injurious and tap water is avoided because it picks up metals in the pipes and may be chlorinated. Natural waters from ponds and lakes are preferred. They may be freed from contaminating organisms either by previous boiling or by fine-filtering — the latter is recommended. These waters will contain dissolved substances natural to the *Stentor* habitat, but many investigators recommend the addition of a mixture of inorganic salts. (I attempt to supply these along with organic materials in the added milk.) Peters (1904) in particular emphasized the importance of the salt content of the medium and suggested the following mixture, figures representing moles of the salts: $CaCl_2$ (0·0005), K_2HPO_4 (0·00015), $NaNO_3$ (0·00015), and $MgSO_4$ (0·00015). This solution was used in the ratio of 500 ml of salt solution to 3500 ml of culture water. The calcium was especially important. Chalkley's solution for amœbas (NaCl, 0·1 g; KCl, 0·004 g; CaCl$_2$, 0·006 g, and 1000 ml glass distilled water) has also been used (Randall and Jackson, 1958), and Hetherington (1932b) suggested 0·06% artificial sea water. Uhlig (unpublished) found that the addition of soil extract and Knop's solution in equal parts produced excellent cultures of *coeruleus*. The formula for Knop's is: MgSO$_4$, 0·25 g; CaNO$_3$, 0·1 g; K$_2$PO$_4$, 0·12 g; KCl, 0·12 g; FeCl$_3$, trace; and 1000 ml of distilled water. In all these additives the guiding principle is of course that essential ions and elements should be supplied in surplus.

Stentor polymorphus has been cultured in soil extract (Hämmerling, 1946) or 0·01% Benecke's solution (Schulze, 1951) with the green alga *Gonium tetras* as food. Randall and Jackson grew these stentors in Chalkley's solution with added gel from wheat grains boiled in the same. Sleigh (1956) grew *polymorphus* in a basic medium each liter of which contained inorganic salts measured in millimoles as follows: NaCl (1·4), KCl (0·05), NaHCO$_3$ (0·045), CaCl$_2$ (0·035) and CaH$_4$(PO$_4$)$_2$.H$_2$O (0·006), made up in distilled water of about pH 6·8. This solution was nutrified with wheat grains and the stentors were fed *Chilomonas*.

These cultures are to be kept in the light if the stentors bear symbiotic chlorellæ, but too bright an illumination is undesirable. The observation that *polymorphus* undergoes fission only at night (Hämmerling, 1946) suggests the possibility of obtaining simultaneous division in well-fed mass cultures transferred from light to darkness.

To the basic fluid medium may be added nutrient materials on which bacteria and other food organisms can live. Hay and hay infusions have not been found satisfactory, perhaps because the culture becomes too acidic. The hydrogen ion concentration should fall between 6·2 and 8·0 (Strom, 1926; Belda and Bowen, 1940). Prowazek (1904) used lettuce leaves but he found that his cultures went through periodic depressions. The same, or lettuce extract if cleaner cultures are desired, was recommended by Belda and Bowen. They remarked that cultures should be grown in a darkened place because growth is not satisfactory where abundant green algæ develop, and I can confirm this. As nutrient, Stolte (1922) used the scum from lettuce infusions, or beef extract. He found the presence of algæ useful, but I think this was because his cultures were quite putrid or over-rich and therefore oxygen deficient. Wheat and barley grains, boiled to prevent germination, are satisfactory (Hyman, 1925, 1931; Weisz, 1948c). The addition of dry leaves and reeds was recommended by Peters and I have simulated this by adding desiccated lettuce, but without conspicuous advantage.

Stentors are to be provided with food organisms. Very likely stentors can accumulate and ingest bacteria but the eating of larger organisms should be more efficient. The following organisms have been observed to be eaten and digested by stentors:

> *Colpidium*
> *Blepharisma*
> *Paramecium bursaria*
> *Minoidium*, and other colorless flagellates
> Small rotifers
> *Chilomonas*
> *Halteria*
> *Tetrahymena*
> *Glaucoma*
> *Gonium*, and other colored flagellates.

With the least trouble, cultures can be inoculated with these organisms, but for cleaner and more abundant cultures the food organisms should be grown separately. Burnside (1929) fed *coeruleus* on *Halteria* grown separately with hay or malted milk. Constant cultures fed with *Colpidium* were set up by Hetherington (1932a). Schwartz (1935) grew his animals in filtered pond water plus soil extract and fed them on *Colpidium* grown separately in a 0·03% solution of yeast extract. *Chilomonas* with *Paramecium* were recommended as food by Turner and Brandwein (1937). Stentors cannot readily capture *Paramecium caudatum* so that smaller and less vigorous species are recommended. Gerstein (1937) and Dawson (1953) used *Blepharisma* grown separately and obtained long-enduring cultures. I also found *Blepharisma* to be excellent food; but the pigment of this ciliate has a photodynamic action (Giese, 1957) which might prove damaging under bright illumination during operations on stentors which have ingested them.

3. Survival on slides

Although Balbiani (1889) reported keeping one stentor alive on a slide for nearly a month with feeding, most students since Johnson have found that stentors isolated into a few drops or even into watch glasses do not long survive. In fact, one gains the impression that the results of many investigations may have been compromised by poor survival on slides and the unfavorable conditions this implies. We have noted, however, that stentors will multiply and clones can be started in deep depression slides containing only about 1 ml. Hetherington (1932b) was able to maintain stentors for a year in Stender dishes, a few dozen to the dish.

Exploring the limits of isolation culture, I kept a normal *coeruleus* for 41 days in 3 drops of medium with some feeding and two transfers to fresh fluid, together with the addition, after 3 weeks, of two squashed stentors which I thought should supply what stentors need. Experimental animals which had been operated on in various ways survived as long as 16 days in 3 drops, but as a rule stentors live only about one week under these conditions. It is quite possible that improvements in isolation culture can be made, and the advantages of adding some stentor brei is indicated. In any event, if specimens or controls do not survive for at least two days, I regard the experiment unreliable.

4. Staining

More or less standard methods have been used for the cytological study of stentors, and suggestions regarding fixation and staining are given in the papers of Johnson (1893), Schwartz (1935), Randall and Jackson (1958) and especially of Weisz (1949a, 1950a). Differing from most other ciliates, stentors have not revealed a neat silver-line system either by the wet or dry methods of silver staining (Villeneuve-Brachon, 1940; Weisz, 1949a). Merton (1932) made a valiant effort to fix and stain stentors in the extended state, but I am inclined to agree with Johnson that semi-contracted animals are good enough for most purposes. To see the form of extended stentors living animals are the best. Treatments which have been used for anæsthetizing the contractile elements have already been discussed in Chapter XIV.

5. Cutting methods

The simplest way of obtaining *Stentor* fragments is to shake the animals briefly but vigorously in a tiny vial. Presumably formation and breaking of bubbles adjacent to the cells splits them into pieces. This was the method first used by Lillie (1896) who well knew that cleaving eggs can be separated into their blastomeres in this manner. If a few bits of broken cover glass are added to the vial, random cutting occurs. For more precise hand sectioning needles are used. Steel needles trimmed and sharpened to a very fine point were used by Prowazek, Schwartz, and Weisz. I employ only glass needles, made by holding the ends of two glass rods in a small gas or alcohol torch flame until they fuse together lightly and form a ball of molten glass between, whereupon the rods are quickly separated as they are withdrawn from the flame and one or two good needles are produced. The pulling must be done at just the right time, when the glass is neither too fluid nor too congealed, and this requires practice. The glass rod should be of soft glass. I do not know the specifications, but if success is not attained one should try a different stock. When properly made (Fig. 97A) glass needles provide the finest points obtainable and are used like a knife in cutting.*

In earlier days, ciliates were cut without quieting by merely confining them to a tiny drop, beside which a large drop of medium was placed, quickly to be flooded into the small one immediately after the operation to prevent drying (Balbiani, 1889). The best quieting agent is a solution of methyl cellulose which greatly retards stentors by its high viscosity. This method was introduced by Marsland (1943) for paramecia and later adopted for stentor experiments by Weisz (1951a). The solution seems more innocuous for stentors than for paramecia, and I noticed that it quickly kills *Blepharisma*. Sleigh (1956), in his studies of ciliary coordination, found that methyl cellulose is entirely reversible in its effect; and I kept *coeruleus* for two days in a thick solution without apparent injury to the animals. Nevertheless, methyl cellulose treatment sometimes showed an inhibiting influence on early primordium formation (Tartar, 1958c). Early dividers in

---

*Uhlig (1960) used a Spemann pipette to remove ectoplasm of the fission line bit by bit to produce doublets by aborted division.

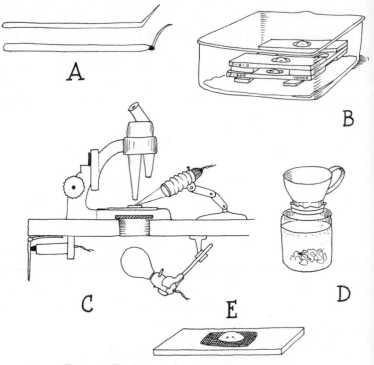

FIG. 97. Equipment for operations on stentors.

A. Glass needle drawn from soft glass rod for cutting; eyelash fastened to handle for rolling over specimens to examine all sides when following operated animals.

B. Moist chamber, a plastic sandwich box with wet filter paper on the bottom and depression slides stacked on 2 bridges.

C. Bench for operating. As he bends over microscope, operator automatically presses hinge at edge which turns on spring switch and embryological lamp. Bench top used for arm rests. Ordinary blue light below hole in bench is used in searching culture samples by transmitted light. Both sources of illumination have glass heat filters.

D. Canning funnel covered with drum-head of fine bolting silk and immersed in culture jar, for maintaining large fusion masses under optimum conditions.

E. Operating slide to which a square of finely woven fabric is applied with melted paraffin carries large drop of methyl cellulose into which stentors have been introduced with the micropipette.

stage 1 and even occasionally at stage 2 resorbed the primordium if they were kept too long in the viscous fluid, and regenerators either did likewise or the anlage was considerably delayed in its appearance. After cutting in methyl cellulose the animals should therefore be washed once by passing them through a large drop of filtered culture medium. Old solutions had a greater inhibiting effect so that it is well not to employ dissolved methyl cellulose which has been kept longer than two months. A stock solution of methyl cellulose may be prepared in the following manner: add 50 ml of dry methyl cellulose to the same amount of boiling filtered lake water used in culturing; stir the fibers to remove air bubbles and assure complete wetting; remove the beaker from the stove and allow it to stand for half an hour, after which another 50 ml of cool lake water is added with stirring; let stand overnight until the solution is cool and the methyl cellulose thoroughly dissolved.

My method of operating is quite simple. I use a stereomicroscope without base or mirror, because the instrument then stands low and the bench itself can be used to give support to the arms during delicate operations with the needle (Fig. 97B). The 'scope should have the highest powers available (about 150×), which still gives sufficient working distance between the lower lens and the specimen to permit operating. Lower magnifications are needed for capturing specimens. Sub-stage illumination is provided by a hole in the bench covered by a heat filter glass with the light underneath. But for operating, reflected light is used from an embryological lamp, also supplied with a heat filter. It is convenient as well as saving of bulbs to arrange a pressure switch with a strap hinge at the edge of the bench so that this light turns on only when one bends over the microscope. Reflected light has the great advantages of not silhouetting the stentor but clearly revealing its entire surface topography, and of avoiding eye-fatiguing glare.

Using a toothpick dip, a fairly large drop of methyl cellulose solution is placed in the center of a piece of finely woven cloth stuck with melted paraffin to a thick slide. The slight roughness of the cloth keeps the specimen from skidding under the needle, as it would on glass, thus helping to hold the animal in place. Paraffining prevents spreading of the drop. A white cloth is used for pigmented forms like *coeruleus* and a black cloth for unpigmented species like *roeseli*. A thick slide is easier to pick off the microscope stage than the common thin ones. I use a depression slide turned upside down.

With a micropipette an animal is then transferred with minimum fluid to the center of the drop of methyl cellulose. The stentor must not be allowed to wander to the surface, for then, oddly enough, the ectoplasm will adhere and tear off when the animal is moved. With an eyelash fastened to a narrow handle the animal is then pushed to the bottom of the drop; reason: a glass needle is too sharp and may impale the specimen.

The glass needle is then taken in hand and after gently moving the stentor into position the proper cut is made. With practice the needle can be precisely "located" under the microscope so that in time breakage becomes infrequent. After cutting at high magnification, the objectives are shifted to low power and the specimen removed with the micropipette and placed in a block cell with several drops of filtered culture medium to wash off the methyl cellulose. Washed specimens are then transferred to two large drops of filtered medium in a shallow depression slide, the code number of the experiment can be written in pencil on the frosted edge, and the slide stacked "pig-stye fashion" in a moist chamber. For the latter I use plastic sandwich boxes, the bottoms of which are covered with a thick layer of wet filter paper. One box will accommodate about 2 dozen stacked slides. (Fig. 97C). At intervals depending on the experiment, the slides are removed from the chamber and examined by reflected light under the microscope, moving them always in the same order, stacking them then in reversed order in another moist chamber. When necessary, the specimen can be transferred briefly to a drop of the methyl cellulose for close examination under high magnification, rolling it into position with the eyelash. On termination of an experiment, the drop is shaken off the slide, leaving some moisture by which it may be rubbed clean and dry with cheese cloth, and the code number erased. I do not use elaborate cleansing methods because these are unnecessary when control of bacterial flora is not involved.

My experience agrees with the pioneer observations of Gruber, that healing of cut surfaces is always prompt and effective. Even if most of the ectoplasm is removed, the remainder will stretch and manage to cover all the endoplasm (see Fig. 25C). Defective healing therefore indicates poor material or conditions of experiment.

Intentional disarrangement of the stripe pattern is illustrated by rotating anterior halves 180° on posterior halves. The cell is first cut through halfway on one side and then gently rolled over and cut through on the other side. The surface is thus completely severed but the two parts remain joined by the endoplasm, the first wound healing while the second is being made. Quickly, and before firm rejoining of the ectoplasm occurs, the side of the needle is spun around the anterior end causing it to be rotated until it takes a position in which the mouthparts are now opposite the primordium meridian on the posterior half. Within a minute, firm healing of the parts in their new orientation will have been effected and the specimen is ready to transfer.

Regeneration, singly or *en masse*, can be induced by brief salt treatment to cause shedding of the membranellar band. For individual specimens in a drop on a slide, I add one drop of 4% urea solution, rescuing the animal as soon as the membranelles are fimbriated. Shedding is completed in a large drop of culture medium to which the animal is transferred for washing. Regeneration is easily evoked in this manner, a procedure useful when cutting would reduce or disarrange the lateral striping.

When many stentors in simultaneous regeneration are required, the following procedure is followed. Place 10 ml of *Stentor* sample in a 25 ml graduated cylinder and, slanting the vessel, introduce drop by drop and with minimum turbulence an equal volume of 4% urea (or other solution having the same effect; see p. 252). Contents of the cylinder are then poured into a caster dish under a dissecting microscope and followed until membranelles begin to be sloughed. Effective time and concentration of the salt may vary with the condition of the animals. The dish is then emptied into a tall olive bottle or 100 ml cylinder and quickly filled with filtered lake water to dilute and stop the action of the chemical. As soon as the animals settle to the bottom, the vessel is decanted and filled again with water for a second washing, after which the settled animals are ready to be set aside or used in experiments.

It may be mentioned here that the studies of Chambers and Kao (1952) and of de Terra (1959) demonstrate that injection and autoradiographic techniques are quite feasible in *Stentor*.

6. Grafting

Ciliates may be said to graft themselves in conjugation or fusion of gametic individuals (e.g. *Metopus*). Heliozoa reincorporate separated pseudopodia and may fuse together in clumps for the purpose of digesting large food organisms. Doubtless for this reason, heliozoa were the first protozoa artificially to be grafted, beginning with Cienkoweski in 1865. The history of these experiments, as well as the generally futile early attempts to fuse amœboid forms, was recounted by Okada (1930) in connection with his own experiments of this type. More recently, Daniels (1951) has been able to fuse giant amœbas, by impaling one cell on top of the other with one needle and breaking the cell membranes together with another. To Gruber (1885a) belongs the credit for conceiving that stentors can be grafted if cut surfaces are brought together quickly before healing. In a few instances he was briefly successful in rejoining cut stentors. Unmindful of Gruber's explorations, Morgan (1901a) forecast *Stentor* grafting but was unsuccessful in realizing it. Ignorant of both, I independently succeeded in fusing as many as 4 stentors together (Tartar, 1941b), this possibility being suggested at once by the ease with which two stentor halves, left attached by a small strand of cytoplasm, fused together again. That grafting should be successful in some other ciliates is at least suggested by Prowazek's (1901) experience with one *Glaucoma scintillans*, cut parts of different individuals being temporarily united under a cover glass. How much may be accomplished by cutting and shifting of parts in forms too small to graft is shown in the excellent experiments of Suzuki (1957) on *Blepharisma*.

The method of grafting was explained in my first paper on this subject (Tartar, 1953). Using the cloth-covered slide already described, two stentors are placed in a large drop of methyl cellulose. The stentors are moved quite close to each other. Each animal is then cut with a sharp needle and the wound surfaces opened widely. By using now a blunter needle, from a stock of needles from which the fine tips have become broken, one animal is pushed so that its gaping wound surface is brought firmly in contact with that of the other. An extra thrust will then spread the two wound surfaces a bit so that the temporary membranes which had been formed over them after cutting are broken afresh, and the two animals will then fuse firmly together (Fig. 98A).

Adhesion is therefore by the naked endoplasm. Sheering of one animal against the other promotes fusion, as if fibrous proteins were then stretched out to expose free bonding points. Even if firm union is achieved at only one point, this is sufficient; for fusion will soon spread throughout the whole wound area.

Large fusion masses are produced by repeating the simple grafting of 2 stentors. To a fresh cut in a joined pair another cut animal is added, and so forth. If masses of 50 or more stentors are desired, I stop occasionally to give both the mass and the operator a rest, washing the specimen free of methyl cellulose by transfer into culture medium where it remains until grafting is continued. If broad adhesion is not secured and parts are left dangling or projecting, there is likelihood that the separate individualities will later pull free. With a blunt needle I therefore poke protruding heads and tails into the mass to give a compact form with uniform surface. Large masses may be kept in a fruit-canning funnel closed with bolting silk to permit fluid exchange with a *Stentor* culture in which the receptacle is immersed (Fig. 97D). Pigmented masses are then easily found and pipetted into block-cells for examination under the microscope.

To graft a patch of ectoplasm onto another stentor, the desired area is cut from one, using the granular stripe pattern as a guide, but the patch is not entirely isolated and the remainder of the cell is now used as a handle, impaling it with the glass needle and carrying the patch to the host, in which a fresh incision has just been made and opened. Adhesion is accomplished by pressing the cell remainder into the cut opening, fusion spreading to the critical patch; but before secure union is effected a tug on the cell remainders orients the patch in place and excess parts are then cut off. In this way the patch is grafted in the desired position without injury from contact with the needle (Fig. 98B).

Similarly, if stentors are to be grafted as heteropolar telobiotics the heads are first cut loose like the lids of flip-top boxes and fused by thrusting them together, whereupon the union extends to the cell bodies, and the heads are then excised (Fig. 98c). The bodies of the animals have then not been touched with the needle and their individual stripe patterns remain wholly normal. An obvious modification of this procedure is used for making head-to-tail tandem grafts or tail-to-tail telobiotics.

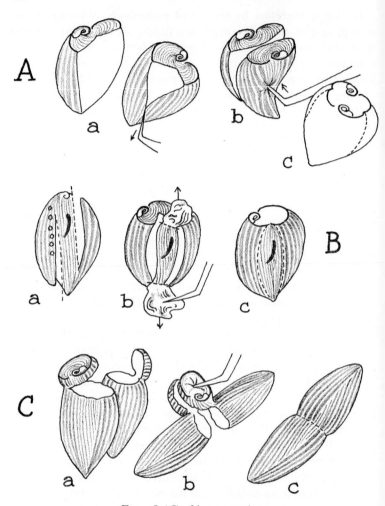

FIG. 98. Grafting operations.

A. Producing a doublet. *a:* Two stentors are split down the back with sharp needle and opened wide to expose the endoplasms. *b:* With a blunt needle (broken tip) animals are orientated and one is pushed against the other, exposed endoplasms pressing together. *c:* Doublet stentor resulting.

B. Implanting a cell sector. *a:* Cuts made from both ends to isolate the primordium sector with or without nuclear nodes, leaving cell remnants at each end. *b:* Host split open and graft

Different species of *Stentor* can be grafted almost as readily as individuals of the same kind by the same methods; and in most cases enduring unions are produced.

7. Minceration

The striped ectoplasm of stentors can be separated into 50 or more disarranged patches by slicing through the surface with the tip of a needle. After repeated cutting, areas will be circumscribed and "float" free on the endoplasm. Further transections of these patches not only cut them in two but drag them into random positions. Maximum randomness is produced if, before mincing, quarter sectors of the stentor are traded — by transverse and longitudinal cuts, first rotating the anterior half 180° on the posterior and then the left on the right half. The latter operation, or beginning minceration, will render the animal incapable of directional swimming and the operation can be continued under optimal conditions in a drop of medium, without further recourse to methyl cellulose.

8. Enucleation and renucleation

If stentors are to be enucleated, abundant animals are first isolated into a caster dish and left to stand for one day. The stentors will then have used up much of the available food material and will be largely free of food vacuoles which might be mistaken for nuclear nodes. A pellucid stentor is transferred to a drop of methyl cellulose on the slide with black silk. If the position of the embryological lamp is adjusted so that it overthrows the specimen a bit, the nodes of the macronucleus will appear as opaque white, or sometimes glowing bluish bodies against the dark background (see Fig. 79A). A slice with the glass needle from the upper right

---

put in place, either homopolar or heteropolar. Posterior remnant pushed into slit to fuse, then each remainder pulled as indicated to orient graft as fusion extends to it. Then cell remnants excised. *c:* Graft in place; in this case its anlage will be caused to resorb by the non-differentiating host.

C. Head-to-head telobiotic. *a:* Heads of two stentors cut but left attached to cell bodies. *b:* Underparts of heads, with exposed endoplasms, thrust together, then excised as fusion spreads to the main bodies. *c:* Resulting telobiotic.

corner of the stentor to near its base is made and the two halves, still attached at the posterior pole, are spread out widely (Fig. 99A). Thus exposed, the nuclear nodes stand out more clearly than ever and are rapidly teased out with the needle or sliced off with minimum cytoplasm. All this can be done while leaving the oral structures entirely intact. When all visible nodes have been removed, the two halves of the specimen are then brought together in normal location to aid their rejoining in normal shape. Then the posterior end of the cell is split apart and the last nodes searched for among

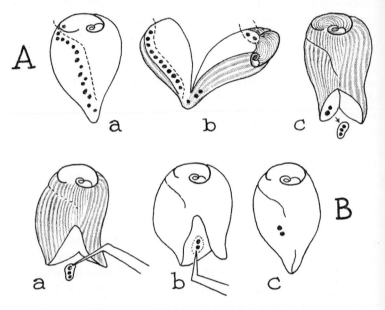

FIG. 99. Enucleation and renucleation.

A. *a:* Incision to enucleate *coeruleus* without disturbing feeding orgenelles and with minimum loss of cytoplasm. *b:* After cell is laid open, margins with macronuclear nodes are excised or nodes teased out. *c:* As specimen heals together, posterior end is opened to cut out remaining nodes obscured by carbohydrate reserves.

B. In renucleation with nodes from same or a different species, enucleated host is split open when endoplasmic sac with nodes is available (*a*); the sac is broken against host wound, the endoplasms fusing; and nuclear nodes are then securely inside (*c*).

the granular carbohydrate reserves which tend to obscure them. Soon after this operation the stentor will appear entirely normal but lacking the macronucleus.

Comandon and de Fonbrune (1939b) devised a method and instrument for transferring the nucleus of one amœba into the cell of another. Essentially, the nucleated cell is pressed against the enucleate one and the nucleus pushed through from the donor into the host. In *Stentor* the procedure is different. A healed, enucleate specimen is returned to a drop of methyl cellulose along with the donor of the new nucleus. The two animals are brought adjacent with the eyelash. The nucleated specimen is then cut open as described and one or more macronuclear nodes are teased out of the cell without ectoplasm but within a thin halo of endoplasm. This endoplasm quickly forms a membrane around itself which serves both to preserve the nucleus from exposure to the medium and to form a means of transfer. The enucleated cell is then cut open and considerable area of free endoplasm is exposed. The free sac of nuclear nodes is picked up with the point of the needle and broken against this endoplasm, whereupon fusion occurs and the nodes are taken in (Fig. 99B). Whole macronuclei can be transferred in the same manner with minimum endoplasm if dividers with compacted nuclei are used as donors. Healing of the host wound firmly traps the nucleus within the cell. Nuclear transfers are possible between different species of *Stentor*, and it can be seen that the foreign nucleus is not ejected but persists in the alien cytoplasm.

The possibility of other techniques should be explored. For instance, it would be desirable to find a non-toxic agent which would permit healing but prevent intimate rejoining of cut edges of the ectoplasm so that stentors would remain as cut; or to discover a means of agglutinating stentors so that they adhere by the ectoplasm without fusing. In the first case, would a mincerated stentor express multiple individuality, and in the second could the impulse to primordium formation be transmitted by contact from cell to cell? Possibly stentors could be grafted by drastic methods not involving individual handling. I have tried forcing highly concentrated *coeruleus* through the finest stainless-steel screens available. A few fusions were made in this way but not large

Y

masses as hoped; for when the openings in the screen are smaller than the diameters of stentor so that the animals are broken open when passing through, the wire diameter is then wider than the pores so that the emerging streams of stentor protoplasm are too widely displaced to meet and fuse immediately following disruption of the cells. Yet these remarks may suggest to others more ingenious approaches increasing the possible techniques with *Stentor* which have by no means been exhaustively explored.

Blepharisma is also a heterotrichous ciliate, with bands of (red) pigment granules lying between the kineties or rows of body cilia. Otherwise stentors and blepharismas are notably different in general aspect. *Blepharisma* is scarcely or not at all contractile, has no holdfast, possesses a terminal contractile vacuole and cytopyge, and has an undulating membrane to the right of the mouthparts, paralleling the peristome or row of membranellar plates. There is no obvious gradation in pigment stripe widths around the cell, but posterior to the mouth lies a ramifying zone where the kineties bifurcate in multiplying, especially during the earliest stages of division. Suzuki's drawing indicates that multiplication of clear stripes begins in the left anterior corner of this V-area, just as in *Stentor*. This region is also the site of oral primordium formation. A groove or rift in the ectoplasm there occurs, and anlagen development shows only two points of difference: first, the primordium separates longitudinally to place the undulating membrane on one side of an oral groove and the membranellar band on the other; and second, the anlage is apparently always parallel to the lateral striping instead of at first cutting across the stripes. This is understandable because *Blepharisma* has no frontal field and lateral striping therefore does not need to be shifted forward. The feeding organelles remain deployed longitudinally on one side of the cell, extending from the anterior pole to about mid-body level instead of being shifted entirely to the anterior end.

Major points of similarity are as follows. In division, the fission line is seen as a clear band from which pigment granules are missing, as in *Stentor*, and its position is determined late in the division cycle. Indifferent ectoplasm blocks the division furrow. Injury apparently causes the resorption of early division primordia, but mid-stage dividers complete division after excision of the original feeding organelles; and if the division furrow is destroyed a divider is converted into a reorganizer. The macronucleus does not necessarily split into two equal parts, for in cut dividing cells a smaller amount is received by smaller than normal daughter cells. After mid-stage, division is completed even in the absence of the nucleus or of the division primordium. If only the nucleus is excised, completion of the opisthe shows that primordia, in what probably correspond to stage 5 of *Stentor*, can complete the oral differentiation. Removal of a substantial part of the membranellar band may incite division, as seems to be the case in stentors.

In reorganization the old mouthparts are resorbed and the new membranellar bands join with that of the old. Micronuclear mitoses occur during reorganization and regeneration as well as in division. There is no evidence for intranuclear differentiation, for all parts of the macronucleus in *Blepharisma* as in *Stentor* were capable at all times of mediating oral regeneration.

Ablations of other than oral parts does not result in regeneration, but the more of the peristome removed the sooner regeneration follows. Primordium formation is therefore inhibited by existing feeding organelles. Suzuki attributed the possibility of anlage development during division to a release from inhibition by reason of partial dedifferentiation of the existing feeding organelles. Gullet and oral pouch also become vague in dividing stentors, but in both organisms the blurring itself seems to occur only after the primordium is well started.

Nucleate anterior fragments of *Blepharisma* behave like longitudinal aboral halves of *Stentor* which also lack the original primordium site. Regeneration is usually much delayed yet does occur. Therefore the normal site is not indispensable and all parts of the ectoplasm are equipotent as regards anlagen formation.

Rotation of the anterior on the posterior half can lead to the formation of doublets and doublet animals could be maintained through a series of divisions lasting a month. Like parts tend to join, as two cytopyges coalesce or tandem membranellar bands join together. Induced reorganization occurs on one side of a doublet when the other side is caused to regenerate, as evident in Suzuki's figure 38Dc. Without grafting, induced resorption of primordia could not have been demonstrated, but if one type of induction is possible the other may be likewise, and blepharismas may also pass through states of activation and inhibition.

Feeding organelles of reversed asymmetry can be produced in *Blepharisma*. These forms were apparently the result of the influence of a posterior pole at the "wrong" end of the primordium, just as peristomes with mouthparts at both ends were formed when two posterior ends were present. As in all other cases of feeding organelles which are a mirror image of the normal, those in *Blepharisma* are unable to feed and a self-reproducing biotype with *situs inversus* cannot be produced. Evidently the posterior pole of the cell induces invagination and mouthparts formation in a terminus of the primordium which lies in or near it.

Homopolar primordium sites are obviously capable of forming anlagen though not in their normal position. Heteropolar pieces tend to creep apart, showing that their polarities are intrinsic and retained. As in stentors, heteropolar primordium sites may not be activated to produce anlagen and smaller reversed patches may be resorbed. When longitudinal halves are rotated upon each other, an extra primordium may appear at the suture, and this indicates a possible inductive action between these stripe areas as at loci of stripe contrast in stentors.

The chief differences in morphogenesis in *Stentor* and *Blepharisma* are now noted. In the latter, Suzuki speaks of an evident "growth zone" at the posterior end of the developing anterior daughter cell which forms a new posterior end during fission. Such is not obvious in stentors, in which Johnson only indicated that something like this increase may occur. Possibly related to the occurrence of this zone is Suzuki's finding that the oral parts in *Blepharisma* induce V-areas or primordium sites in any indifferent region lying posterior to them. Thus, when the cell was transected and feeding organelles shifted to the side opposite the original primordium site, a new site then developed posterior to the displaced organelles and doublets were produced. This does not occur in *Stentor*; for if the head is rotated 180° the anlage appears only in the original primordium site and a new site is not generated posterior to a displaced mouth. Also, in *Stentor* doublets converting to singles, a primordium site may be obliterated posterior to one of the mouths, which remains intact.

Doublet animals behave differently in other ways. Removal of one set of mouthparts did not result in regeneration in *Blepharisma*. Apparently one set of organelles can inhibit anlagen formation in two primordium sites; but in stentors double regeneration-reorganization always occurred if one site was not subtended by a set of mouthparts. *Blepharisma* doublets could not remodel directly into singles, as stentors do. They achieved this end rather by exaggerating their doubleness and splitting apart from the anterior end. Hence these two ciliates exemplify the two types of transformation to singles defined by Fauré-Fremiet (1948b). Finally, it may be noted that when the anterior end of a pre-

divisional *Blepharisma* was excised, both division and the regeneration of the proter proceeded simultaneously, contrasting with
Stentor in which regeneration of the anterior daughter is always
delayed until after fission is completed.

These differences are minor, though instructive, and should not
be allowed to detract from the demonstration of a remarkable
similarity between the two ciliates. In both genera, micrurgical
studies show how important is the pattern of the ectoplasm for
the course of cytodifferentiation.

In the manner of elaboration of cytoplasmic structures *Stentor*
is also not remote from other ciliates (see Klein, 1932; Tartar,
1941b; Fauré-Fremiet, 1948b; and Lwoff, 1950). Starting with the
flagellates from which all agree that the ciliates have evolved, the
general picture, as developed by Fauré-Fremiet (1954), seems to
be as follows. The centrosome was originally developed to produce
spindle fibers for mitotic division of the nucleus. In flagellates the
centrosome also assumed the new role of producing an external,
fibrous flagellum and its associated organelles. By delegating this
function to other granules (blephoroplasts) derived from the
centrosome and also self-replicating, the number of flagellæ and
complexity of organization could be increased. In ciliates, the
fibrogenic granules lose their morphological association with the
nucleus, increase greatly in number, becoming the semi-autonomous kinetosomes which produce short flagellæ (i.e., cilia, with
the same fibrous structure). The transition form, *Opalina*, shows
uniform ciliation and there is still a certain lack of autonomy in
that the basal bodies all stem from one or two generative kineties.
But the large population of kinetosomes and their self-reproduction
in ciliates provided the possibility of specialization of the fibers
derived from them as well as for the association of parts into
organelles. The organelles, specifically the mouthparts (and in the
case of *Lichnophora*, the pedal disc), in turn become in a manner
themselves self-reproducing in that new mouthparts are developed
at least in close association with the old. But, just as the kinetosomes become morphologically (yet not physiologically) independent of the nucleus, so the oral anlagen became more autonomous
and, in *Stentor*, originate far from the preexisting mouthparts. A
vestige of the old relationship (as when in Euplotes the new
membranellar band always forms near the posterior end of the old)

may be evident in *Blepharisma* in which the present feeding organelles induce not primordia but sites for primordia. The eventual evolutionary development therefore provides a cell cortex with a persisting pattern and polarity (not labile as in flagellates) as well as semiautonomous units of ectoplasmic structure whose organization is apparently controlled by that pattern. Possibly the greatest persistence and fixity of cortical pattern is to be found in *Paramecium*, which cannot remodel a defective pattern as stentors do and rounds out the contour of the cell after an end has been cut off only by subsequent feeding and structural growth (Tartar, 1954).

2. Hypotheses concerning morphogenesis of ciliates

A cortical pattern in ciliates is best revealed by silver staining. By this method Klein showed that the surface of ciliates presents a network in orderly relation to which are found the ciliary kinetosomes, oral structures, and other ectoplasmic organelles. Certain fibers, as others had suggested, are probably concerned with the coordination of ciliary organelles in swimming, searching, and feeding behavior. But Klein (1932) also conceived that the ground network might produce the ciliary and other organelles or at least guide their organization into specific patterns. Many have differed with Klein, on the grounds that certain of his networks are mere sculpturings in a " dead " pellicle and hence are an end result rather than a possible cause of morphogenesis, as well as that fibers do not produce kinetosomes but the reverse. Klein's work has therefore been much neglected because of these differences of interpretation, though Gelei (1936) made notable contributions in a similar approach. Yet the idea of some cortical pattern which, as a continuum, affords the basis for integrating all ectoplasmic differentiation and, as a geometric scaffolding, provides for their orderly deployment has endured because it fulfils a logical requirement.

In Fauré-Fremiet's (1950,1954) conception, there is a basic cortical pattern but it is on a finer level and consists in the orientation and association of molecules in orderly arrangements. We are therefore provided a link with the biochemical basis of the organism, structure being successively compounded on pre-existing structure until the visible form and differentiation of the ciliate is achieved. Important among these derived structures is the infraciliary network, and Fauré-Fremiet (1948a) suggested that this pattern could be viewed as a morphogenetic field, tending to recover from distortions and capable of regaining its equilibrium wholeness following excision of parts. Doublet ciliates are instructive as manifesting doubleness of fields in balance, but any disequilibrium between the two sides leads in most ciliates to removal of structural constraint and hence to remodeling of the complex toward the single form.

According to Lwoff (1950) this cortical network or anisotropic field would tend to become "saturated" with kinetosomes in certain areas where we observe the organelles. If still more kinetosomes are produced, these would be left free to produce their own field or be guided into a separate field which would become a primordium.

Although evoking an ectoplasmic pattern on the basis of their orderly arrangement, Lwoff stressed the importance of the kinetosomes in the differentiation of ciliates. This emphasis naturally stemmed from his classical studies with Chatton on the developmental cycles of apostomatous ciliates (Chatton and Lwoff, 1935a) indicating a genetic continuity of the kinetosomes and a pluripotentiality with respect to what they produce. That is to say, the kinetosomes are self-reproducing and new ones arise only by multiplication of others preexisting; and daughter granules elaborate body cilia, oral cilia, trichites, or trichocysts, etc., depending on how they are determined to develop by their biochemical surroundings or organizing relations with respect to the patterned cortex. That nucleated endoplasmic spheres of stentors entirely bereft of their ectoplasm can regenerate neither the structured ectoplasm nor the feeding organelles (unpublished) also suggests a genetic continuity of kinetosomes, although it cannot be excluded that the morphogenetic failure of these spheres may be due to the absence of normal outer membranes which upsets the entire "metabolism" of the cell.

Perhaps the best evidence for division of kinetosomes is to be found in the work of Hammond (1937) on *Euplotes*. At the level of the division furrow the basal bodies of the dorsal bristles were seen to increase in number and this occurred within a lengthening, sub-pellicular tubule which would seem to exclude the migration of kinetosomes into this area from, say, the nucleus or from any other source, save that of the preexisting kinetosomes. In oral primordium formation in ciliates in general, a disorganized aggregation or "anarchic field" of additional kinetosomes appears at the site of development. If these in fact arise from multiplication of adjacent basal bodies of the lateral cilia, this would explain the origin of the "building blocks" or structural components of organelles. Yet, as Lwoff said, ". . . if kinetosomes are necessary for morphogenesis, they seem not to 'command' but to obey some mysterious force which is responsible for their orientation". The alignment and organization of kinetosomes into complex structures and determination of what type of fibrous elaborations these granules will produce thus implies an additional agency, a pattern of "molecular ecologies" or of some preexisting ground structure in the cortex.

Working with *Paramecium*, Ehret and Powers (1959) have challenged previous conceptions regarding the genetic continuity of kinetosomes and the importance of fibrous networks in organizing the ciliate cortex. Briefly, they find that the cilia of the oral primordium arise not from kinetosomes but from different entities which might be "microsomes"; and they conceive the unit of cortical structure as a ciliary corpuscle which usually bears one or double cilia and associated elements, the close packing of these spherules producing the appearance of hexagonal and rhomboidal fibrous patterns. This interpretation is contrary to that of Yusa (1957) and Roque (1956) who retain the postulate of the genetic continuity of kinetosomes and agreement has not yet been reached, yet the revolutionary conceptions of Ehret and Powers at least have the merit of keeping the problems of ciliate morphogenesis in a fruitfully flocculent state. The crowding of cortical granules, apparently of internal origin, into every available space in the ectoplasm of *Stentor coeruleus* would seem to offer a parallel to the packing of ciliary corpuscles. But the unextensible, relatively thick and solid ectoplasm of forms such as *Paramecium* and *Frontonia* may represent a special and peculiar evolutionary development (Tartar, 1954) and, as these investigators grant, it remains to be seen how far their intriguing ideas are applicable to other ciliates. The orderly packing and morphogenetic control of corpuscular units, even in *Paramecium*, would seem to require, as with kinetosomal orientation, some pattern factor in addition.

Specifically in reference to his studies on *Stentor* (Weisz, 1951c, 1954) developed a theory of morphogenesis in ciliates involving three postulates: first, that self-reproducing kinetosomes represent a hierarchy, with oral granules dominant over those of a stomatogenic kinety or primordium site and these in turn dominant over those of other kineties of the more generalized lateral body surface; second, that this hierarchy represents the degree of ascendency in competition of the kinetosomes for their "food" or the special metabolites supplied by the endoplasm from biochemical activities supported by the macronucleus which they require both to grow and to maintain themselves; and third, that the kinetosomes in turn act back, enzymatically, on the part of the macronucleus nearest them. How this system was thought to operate may be illustrated by the case of regeneration. When the feeding organelles are excised, the upper level of the kinetosomal hierarchy is vacated so that the metabolites can flow to the kinetosomes of the next level — those of the stomatogenic kinety or, if this was also removed, then the next adjacent body kinety — which are then able to multiply and produce oral cilia for the anlage of a new set of feeding organelles. Once formed, this new set again exhausts the special metabolites for oral cilia so that further primordium formation is inhibited. (In division and reorganization, the oral kinetosomes somehow lose their competitive ascendancy so that the kinetosomes of the stomatogenic kinety are no longer held in check.) The oral kinetosomes in place now react with adjacent nodes of the nucleus, maintaining their capacity to produce the special metabolites, while those far distant lose their capability, and morphostasis is hence stabilized.

The effectiveness of this hypothesis depends upon two points: first, that the postulated metabolites are necessary for the maintenance of existing feeding organelles, and second, that these metabolites are present only in limited quantity. Only on the basis of these assumptions would there occur that competition which would explain the integration of the organism, e.g., that it never has more than one set of feeding organelles. Yet I do not think that either of these points have been substantiated by subsequent studies. The formed feeding organelles and body cilia of enucleates are often maintained to the point of death or at least they continue intact for a whole week and undergo dissolution only just before the death of the specimen at which time the appearance of a general necrosis could just as well account for structural disintegration. I have observed nothing like an intimate nutritive relationship between the nucleus and the feeding organelles such that removal of the nucleus withdraws their maintenance and results in the prompt resorption of specialized organelles. In fact, the failure of excised heads to reduce the feeding organelles to a size proportionate to the small fragment, if enucleate, indicates just the opposite: that the nucleus is necessary for the resorption of formed organelles. Nor is there any substantiation that the hypothetical metabolites are present in limited quantity. Arguing against this assumption is the fact that grafted pairs of stentor produce one, two, or three primordia and sets of feeding organelles regardless of the amount of nuclear material present; and grafting of an enucleated stentor to a normal animal may lead to the production of a doublet just as readily as when both nuclei are present (Tartar, 1954). Similarly, if the fine-line zone of a stentor is split by an enucleated meridional patch of wide striping, three anlagen of normal size are usually formed instead of one (Tartar, 1956a). On Weisz's hypothesis this would imply that the single animal is quite able to produce three "quanta" of oral metabolites. If so, there is no reason to suppose that an intact set of feeding organelles would monopolize them and in this way exert inhibitive action on the primordium site. The additional postulate — that the kinetosomes act back on the nucleus to produce internodal differences — was also not confirmed; for in later tests all sections of the macronucleus were found to be equivalent (Tartar, 1957b).

Form in ciliates is still without satisfactory causal analysis; but this is no wonder since no adequate theory of morphogenesis of any organism has yet been achieved. In this perspective, the progress with ciliate protozoa appears promising and we may ask how, if eventually successful, a verifiable explanation of their development might be pertinent to general problems of cytodifferentiation.

3. Stentors and cells

First we shall consider whether a ciliate like *Stentor* is a cell, or properly should be included in the class of those things called cells, and therefore whether *Stentor* studies are relevant to analysis of the potentialities of cells in general. My opinion is already evident from the fact that stentors have throughout this study been referred to as cells. This follows if we define the cell as a packaged nucleo-cytoplasmic duality capable in some degree of independent life. We can allow that these "packages" sometimes may have "holes" in them connecting to other packages (cell bridges), and that the enclosed nuclear phase may consist of one or more nuclei of one or two types. These units may be wholly free-living, like *Stentor*. They may be autonomous but not free-living as in the case of parasitic protozoa. Or as tissue cells they may be subject to a system of intercellular reactions leading to the morphological and functional wholeness of cellular organs and organisms. Even in the latter case, the cell lives a double life, both dependent and independent, as one of the authors of the Cell Theory, Schleiden, remarked. A tissue cell is dependent on the organism for its sustenance and participates in multicellular interaction and organizing relations, yet its capacity for independent life is abundantly demonstrated by culture outside the organism; just as its self-dependence is shown by the fact that if the long process of a nerve cell is separated from its nucleated cell body, neither proximity to countless nucleated fellow cells nor being continually bathed in blood plasma can save that nerve from disintegration after its nucleo-cytoplasmic integrity has been violated. Indeed, the study of somatic deletions in *Drosophila* has shown that the absence of a single genetic locus, which may be tagged by its correlation with yellow color, results in the independent death of the cells which lack it, as if all the nucleus is needed all the time just to maintain the life of the cell itself (Demerec, 1934).

That larger organisms are comprised of multitudes of cells would seem to imply the interaction between nucleus and cytoplasm is so intimate that no portion of the cytoplasm can be far from an associated nucleus. The nuclear phase is not aggregated into one "gland". Even in the neurone, in which the cytoplasm may extend several feet from the major cell body with its nucleus, specialized organelles — the neurofibrils — may have been developed to allow nucleo-cytoplasmic interactions even at this distance (Parker, 1929).

All grades are found between complete independence of cells, as in free-living protozoa, and a total dependence which might best be exemplified by the anucleate mammalian red blood cell — whose fellow traveler in the blood stream, the leucocyte, is relatively autonomous and practically indistinguishable from parasitic amœbas. In the cellular slime molds free-living amœbas cooperate in forming multicellular fruiting bodies. What remains constant throughout is self-dependence of the cell as a packaged nuclear-cytoplasmic duality capable of some degree of independent life.

The further similarity between unicellular organisms and tissue cells is found in the fact that the genome of protozoa is evidently just as complex as that of metazoa and their tissue and germ cells. Higher organisms do not have larger or longer or more numerous chromosomes and hence, evidently, have not a correspondingly greater number of genes, nor is the behavior of their nuclei more complex. In present-day terms, this implies that the protozoan nucleus contains as much "information" as the egg or tissue cell (Elsasser, 1958). This uniformity suggests that the nucleus is concerned first of all with the life of the individual cell, and that in multicellular forms there is developed among the cells another system of intercellular reactions, about which we still know practically nothing, which provide the information for multicellular differentiation. Evolution, with its teaching of the continuity of life, leads us to regard free-living and tissue cells as basically the same, multicellular organisms arising either by the adherence of products of cell division, as in the algæ, or by a partitioning of a multinucleated cell into a multicellular body as seen in the Acœla or in insects. A transcending unity of all cells, not as parts but as expressing what Woodger (1929) called the cell type of organization, certainly provides the most hopeful heuristic principle. This does not exclude the possibility that protozoa have taken this type of organization to extremes of multiple specialization of the cytoplasmic phase, or that we can learn as much from them by contrast as by comparison with other cells.

4. Stentor and metazoa

Stentors elaborate themselves in only one direction, to form another stentor. In this regard they are like eggs but lack the multiple potentialities of embryonic cells. Repeated cleavage without feeding but also without intercellular differentiation occurs in some ciliates, as when the large form of *Ichthyophthirius* produces multitudes of small forms (Mugard, 1948). The beginnings of cellular differentiations may be seen in the formation of mating types or the gametic differentiation of some ciliates, as well as in multicellular stages of certain Sporozoa, the Cnidosporidea. In clonal cell cultures, metazoa are being, as it were, reduced to "protozoa". And in *Chætopterus*, Lillie (1906) was able to suppress cleavage of the egg and yet obtained unicellular embryos of fairly normal shape in which the elaboration of cilia, with a particulate contribution from the nucleus, and imprecise segregation processes led to a fairly recognizable early embryo. Being cytoplasmic continuums, *Stentor* masses are not multicellular though they do show the emergence of new capacities for morphogenesis.

Another major point of correspondence lies in the cilia and ciliation. We now know that the basic structure of cilia and flagella are the same in all organisms. Many animals have ciliated epithelia and in these the joining of the cilia by fibrous connectives does not differ fundamentally from that in ciliates. Gruber commented on the remarkably similar construction of the membranelles of *Stentor* and those occurring in the "corner cells" of certain molluscs, notably *Cyclas cornea*. Whitman (1893) used this correspondence in argument for the inadequacy of the cell theory of development, having to emphasize at that time the neglected and still baffling intercellular organizing relations through which the separate cells, regardless of their size or number, are formed into an embryo. *Stentor* makes many such membranelles in one cell; a mollusc, one in each of many cells. In their embryonic stages many multicellular organisms are conspicuously ciliated, offering the possibility that something like ciliate morphogenesis may play a significant role in their early development. In the shipworm a silver-staining material is segregated into specific blastomeres (Fauré-Fremiet and Mugard, 1948); and in the sea urchin certain cells come to show an argentophile network with apparently a centrosome–kinetosome in each cell which becomes part of a ciliated structure (Mugard, 1957), but there is still no proof that these are causal factors in development.

Embryologists are generally agreed that development implies an initial cytoarchitecture in the cortex of the egg as a guide for orderly transformations. *Stentor* has such an architecture or cortical pattern which is even visible in its heterogeneity in the living organism and therefore can be rearranged at will. In dividing stentors the migrations of the carbohydrate reserves mimics the segregation of distinctive ooplasms in certain eggs, while in the egg coat which Holtfreter (1949) has shown to be so important in embryogenesis we may have a direct descendant of the ciliate pellicle. We are reminded, too, that lithium has marked morphogenetic effects on stentors as it does on embryos. Truly, we do not know which of these resemblances are superficial and which are fundamental, but no possible correspondencies should be ignored.

5. Theoretical considerations

Before the nucleus was discovered and even after this cell organelle was found to be present but not obviously active except in reproducing itself at cell division, the emphasis was on the cytoplasm as the basis of life. All cytoplasms were said to have a common denominator in "protoplasm", a semifluid substance conceived as "living matter". Of this view there remains today only the fact that living organisms are intimately involved with the colloidal state, and the hope that all living phenomena will be explainable in terms of molecules and their interactions. With the discovery of the nucleus and its importance in inheritance the emphasis shifted in the other direction, and the nucleus was regarded as "the heart of the cell", or, currently, as "containing all the information for the organism". Yet both cytoplasm and nucleus are necessary as a natural and inescapable dualism presented by the cell. Of course these two parts of the cell interact, and Verworn (1892) early conceived a scheme embracing possible interactions, excepting the more sophisticated modern concept of steady states. Simply stated, we want to know what the nucleus does and how it does it, what the cytoplasm does and how this is accomplished, as well as how the two phases cooperate in the life of the cell.

The nucleus seems to serve as a chemical factory for the cytoplasm, producing essential substances or the means of their production, apparently coenzymes. Apart from itself growing and replicating, the nucleus contributes substances into the cytoplasm where reactions leading to metabolism and structural growth take place. The cytoplasm would have at any moment a store of these substances, exhaustible if the nucleus is removed. The nucleus has therefore been regarded as the source of the regeneration of enzyme systems present and acting in the cytoplasm (Mazia, 1952).

Stentors emphasize the importance of this trophic function of the nucleus. The micronuclei are significant only in genetic recombination during conjugation. It is the macronucleus which supports the life of the cell, though this involves the expression of specific genetic determinants derived from its progenitor, the micronucleus, as was demonstrated for *Paramecium* by Sonneborn (1947). In metazoa the metabolic function of the nucleus is cryptic and not obvious, or is revealed only by special demonstrations as in neurone regeneration or the somatic deletion studies of Demerec. But in protozoa, as in studies of microbial genetics and the new work on *Neurospora*, the trophic role of the nucleus is apparent.

In stentors, the macronucleus is clearly necessary for both digestion and synthesis which leads to growth. Therefore it should make possible the formation of enzymes and may be a source of RNA, via nucleolar extrusion, for protein synthesis. This nucleus also probably sustains respiration, for though energy metabolism long continues in enucleates it gradually diminishes. Several instances have been cited which show that the quantitative relationship between nucleus and cytoplasm is important for these physiological or biochemical processes; and it is in the relatively simple alterability of the nucleo-cytoplasmic ratio that stentors should prove most fruitful in studies of cell physiology.

Some portion of the macronucleus is essential for cytodifferentiation in oral regeneration. Presumably this support is either a synthesis or a mobilization of structural proteins; but in spite of the sameness of stentor organelles this action is fraught with specificities, for the nucleus of one species of *Stentor* can rarely be exchanged for another to yield an effective nucleo-cytoplasmic combination. And where and how the building blocks are put together in formed organelles is very probably the work of the ectoplasm and its pre-formed structure.

This view was previsioned by Prowazek in the course of his investigations on *Stentor* and has been enlarged upon by others up to the present day (Tartar, 1941b; Sonneborn, 1951; Ephrussi, 1953; Weisz, 1954; Danielli, 1958). Noting that the nucleus is not

z

bound to the cytoplasm by any intimate structure and requires no specific geometric relationship with the cytoplasm for its effective action, Prowazek (1904) inferred that there is only a substance relation between the two phases of the cell which could well be explained in chemical terms. Neither can the form of the cell, nor that of the organism in the case of protozoa, be related to the flowing endoplasm which indeed has been shown in *Condylostoma* (Tartar, 1941b) and in the regeneration of stentor "skins" (unpublished) to be dispensable. Therefore nucleus and cytoplasm presumably interact by chemical contributions to each other, and guidance of the elaboration of formed parts in the cytoplasm is to be sought in neither a nucleus of unprescribed location nor a flowing endoplasm but in the most solid portion of cell, namely, the ectoplasm (Prowazek, 1913).

Events in the ectoplasm of *Stentor* also clearly exert control over the behavior of the nuclei. Micronuclei divide whenever an oral primordium is formed, even when there is no cytosomal fission. Macronuclei coalesce, re-nodulate, or are divided according to the phase of the cytoplasm in which they find themselves. Compensatory increase in macronuclear volume occurs only if primordia are formed. And the disposition of the macronuclear nodes is evidently determined in large part by the pattern of ectoplasmic striping.

The cytoplasm may have its own replicating units, including kinetosomes as important elements of ectoplasmic structure. Self-reproducing entities are of limited explanatory value because they refer us back to another of the same type of entity which we seek to analyze and explain. Yet to establish a genetic continuity of cytoplasmic parts would tell us whence new entities arise, i.e., from preexisting ones, and this is a great aid in narrowing the field of inquiry. Moreover, replicating units and their elaborations alone would not make an organism but merely an assemblage. "Is anyone willing to believe", asks Sonneborn (1951), "that, if all such self-duplicating components of the cell were thrown together in a test tube in the proper portions with adequate food for their multiplication, a *Chilomonas* cell or any cell at all would result?" Something more seems to be needed and this is a cortical pattern factor itself having genetic continuity.

In *Stentor*, development is organized because there is always a previous pattern. A cortical pattern of polarized, anisotropic lateral striping is always visibly present no matter how we fragment the cell. The location, number, length and direction of asymmetry of the oral primordium are determined by the pattern of the ectoplasm, quite independently of the location or quantity of the nucleus and endoplasm. Induction of mouthparts at the terminus of the anlage is also to be correlated with the polar ectoplasm, for in heteropolar implants two sets of mouthparts are produced in correspondence with two separate posterior poles although the endoplasms would mingle indiscriminately and the nuclear nodes may be located anywhere. Even the smallest, nucleated pieces bear short lengths of a few lateral ciliary bands which are separated at graded distances by granular stripes so that healing produces a locus of stripe-width contrast and regeneration of a whole is always guided by this preexisting polarity and anisotropy. Even in the relatively dedifferentiated cyst stage, striping and polarity are evident, according to the drawings of Stein; and in other ciliates which have been carefully studied all landmarks do not disappear and some cortical pattern evidently persists (e.g., Garnjobst, 1937).

Empirically, *Stentor* possesses at all times — in all our experimental situations save one: denudation of the ectoplasm — an obviously persistent visible pattern. However the basic cortical pattern may be conceived, to postulate it as axiomatic or as a factor always present from the initial state in any experiment we can perform, has an important consequence. This is that we need not and cannot derive the final form and pattern from molecules and their spontaneous aggregation or interactions as such. True, these cortical cell patterns would have arisen at some time in the early evolution of life, and phenomena such as the association of collogen into fibrous sheets may give us some hint of how this could have been brought about. Once developed, the relatively large scale patterns we have in mind, like such replicating units as macromolecules, chromosomes, and perhaps kinetosomes, could have been carefully conserved and never destroyed but passed on by genetic continuity, pattern producing further pattern, and these patterns gradually evolving in complexity, on the one hand into very complicated unicellular flagellates and ciliates and on the other into equally complex yet cryptic egg patterns capable of guiding the development of the whole range of elaborate multicellular organisms. Therefore, in any experiment we perform today we do not have to demonstrate the origin of life by reducing the results to molecules and their interactions, for pattern is always there to start with. This pattern factor may have undreamed of capabilities, itself constituting a primary determinate of what kind of molecules are synthesized in association with it and how they behave, for example, in contributing to growth or increase in that pattern.

These patterns would be in one sense " of molecules "; in precisely this sense, that the organism is obviously reducible to a collection of identifiable molecules after chemical treatment and destruction in a test tube. This would explain why organisms in their functions and even in their forms are very definitely and sometimes grossly affected by the presence of certain types of molecules. Even a single ion like lithium exerts great influence on morphogenesis in both embryos and stentors. For if the patterns are "made up of molecules" the kinds of molecules and ions available would clearly have a substantial effect on these patterns. The patterns themselves could have just as much influence in the formation and behavior of the molecules. There is some evidence, for instance, that the molecules we analyze in the test tube do not exist as such in the organism (see Needham, 1933). Picric acid is said to precipitate proteins in solution but not when injected into amœbas, and sea urchin eggs do not show the characteristic ultraviolet absorption spectrum of proteins until they are killed.

From these considerations it follows that pattern and substance are two irreducible aspects of the organism. They may be related in the sense of Neils Bohr's principle of complementarity, as he has himself suggested (1958).

It would appear, therefore, that our greatest lack and most fruitful opportunity in biology lies in conceiving and testing the nature and capabilities of persistent supramolecular patterns. For this task stentors should be highly appropriate because they present us with a visible cortical geometry as an empirical reality, and stentors as the most operable of all cells have already shown how important this pattern is in determining form and cyto-differentiation.

Any indication, however general, of the possible nature of basic cortical patterns in ciliates and in eggs should help in transcending this most important gap in our understanding of organisms. Proceeding from the *Stentor* studies we may suggest that one characteristic of the cortical pattern is that it is beyond individuality but bears intrinsically the tendency or capacity to integrate as one or more than one individuality. In terms of a model, the pattern might therefore be conceived as a network which is a type of repeat pattern, somehow capable of deriving a wholeness while maintaining its repeat character and potentialities beyond individuality. Thus fragments of a stentor or an egg when physically isolated can themselves become wholes, so that the original individuality is seen to have contained multiple nascent individualities. When a stentor or cell normally divides the original integrated pattern is obviously converted into two. Conversely, two or more whole eggs or stentors can be fused together to produce only a single individuality from the several original ones. Therefore, whatever is operating and determinant in these experimental situations is something which is beyond individuality but tends to individuate. It is this characteristic which has made pattern unmechanical and so difficult to pin down, even in the case of mosaic eggs; for in experiments the pattern reintegrates after disturbances and deletions so that there is no point to point correspondence on which to base analysis until the work of determination has already been accomplished. If the pattern factor is beyond individuality, an important consequence is that wholeness is not, as many have maintained, an irreducible, axiomatic presupposition about any organism but rather a result or an achievement, as McDougall (1938) has well stated. At the moment when a fragment of an egg or a ciliate is cut there is no wholeness except in the sense of an object which has been physically isolated, nor is there a wholeness at the moment when two organisms are fused. Instead, there are molecules, replicating units, and above all a pattern factor which is beyond individuality through which a wholeness is later achieved. In learning how this may come about, *Stentor* may be an invaluable guide. Though *Stentor* is a single cell and can presumably teach us nothing of the complex intercellular relations which form the multicellular organism, it may well be that comprehending the organization of a unicellular animal is a fruitful if not essential step towards evolving a satisfactory theory of more complex developments.

BIBLIOGRAPHY OF STENTOR

ADOLPH, E. F. (1931): *The Regulation of Size as Illustrated in Unicellular Organisms.* Thomas, Springfield, Illinois. (Review of size in relation to regeneration.)

ALLESCHER, MARIE (1912): Über den Einfluss der Gestalt des Kernes auf die Grössenabnahme hungernder Infusorien. *Arch. Protistenk.* **27,** 129–171.

ALVERDES, F. (1922): Zur Lokalisation des chemischen und thermischen Sinnes bei *Paramœcium* und *Stentor. Zool. Anz.* **55,** 19–21.

ANDREWS, E. A. (1945): Stentor's anchoring organs. *J. Morph.* **77,** 219–232.

ANDREWS, E. A. (1946): Ingestion organs in Folliculinids and in Stentors. *J. Morph.* **79,** 419–444.

ANDREWS, E. A. (1948a): Folliculinids and Stentors in British Columbia. *Trans. Am. Micros. Soc.* **67,** 61–65.

ANDREWS, E. A. (1948b): Surface parts of the contractile vesicle of Stentor coeruleus. *J. Morph.* **82,** 257–268.

BALAMUTH, W. (1940): Regeneration in protozoa: a problem of morphogenesis. *Quart. Rev. Biol.* **15,** 290–337.

BALBIANI, E. G. (1861): Recherches sur les phénomènes sexuelles des Infusoires. *J. de Physiol.* t.IV. (Not seen).

BALBIANI, E. G. (1882): Les Protozoires. Leçons faites au College de France. *Jour. de Micrographie* t.VI, p. 474 (or 1881? Not seen).

BALBIANI, E. G. (1889): Recherches expérimentales sur la mérotomie des infusoires ciliés. Contribution á l'étude du rôle du noyau cellulaire. *Recueil Zoologique Suisse* **5,** 1–72.

BALBIANI, E. G. (1891a): Sur les régénérations successives du péristome comme caractère d'âge chez les Stentors et sur le rôle du noyau dans ce phénomène. *Zool. Anz.* **14,** 312–316; 323–327.

BALBIANI, E. G. (1891b): Sur la formation des monstres doubles chez les Infusoires. *J. de l'Anat u. de la Physiol.* **27,** 169–196.

BALBIANI, E. G. (1891c–2): Nouvelles recherches expérimentales sur la mérotomie des infusoires ciliés. *Annales de micrographie* **4,** 369–407; 449–489.

BALBIANI, E. G. (1893): Nouvelles recherches expérimentales sur la mérotomie des infusoires ciliés. *Ibid.* **5,** 1–25; 49–84; 113–134.

BARBIER, M., E. FAURÉ-FREMIET, and E. LEDERER (1956): Sur les pigments du cilié *Stentor niger. C. R. Acad. Sci.,* Paris **242,** 2182–2184.

BARY, B. M. (1950): Four new species of fresh-water ciliates from New Zealand. Zoology publications from Victoria Univ. College (N.Z.), No. 2.

BELDA, W. H. and W. J. BOWEN (1940): A tested method of growing *Stentor coeruleus. Science* **92**, 206.

BISHOP, ANN (1927): The cytoplasmic structure of *Spirostomum ambiguum*, Ehrenberg. *Quart. J. Micros. Sci.* **71**, 147–172. (Containing review of fiber systems in Stentor.)

BRACHET, J. (1957): *Biochemical Cytology*, Academic Press, New York.

BRAUER, A. (1885): *Bursaria truncatella* unter Berücksichtigung anderer Heterotrichen und der Vorticellen. Jena. *Z. Naturwiss.* **19**, 489–519. (With notes on stripe multiplication in Stentor.)

BULLINGTON, W. E. (1925): A study of spiral movement in the ciliate infusoria. *Arch. Protistenk.*, **50**, 219–274.

BURNSIDE, L. H. (1929): Relation of body size to nuclear size in Stentor coeruleus. *J. Exptl. Zool.* **54**, 473–483.

CAUSIN, M. (1931): La régénération du *Stentor coeruleus. Arch. d'Anat. Micros.* **27**, 107–125.

CHAMBERS, R. and C.-Y. KAO (1952): The effect of electrolytes on the physical state of the nerve axon of the squid and of Stentor, a protozoon. *Exptl. Cell Research* **3**, 564–573.

CHILD, C. M. (1914): The axial gradient in ciliate Infusoria. *Biol. Bull.* **26**, 36–54.

CHILD, C. M. (1949): A further study of indicator patterns in ciliate protozoa. *J. Exptl. Zool.*, **111**, 315–347.

CLAPARÈDE, É. and J. LACHMANN (1857): Note sur la reproduction des Infusoires. *Ann. Sci. nat., Zool.*, **4**, 221–244. (Not seen).

CLAPARÈDE, É. and J. LACHMANN (1858–61): Études sur les Infusoires et les Rhizopodes. Genève, 2 vols. *Mém. Inst. nat. genev.*, **5; 6; 7**, 1–291. (Not seen).

COX, J. D. (1876): Multiplication by fission of Stentor mülleri. *Am. Naturalist* **10**, 275–278. (Incidental).

DABROWSKA, J. (1956): Tresura *Paramecium caudatum, Stentor coeruleus, Spirostomum ambiguum* na budźce świetne. *Folia Biologica, Polska Akademia Nauk.* **4**, 77–91. (With English summary).

DANIEL, J. F. (1909): Adaptation and immunity of lower organisms to ethyl alcohol. *J. Exptl. Zool.* **6**, 571–611.

DAVENPORT, C. B. and H. V. NEAL (1896). Studies in morphogenesis, V. On the acclimatization of organisms to poisonous chemical substances. *Archiv. f. Entw.-mech.* **2**, 564–583.

DAWSON, J. A. (1953): The culture of Blepharisma undulans and Stentor coeruleus. *Bio. Rev. College City of New York*, **15**, 13–15. (Not seen).

DE TERRA, Noël (1959): Personal communication.

DE TERRA, Noël (1960): Studies of nucleo-cytoplasmic interactions and P³² uptake during cell division in *Stentor coeruleus. Exptl. Cell Research.* (In press.)

DIERKS, K. (1926a): Untersuchungen über die Morphologie und Physiologie des *Stentor coeruleus* mit besonderer Brücksichtigung seiner kontraktilen und konduktilen Elemente. *Arch. Protistenk.*, **54**, 1–91.

DIERKS, K. (1926b): Lähmungsversuche an Stentor coeruleus durch Kaliumionen. *Zool. Anz.* **67**, 207–218.

FAURÉ-FREMIET, E. (1906): Sur un cas de monstruosité chez *Stentor coeruleus*. *Arch. d'Anat. Micros.*, **8**, 660–666.

FAURÉ-FREMIET, E. (1936): *Condylostoma (Stentor)* auriculatus (Gruber). *Bull. de la Soc. Zool. de France* **61**, 511–519.

FAURÉ-FREMIET, E. and E. LEDERER (1956): Microscopie électronique de quelque ciliés. *Bull. soc. zool. France* **81**, 9–11.

FAURÉ-FREMIET, E. and C. ROUILLER (1955): Microscopie électronique des structures ectoplasmiques chez les ciliés du genre *Stentor*. *C.R. Acad. Sci., Paris* **241**, 678–680.

FAURÉ-FREMIET, E., C. ROUILLER, and M. GAUCHERY (1956): Les structures myoïdes chez les ciliés. Étude au microscope électronique. *Arch. d'Anat. micros. Morph. exp.* **45**, 139–161.

GELEI, J. v. (1925): Über der Kannibalismus bei Stentoren. *Arch. Protistenk.* **52**, 404–417.

GELEI, J. v. (1926): Sind die Neurophane von NERESHEIMER neuroide Elemente? *Arch. Protistenk.* **54**, 232–242.

GELEI, J. v. (1927): Angaben zur der Symbiosefrage von *Chlorella*. *Biol. Zentralbl.* **47**, 449–461. (Including some remarks on Stentor.)

GELFAN, S. (1927): The electrical conductivity of protoplasm and a new method of its determination. *Univ. Calif. Publ. Zool.* **29**, 453–456.

GERSTEIN, J. (1937): The culture and division rate of Stentor coeruleus. *Proc. Soc. Exptl. Biol. Med.* **37**, 210–211.

GREELEY, A. W. (1901): On the analogy between the effects of loss of water in lowering of the temperature. *Am. J. Physiol.* **6**, (1901–2), 122–128.

GRUBER, A. (1878): Die Haftorgane der Stentoren. *Zool. Anz.* **1**, 390–391.

GRUBER, A. (1883): Ueber die Einflusslosigkeit des Kerns auf die Bewegung, die Ernährung und das Wachstum einzelliger Tiere. *Biol. Zentralbl.* **3**, 580–582.

GRUBER, A. (1885a): Ueber künstliche Teilung bei Infusorien. *Ibid.* **4**, 717–722.

GRUBER, A. (1885b): Ueber kunstliche Teilung bei Infusorien (II). *Ibid.* **5**, 137–141.

GRUBER, A. (1886): Beitrage zur Kenntniss der Physiologie und Biologie der Protozoen. *Ber. naturf. Ges. Freiburg, i.B.* **1**, 33–56.

GUTTES, E. and Sophie GUTTES (1959): Regulations of mitosis in *Stentor coeruleus*. *Science* **129**, 1483.

HAMBURGER, Clara (1908): Zur Kenntnis der Conjugation von *Stentor coeruleus* nebst einigen allgemeinen Bemerkungen über die Conjugation der Infusorien. *Z. wiss. Zool.* **90**, 421–433.

HÄMMERLING, J. (1946): Über die Symbiose von Stentor polymorphus. *Biol. Zentralbl.* **65**, 52–61.

HARTMANN, M. (1922): Über den dauernden Ersatz der ungeschlecht-lichen Fortpflanzung durch fortgesetzte Regenerationen. *Ibid.* **42**, 364–381.

HAUSMANN, Gertrud (1927): Über die Bewegungen einigen ciliaten Protozoen im Wechselstrom. *Biol. Generalis* **3**, 463–474.

HAYE, A. (1930): Über den Extretionsapparat bei den Protisten, nebst Bemerkungen über einige andere feinere Strukturverhaltnisse der untersuchten Arten. *Arch. Protistenk.* **70**, 1–86.

HEGNER, R. W. (1926): The interrelations of protozoa and the utricles of *Utricularia. Biol. Bull.* **50**, 239–270.

HEILBRUNN, L. V. (1928): The colloid chemistry of protoplasm. *Protoplasm-Monographien* Vol. 1, Berlin.

HEILBRUNN, L. V. (1943 or 1952): *An Outline of General Physiology*, either 2nd or 3rd ed. Saunders, Philadelphia.

HETHERINGTON, A. (1932a): The constant culture of *Stentor coeruleus. Arch. Protistenk.* **76**, 118–129.

HETHERINGTON, A. (1932b): On the absence of physiological regeneration in *Stentor coeruleus. Ibid.* **77**, 58–63.

HOFER, B. (1890): Ueber die lähmende Wirkung des Hydroxylamines auf die contractilen Elemente. *Z. wiss. Mikr.* **7**, 318–326 (*S. coeruleus* included).

HOLT, E. B. and F. S. LEE (1901): The theory of phototactic response. *Am. J. Physiol.* **4**, 460–481.

HOWLAND, Ruth B. (1928): A note on *Astasia captive* Beauchamp. *Science*, **68**, 37.

HYMAN, Libbie H. (1925, 1931): Methods of securing and cultivating protozoa. *Trans. Am. Micros. Soc.* **44**, 216–221; **50**, 50–57.

ISHIKAWA, H. (1912): Wundheilungs- und Regenerationsvorgänge bei Infusorien. *Arch. Entw.-mech.* **35**, 1–29.

IVANIĆ, M. (1926): Zur Auffassung der Kernverhältnisse bei Stentor coeruleus und Stentor polymorphus, nebst Bemerkung über einige Kernverhältnisse bei Infusorien im allgemeinen. *Zool. Anz.* **66**, 55–61. (Dubious).

IVANIĆ, M. (1927): Über der Kannibalismus bei Amœba verrucosa (Ehrb.), nebst Bemerkung über den Kannibalismus bei Protozoen im allgemeinen. *Ibid.* **74**, 313–321. (Dubious).

JENNINGS, H. S. (1899): Studies on reactions to stimuli in unicellular organisms. III. Reactions to localized stimuli in *Spirostomum* and *Stentor. Am. Naturalist* **33**, 373–389.

JENNINGS, H. S. (1902): Studies on reactions to stimuli in unicellular organisms. IX. On the behavior of fixed Infusoria (*Stentor* and *Vorticella*), with special reference to the modifiability of Protozoon reactions. *Am. J. Physiol.* **8**, (1902–3), 23–60.

JENNINGS, H. S. and C. JAMIESON (1902): Studies on reactions to stimuli in unicellular organisms. X. The movements and reactions of pieces of ciliate infusoria. *Biol. Bull.* **3**, 225–234.

JENNINGS, H. S. and E. M. MOORE (1902): Studies on reactions to stimuli in unicellular organisms. VIII. On the reactions of Infusoria to carbonic and other acids, with especial reference to the causes of the gatherings spontaneously formed. *Am. J. Physiol.* **6**, (1901–2), 233–350.

JOHNSON, H. P. (1893): A contribution to the morphology and biology of the Stentors. *J. Morph.* **8**, 467–562.

KAHL, A. (1935): Wimperthiere oder Ciliata. In *Die Tierwelt Deutschlands*, 25th Teil, Part 3, " Spirotricha ", 457–466. Jena.

KALMUS, H. (1928): Über den Bodenfauna der Moldau im Gebiete von Prag. Ein Jahreszyklus. II. Protozoa, etc. Mit einem Anhang: Ökologische Beobachtungen und Versuche. *Internat. Rev. Hydrobiol.* **19**, 349–429.

KENT, W. S. (1881–2): *A Manual of the Infusoria.* London, Vol. II, pp. 588–596.

KESSLER, G. (1882): Ein Beitrag zur Lehre von der Symbiose. *Arch. f. Anat. u. Physiol.* **1882**, 490–492. (Not seen.)

KIMBALL, R. F. (1958): Experiments with *Stentor coeruleus* on the nature of the radiation-induced delay in fission in the ciliates. *J. Protozool.* **5**, 151–155.

KIRBY, H., Jr. (1941a): Relationships between certain protozoa and other animals. In *Protozoa in Biological Research* (edited by Calkins and Summers) Columbia University Press, pp. 890–1008.

KIRBY, H., Jr. (1941b): Organisms living on and in protozoa. *Ibid.*, 1009–1113.

KIRBY, H., Jr. (1956): In: Opinion 418. *Opin. Internat. Comm. Zool. Nom.* **14**, 46–68.

LANKESTER, E. R. (1873): Blue stentorin, the coloring matter of *Stentor coeruleus*. *Quart. J. Micros. Sci.* **13**, 139–142.

LIEBERKÜHN, N. (1857): (Muskelfasern in *Stentor*, etc.—fibrillar and contractile structures in protozoa.) *Arch. Anat. u. Physiol.* **3**, 20. (Not seen.)

LILLIE, F. R. (1896): On the smallest parts of stentor capable of regeneration; a contribution on the limits of divisibility of living matter. *J. Morph.* **12**, 239–249.

MADLEN, J. (1946): (The significance and occurrence of micro-organisms in forest soils.) Lesnická Práce 25 (1/2), 20–31. (*S. polymorphus* incorrectly listed as a soil organism). (Not seen.)

MAIER, N. H. (1903): Über den feineren Bau der Wimperapparate der Infusorien. *Arch. Protistenk.* **2**, 71–179.

MAST, S. O. (1906): Light reactions in lower organisms. I. *Stentor coeruleus. J. Expl. Zool.* **3**, 359–399.

MAUPAS, E. (1879): Micronucleus of *Stentor coeruleus* and *Spirostomum ambiguum*. *C. R. Acad. Sci.*, Paris (1879), 1274.

MAUPAS, E. (1883): Contribution a l'étude morphologique et anatomique des Infusoires ciliés. *Arch. Zool. exper. et gén.* **1**, 427–644.

MAUPAS, E. (1888): Recherches expérimentales sur la multiplication des infusoires ciliés. *Arch. Zool. exp. et gén.* **6**, 165–277.

MEISSNER, M. (1888): Beiträge zur Ernährungsphysiologie der Protozoen. *Z. wiss. Zool.* **46**, 498–516.

MERTON, H. (1932): Gestalterhaltende Fixierungs — versuche an besonders kontraktilen Infusorien nebst Beobachtungen über das Verhalten des lebenden Myoneme und Wimpern bei *Stentor*. *Arch. Protistenk.* **77**, 491–521.

MERTON, H. (1935): Zwangsreaktionen bei Stentor als Folge bestimmter Salzwirkung. *Biol. ZenTralbl.* **55**, 268–285.

MØLLER, K. M. (1960): On the nature of Stentorin. *Compt. rend. trav. Lab. Carlsberg* (in press).

MONOD, J. (1933): Mise en évidence du gradient axial chez les infusoires ciliés par photolyse à l'aide des rayons ultraviolets. *C. R. Acad. Sci., Paris* **196**, 212–214.

MORGAN, T. H. (1901a): Regeneration of proportionate structures in *Stentor*. *Biol. Bull.* **2**, 311–328.

MORGAN, T. H. (1901b): *Regeneration*. Macmillan, London.

MOXON, W. (1869): On some points in the anatomy of Stentor and on its mode of division. *J. Anat. and Physiol.* **3**, 279–293. (Cambridge).

MUGARD, Hélène and Bernadette COURTNEY (1955): Paralysie des Infusoires Ciliés au moyen des phosphates alcalins. *Bull. Soc. Zool. France* **80**, 196–205.

MÜLLER, J. (1856): Einige Beobachtungen an Infusorien. *Monatsber. preuss. Akad. Wissensch.* 1856, 389, 393 (Not seen).

MULSOW, W. (1913): Die Conjugation von *Stentor coeruleus* und *Stentor polymorphus*. *Arch. Protistenk.* **28**, 363–388.

NERESHEIMER, E. R. (1903): Ueber die Höhe histologischen Differenzierung bei heterotrichen Ciliaten. *Ibid.* **2**, 305–324.

NERESHEIMER, E. R. (1907): Nochmals über *Stentor coeruleus*. *Ibid.* **9**, 137–138.

OKEN, L. (1815): *Lehrbuch der Naturgeschichte*, 3 Teil. Zoologique. Erste Abt. Fleischlose Thiere. Jena. (Not seen.)

OTTERSTRØM, C. V. and K. LARSEN (1946): Extensive mortality caused by the infusorian *Stentor polymorphus* Ehrenb. *Rept. Danish Biol. Sta.* **48**, (1943–5), 53–57. (Dubious).

PACKARD, C. E. (1937): Oblique division in Stentor. *Trans. Am. Micros. Soc.* **56**, 191–192. (Incidental).

PARK, O. (1929): The osmiophilic bodies of the protozoans, Stentor and Leucophrys. *Trans. Am. Micros. Soc.* **48**, 20–29.

PENARD, E. (1922): *Études sur les Infusoires d'Eau douce*. Genève.

PETERS, A. W. (1904): Metabolism and division in protozoa. *Proc. Am. Acad. Arts, Sci.* **39**, 441–516.

PETERS, A. W. (1908): Chemical studies on the cell and its medium. III. The function of the inorganic salts of the Protozoan cell and its medium. *Am. J. Physiol.* **21**, 105–125.

POPOFF, M. (1908): Experimentelle Zellstudien. *Arch. Zellforsch.* **1**, 245–379.

POPOFF, M. (1909): Experimentelle Zellstudien. II. Über die Zellgrösse, ihre fixierung und Vererbung. *Ibid.*, **3**, 124–180.

PROWAZEK, S. (1901): Beiträge zur Protoplasmaphysiologie *Biol. Zentralbl.* **21**, 87–95; 144–155.

PROWAZEK, S. (1904): Beitrag zur Kenntnis der Regeneration und Biologie der Protozoen. *Arch. Protistenk.* **3**, 44–59.

PROWAZEK, S. (1913): Studien zur Biologie der Protozoen. VI. *Arch. Protistenk.* **31**, 47–71.

RANDALL, J. T. (1956): Fine structure of some ciliate protozoa. *Nature*, **178**, 9–14.

RANDALL, J. T. and SYLVIA JACKSON (1958): Fine structure in *Stentor polymorphus. J. Biophys. Biochem. Cytol.* **4**, 807–830.

ROESLE, E. (1902): Die Reaktion einiger Infusorien auf einzelne Induktionsschläge. *Z. allgem. Physiol.* **2**, 139–168. (Not seen.)

ROSKIN, G. (1915): La structure des myonèmes contractiles de *Stentor coeruleus.* Tirage à part de " Memoires Scientifiques des Chaniavsky Université de Moscou ", Vol. 1. (Not seen.)

ROSKIN, G. (1922): Über den Bau von kontraktilen Elementen und Stützsubstanzen bei einigen Protozoen. (Russ. with Ger. summary.) *Arch. Soc. Russe Protist. Moscow* **1**, 35–45. (Not seen.)

ROSKIN, G. (1923): La structure des myonèmes des Infusoires. *Bull. Biol., France et Belg.* **57**, 143–151.

ROSKIN, G., i. V. SEMENOV (1933): (Study of oxidation–reduction processes in the cell). *Arch. Russes, Anat. Hist. et Embryol.* **12** (1), Russ., 27–55; German trans. 180–182. (Not seen.)

SCHAEFFER, A. A. (1910): Selection of food in *Stentor coeruleus* (Ehr.). *J. Exptl. Zool.*, **8**, 75–132.

SCHÖNFELD, C. (1959): Über das parasitische Verhalten einer *Astasia*—Art in *Stentor coeruleus. Arch. Protistenk.* **104**, 261–264.

SCHRÖDER, O. (1907): Beiträge zur Kenntnis von *Stentor coeruleus* Ehrbg. und *St. roeselii* Ehrbg. *Ibid.* **8**, 1–16.

SCHUBERG, A. (1890): Zur Kenntnis der *Stentor coeruleus. Zool. Jahrb.*, Abt. Anat. **4**, 197–238.

SCHUBERG, A. (1905): Über Cilien und Trichocysten einiger Infusorien. *Arch. Protistenk.* **6**, 61–110.

SCHULZE, K. L. (1951): Experimentelle Untersuchungen über die Chlorellen-symbiose bei Ciliaten. *Biol. gen.* (*Vienna*), **19**, 281–298.

SCHWALBE, G. (1866): Über die kontraktilen Behälter der Infusorien. *Arch. f. mikr. Anat.* **2**, 351–371.

SCHWARTZ, V. (1934): Versuche über Regeneration und Kerndimorphismus der Ciliaten. *Nachr. Ges. Wiss. Göttingen*, N.S. **1**, 143–155.

SCHWARTZ, V. (1935): Versuche über Regeneration und Kerndimorphismus bei *Stentor coeruleus* Ehrbg. *Arch. Protistenk.* **85**, 100–139.

SILÉN, L. (1948): On a new stentor from the west coast of Sweden. *Ark. Zool.* (*Stockholm*) **40A** (No. 8), 1–10.

SIMROTH, H. (1876): Zur Kenntnis des Bewegungsapparates der Infusionsthiere. *Arch. micr. Anat.* **12**, (Not seen).

SLEIGH, M. A. (1956): Metachronism and frequency of beat in the peristomial cilia of *Stentor. J. Exptl. Biol.* **33**, 15–28.

SLEIGH, M. A. (1957): Further observations on co-ordination and the determination of frequency in the peristomial cilia of *Stentor*. *Ibid.* **34**, 106–115.

SLEIGH, M. A. (1960): The form of beat in cilia of *Stentor* and *Opalina*. *Ibid.* **37**, 1–10.

SOKOLOFF, B. (1923): Hunger and regeneration. *J. Roy. Micros. Soc., London*, (1923), 183–189.

SOKOLOFF, B. (1924): Das Regenerations problem bei Protozoen. *Arch. Protistenk.* **47**, 143–252.

SOKOLOFF, D. (1930a): Las particularidades del *Stentor viridis* de Xochimilco. *An. Inst. Biol. (Univ. Nac. Mexico)* **1** (1), 83–86. (Not seen. See Kahl.)

SOKOLOFF, D. (1930b): *Stentor oligonucleatus*, sp. nov. *Ibid.* **1**, 327–328. (Not seen. See Kahl.)

SOSNOWSKI, J. (1899): Relations entre le noyeau et le Protoplasme chez les protozoaires. *Trans. Lab. Zoot. Varsovie.* **20**, 1–47 (Not seen).

SPRUGEL, G., Jr. (1951): Vertical distribution of *Stentor coeruleus* in relation to dissolved oxygen levels in an Iowa pond. *Ecology* **32**, 147–149.

STEIN, F. (1867): Der Organismus der Infusionsthiere. Abt. II. Leipzig.

STEVENS, NELLIE M. (1903): Notes on regeneration in *Stentor coeruleus*. *Arch. Entw.-mech.* **16**, 461–475.

STOLTE, H. A. (1922): Der Einfluss der Umwelt auf Macronucleus und Plasma von *Stentor coeruleus* Ehrbg. Ein experimentelles Beitrag zur Frage der Kernplasmabeziehungen. *Arch. Protistenk.* **45**, 344–389.

STROM, K. M. (1926): The influence of altered H-ion concentrations on *Stentor*, *Diaptomus* and *Daphnia*. *Nyt. Mag. Naturvidenskab* **64**, 109–115. (Not seen.)

SWARCZEWSKY, B. (1929): Zur Kenntnis der Baikalprotistenfauna. Die an den Baikalgammariden lebenden Infusorien. VI. Stentorina. *Arch. Protistenk.* **65**, 38–44.

TARTAR, V. (1941a): Grafting and reconstitution in a ciliate protozoan. (Abstr.) *Anat. Rec.*, **81** Suppl. p. 132.

TARTAR, V. (1941b): Intracellular patterns: Facts and principles concerning patterns exhibited in the morphogenesis and regeneration of ciliate protozoa. *Growth* (suppl.) **5**, 21–40.

TARTAR, V. (1950): Methods for the study and cultivation of protozoa. In, *Studies Honoring Trevor Kincaid*, (Edited by M. E. Hatch), University of Washington Press, Seattle.

TARTAR, V. (1953): Chimeras and nuclear transplantations in ciliates, *Stentor coeruleus* × *S. polymorphus*. *J. Exptl. Zool.* **124**, 63–104.

TARTAR, V. (1954): Reactions of *Stentor coeruleus* to homoplastic grafting. *Ibid.* **127**, 511–576.

TARTAR, V. (1956a): Grafting experiments concerning primordium formation in *Stentor coeruleus*. *Ibid.* **131**, 75–122.

TARTAR, V. (1956b): Further experiments correlating primordium sites with cytoplasmic pattern in *Stentor coeruleus*. *Ibid.* **132**, 269–298.

TARTAR, V. (1956c): Pattern and substance in Stentor. In *Cellular Mechanisms in Differentiations and Growth* (Edited by D. Rudnick), Princeton University Press.

TARTAR, V. (1957a): Reactions of *Stentor coeruleus* to certain substances added to the medium. *Exptl. Cell Research.* **13**, 317–332.

TARTAR, V. (1957b): Equivalence of macronuclear nodes. *J. Exptl. Zool.* **135**, 387–402.

TARTAR, V. (1957c): Deletion experiments on the oral primordium of *Stentor coeruleus. Ibid.* **136**, 53–74.

TARTAR, V. (1958a): *Stentor introversus*, n. sp. *J. Protozool*, **5**, 93–95.

TARTAR, V. (1958b): Induced resorption of oral primordia in regenerating *Stentor coeruleus. J. Exptl. Zool.* **139**, 1–32.

TARTAR, V. (1958c): Specific inhibition of the oral primordium by formed oral structures in *Stentor coeruleus. Ibid.* **139**, 479–505.

TARTAR, V. (1959a): Equational division of carbohydrate reserves in *Stentor coeruleus. Ibid*, **140**, 269–280.

TARTAR, V. (1959b): Effects of misorientation by rotation of the ectoplasmic pattern of *S. coeruleus.* (Abstr.) *J. Protozool.* Suppl. **6**, 32.

TARTAR, V. (1959c): Division of the macronucleus in *Stentor coeruleus* with regard to nodulation. (Abstr.) *Ibid.* **6**, 32.

TARTAR, V. (1959d): New findings on oral regeneration in *Stentor coeruleus. (Abstr.) Ibid.* **6**, 32.

TARTAR, V. (1959e): Persisting division in *Stentor coeruleus* regardless of removal of parts. (Abstr.) *Anat. Rec.* Suppl. **134**, 644.

TARTAR, V. (1959f): A reproducible lethal abnormality in *Stentor coeruleus.* (Abstr.) *Anat. Rec.* Suppl. **134**, 645.

TARTAR, V. (1959g): Some effects of altered nucleo-plasmic ratio in *Stentor coeruleus.* (Abstr.) *Ibid.* **134**, 645.

TREMBLEY, A. (1744): Translation of a letter from Mr. Abraham Trembley, F.R.S., to the President, with observations upon several newly discovered species of fresh water polypi. *Phil. Trans. Royal Soc. (London)* **43**, 169–183.

TUFFRAU, M. (1957): Les facteurs essentiels du phototropisme chez le Cilié hétérotriche *Stentor niger. Bull. Soc. Zool.*, France **82**, 354–356.

TURNER, J. P. and P. BRANDWEIN (1937): (Culture of Stentor). In, *Culture Methods for Invertebrates*, (Edited by P. Galtsoff *et al.*) Ithica, New York, pp. 60–64.

UHLIG, G. (1959): Polaritätsabhängige Anlagenentwicklung bei *Stentor coeruleus. Z. Naturforsch. Tübigen.* **14b**, 353–354.

UHLIG, G. (1960): Entwicklungsphysiologische Untersuchungen zur Morphogenese von *Stentor coeruleus* Ehrbg. (Doctoral dissertation, Tübigen Univ.) *Arch. Protistenk.* **105**, 1–109.

VERWORN, M. (1892): Die physiologische Bedeutung des Zellkerns. *Pflüger's Archiv.* **51**, 1–118.

VILLENEUVE-BRACHON, Simone (1940): Recherches sur les ciliés hétérotriches, cinétome, argyrome, myonèmes, formes nouvelles ou peu connues. *Arch. Zool. exper. et gén.* **82**, 1–180.

WEISZ, P. B. (1948a): Time, polarity, size and nuclear content in the regeneration of Stentor fragments. *J. Exptl. Zool.* **107**, 269–287.

WEISZ, P. B. (1948b): The role of carbohydrate reserves in the regeneration of *Stentor* fragments. *Ibid.* **108**, 263–278.

WEISZ, P. B. (1948c): On the growth of regenerating fragments in Stentor coeruleus. *Ibid.* **109**, 427–437.

WEISZ, P. B. (1948d): Regeneration in *Stentor* and the gradient theory. *Ibid.* **109**, 439–449.

WEISZ, P. B. (1949a): A cytochemical and cytological study of differentiation in normal and reorganizational stages of *Stentor coeruleus. J. Morph.* **84**, 335–363.

WEISZ, P. B. (1949b): Phosphatases in normal and reorganizing *Stentors*. *Biol. Bull.* **97**, 108–110.

WEISZ, P. B. (1949c): The role of specific macronuclear nodes in the differentiation and the maintenance of the oral area in *Stentor*. *J. Exptl. Zool.* **111**, 141–156.

WEISZ, P. B. (1950a): On the mitochondrial nature of the pigmented granules in *Stentor* and *Blepharisma. J. Morph.* **86**, 177–184.

WEISZ, P. B. (1950b): A correlation between macronuclear thymonucleic acid concentration and the capacity of morphogenesis in *Stentor*. *Ibid.* **87**, 275–286.

WEISZ, P. B. (1951a): Homoplastic grafting in *Stentor coeruleus. Biol. Bull.* **100**, 116–126.

WEISZ, P. B. (1951b): An experimental analysis of morphogenesis in *Stentor coeruleus. J. Exptl. Zool.* **116**, 231–257.

WEISZ, P. B. (1951c): A general mechanism of differentiation based on morphogenetic studies in ciliates. *Am. Naturalist* **85**, 293–311.

WEISZ, P. B. (1953): The embryologist and the protozoon. *Scientific American* **188**, 76–82.

WEISZ, P. B. (1954): Morphogenesis in protozoa. *Quart. Rev. Biol.* **29**, 207–229.

WEISZ, P. B. (1955): Chemical inhibition of regeneration in *Stentor coeruleus. J. Cell. Comp. Physiol.* **46**, 517–527.

WEISZ, P. B. (1956): Experiments on the initiation of division in *Stentor coeruleus. J. Exptl. Zool.* **131**, 137–162.

WETZEL, A. (1925): Vergleichende cytologische Untersuchungen an Ciliaten. *Arch. Protistenk.* **51**, 207–304.

WHITELEY, A. H. (1956): Respiratory patterns in regenerating nucleate and enucleate fragments of *Stentor coeruleus*. (Abstr.) *J. Cell. Comp. Physiol.*, **48**, 344–345.

WHITELEY, A. H. (1960): (Same title.) *C.R. Trav. Lab. Carlsberg.* (In press).

WORCESTER, G. W. (1884): Life history of *Stentor coeruleus. Proc. Centr. Ohio Sci. Assoc.*, **1**, 97. (Dubious).

WORLEY, L. G. (1934): Ciliary metachronism and reversal in *Paramecium, Spirostomum* and *Stentor. J. Cell. Comp. Physiol.* **5**, 53–72.

ZHINKIN, L. (1930): Zur frage der Reservestoffe bei Infusorien (Fett und Glykogen bei *Stentor polymorphus*). *Z. Morph. u. Ökol. Tiere.* (*Z. wissenschaftliche Biologie*, Abteilung A.) **18**, 217–248.

ZHINKIN, L. and P. OBRAZTSOV (1930): (Ecology of *Stentor polymorphus* and *Stentor coeruleus.*) Russian with German summary. *Hydrobiol. Z. USSR.* **9**, 151–153. (Not seen.)

ZINGHER, J. A. (1933): Beobachtung an Fetteinschlüssen bei einigen Protozoen. *Arch. Protistenk.* **81**, 57–87.

ZINGHER, J. A. and W. W. FISIKOW (1931): Biometrische Untersuchungen an Infusorien. 1. Über die Mittelgrösse von *Stentor coeruleus* Ehrbg. *Ibid.* **73**, 482–486.

OTHER REFERENCES CITED

ANDREWS, E. A. (1923): *Folliculina:* case-making, anatomy and transformation. *J. Morph.* **38**, 207–277.

ANDREWS, E. A. (1947): Temperature effect upon rate of feeding in a folliculinid. *Physiol. Zool.* **20**, 1–4.

ANDREWS, E. A. (1949): Folliculinid life-cycle. *J. Morph.* **84**, 401–409.

BERGLAS, A. (1957): *Cancer: Nature, Cause and Cure.* Inst. Pasteur, Paris.

BOHR, N. (1958): *Atomic Physics and Human Knowledge.* New York.

BONNER, J. T. (1954): The development of cirri and bristles during binary fission in the ciliate *Euplotes eurystomus J. Morph.* **95**, 95–108.

BONNER, J. T. (1958): *The Evolution of Development.* Cambridge University Press, England.

BRACHET, J. (1955): Recherches sur les interactions biochimiques entre le noyau et le cytoplasme chez les organismes unicellulaires. *Biochim. Biophys. Acta* **18**, 247–268.

BRIGGS, R. and T. J. KING (1955): Specificity of nuclear function in embryonic development. In, *Biological Specificity and Growth* (Edited by E. G. Butler), Princeton University Press.

BRØNSTED, H. V. (1955): Planarian regeneration. *Biol. Rev.* **30**, 65–126.

CALKINS, G. N. (1911a): Regeneration and cell division in *Uronychia. J. Exptl. Zool.* **10**, 95–116.

CALKINS, G. N. (1911b): Effects produced by cutting Paramecium cells. *Biol. Bull.* **21**, 36–72.

CHATTON, E. and A. LWOFF (1935a): Les Ciliés apostomes. I. Aperçu historique et général; étude monographique des genres et des espèces. *Arch. Zool. exp. et gén.* **77**, 1–453.

CHATTON, E. and A. LWOFF (1935b): La constitution primitive de la strie ciliare des infusoires. La desmodexie. *C.R. Soc. Biol., Paris* **118**, 1068–1072.

CHATTON, E. and Josephine SÉGUÉLA (1940): La continuité génétique des formations ciliares chez les ciliés hypotriches. Le cinétome et l'argyrome au cours de la division. *Bull. Biol. de France-Belg.* **74**, 1-94.

CHEN, Y. T. (1944): Studies on the neuromotor systems of *Stylonychia pustulata* and *Stylonychia mytilus*. *J. Morph.* **75**, 335-345.

CHILD, C. M. (1941): *Patterns and Problems of Development*. University of Chicago Press.

CIENKOWSKI, L. (1865): Beiträge zur Kenntnis der Monaden. *Arch. mikr. Anat.* **1**, 201-232. (Not seen.)

COMANDON, J. and P. DE FONBRUNE (1939a): Ablation du noyau chez une Amibe. Réactions cinétiques a la piqûre de l'amibe normal ou dénucléie. *C.R. Soc. Biol.*, Paris **130**, 740-744.

COMANDON, J. and P. DE FONBRUNE (1939b): Greffe nucléaire totale, simple, ou multiple, chez un Amibe. *Ibid.* **130**, 744-748.

DANIELLI, J. F. (1958): Studies of inheritance in amœbæ by the technique of nuclear transfer. *Proc. Roy. Soc. (London)* B **148**, 321-331.

DANIELLI, J. F. (1959): The cell-to-cell transfer of nuclei in Amœba and a comprehensive cell theory. *Ann. N. Y. Acad. Sci.* **78**, 675-687.

DANIELLI, J. F., I. J. LORCH, M. J. ORD, and E. G. WILSON (1955): Nucleus and cytoplasm in cellular inheritance. *Nature* **176**, 1114.

DANIELS, E. W. (1951): Studies on the effect of x-irradiation upon *Pelomyxa carolinensis* with special reference to nuclear division and plasmotomy. *J. Exptl. Zool.* **117**, 189-210.

DELBRÜCK, M. and W. REICHARDT (1956): System analysis for the light growth reactions of Phycomyces. In, *Cellular Mechanisms in Differentiation and Growth* (Edited by Rudnick), Princeton University Press.

DEMBOWSKA, W. S. (1938): Körperreorganisation von *Stylonychia mytilus* beim Hungern. *Arch. Protistenk.* **91**, 89-105.

DEMERIC, M. (1934): Biological action of small deficiencies of X-chromosome of *Drosophila melanogaster*. *Proc. Natl. Acad. Sci., U.S.* **20**, 354-359.

EHRET, C. F., and E. L. POWERS (1959): The cell surface of Paramecium. *Intern. Rev. Cytol.* **8**, 97-133.

ELSASSER, W. M. (1958): *The Physical Foundation of Biology*. Pergamon Press, London and New York.

EPHRUSSI, B. (1953): *Nucleo-cytoplasmic Relations in Micro-organisms*. Oxford University Press.

FAURÉ-FREMIET, E. (1932): Division et morphogenèse chez *Folliculina ampulla* O. F. Müller. *Bull. biol., France-Belg.* **66**, 77-110.

FAURÉ-FREMIET, E. (1945a): Symétrie et polarité chez les cilies bi- ou multi-composites. *Ibid.* **79**, 106-150.

FAURÉ-FREMIET, E. (1948a): Doublets homopolaires et régulation morphogénétique chez le cilié *Leucophrys patula*. *Arch. Anat. micros. et Morphol. expér.* **37**, 183-203.

FAURÉ-FREMIET, E. (1948b): Les mécanismes de la morphogenèse chez les Ciliés. *Folia Biotheoretica* **3**, 25-58.

FAURÉ-FREMIET, E. (1949): Action du lithium sur la stometogenèse chez les Ciliés. *Belg.-Nederl. Cytoembryol. Dagen. Genet.* **1949**, 100–102.

FAURÉ-FREMIET, E. (1950): Problème moléculaire de la morphogenèse. *Ann. Biol.* **26**, 361–379.

FAURÉ-FREMIET, E. (1954): Les problèmes de la différentiation chez les protistes. *Bull. Soc. zool. France* **79**, 311–329.

FAURÉ-FREMIET, E. and H. MUGARD (1948): Ségrégation d'un matériel cortical au cours de la segmentation chez l'œuf de *Teredo norvegica*. *C.R. Acad. Sci., Paris* **227**, 1405–1411.

FAWCETT, D. W. and K. R. PORTER (1954): A study of the fine structure of ciliated epithelia. *J. Morph.* **94**, 221–281.

GARNJOBST, LAURA (1937): A comparative study of protoplasmic re-organization in two hypotrichous ciliates, *Stylonethes sterkii* and *Euplotes taylori*, with special reference to encystment. *Arch. Protistenk.* **89**, 317–381.

GELEI, J. v. (1936): Das erregungsleitende System der Ciliaten. *C.R. 12th Congrès Internat. de Zool.* (Lisbonne, 1935) **1**, 174–206.

GIESE, A. C. (1938): Cannibalism and gigantism in *Blepharisma*. *Trans. Am. Micros. Soc.* **57**, 245–255.

GIESE, A. C. (1949): A cytotoxin from *Blepharisma*. *Biol. Bull.*, **87**, 145–149.

GIESE, A. C. (1957): Photodynamic effect of Blepharisma pigment on nerve. *J. Cell. Comp. Physiol.* **49**, 295–302.

GIESE, A. C. and R. H. ALDEN (1938): Cannibalism and giant formation in *Stylonychia*. *J. Exptl. Zool.* **78**, 117–134.

GOLDSCHMIDT, R. (1940): Chromosomes and genes. In, *The Cell and Protoplasm*, (Edited by F. R. Moulton), Science Press, Washington, D.C., pp. 56–66.

GUSTAFSON, T. (1954): Enzymatic aspects of embryonic differentiation. *Intern. Rev. Cytol.* **3**, 277–327.

HÄMMERLING, J. (1953): Nucleo-cytoplasmic relationships in the development of Acetabularia. *Intern. Rev. Cytol.* **2**, 475–498.

HAMMOND, D. M. (1937): The neuromotor system of *Euplotes patella* during binary fission and conjugation. *Quart. J. Micros. Sci.* **79**, 507–557.

HARTMANN, M. (1928): Ueber experimentelle Unsterblichkeit von Protozoen–Individuen. *Zool. Jahrb.* **45**, 973–987.

HOFER, B. (1890): Experimentelle Untersuchungen über den Einfluss des Kerns auf das Protoplasma. Jena. *Z. Naturwiss.* **24**, 105–176.

HOLMES, S. J. (1907): The behaviour of *Loxophyllum* and its relation to regeneration. *J. Exptl. Zool.* **4**, 399–430.

HOLTFRETER, J. (1949): Phenomena relating to the cell membrane in embryonic processes. *Exptl. Cell Research*, Suppl. **1** (1949), 497–510.

HORNING, E. S. (1927): On the orientation of mitochondria in the surface cytoplasm of Infusorians. *Austral. J. Exptl. Biol. Med.* **4**, 187–190.

Hörstadius, S. (1950): Transplantation experiments to elucidate inter-actions and regulations within the gradient system of the developing sea urchin egg. *J. Exptl. Zool.* **113**, 245–276.

Jones, E. E., Jr. (1951): Encystment, excystment, and the nuclear cycle in the ciliate *Dileptus anser*. *J. Elisha Mitchell Sci. Soc.* **67**, 205–218.

Klein, B. M. (1932): Das Ciliensystem in seiner Bedeutung für Loko-motion, Koordination und Formbildung mit besonderer Berück-sichtigung der Ciliaten. *Ergebn. d. Biol.* **8**, 75–179.

Lewin, K. R. (1911–12): The behaviour of the infusorian micronucleus in regeneration. *Proc. Roy. Soc.* (*London*) **B84**, 332–344.

Lillie, F. R. (1906): Observations and experiments concerning the elementary phenomena of embryonic development in *Chætopterus*. *J. Exptl. Zool.* **3**, 153–268.

Loefer, J. B. (1936): Isolation and growth characteristics of the " Zoochlorella " of *Paramecium bursaria*. *Am. Naturalist* **70**, 184–188.

Lorch, I. Joan and J. F. Danielli (1950): Transplantation of nuclei from cell to cell. *Nature* **166**, 329–330.

Lorch, I. Joan and J. F. Danielli (1953): Nuclear transplantation in Amœba. I. Some species characters of *Amœba proteus* and *Amœba discoides*. *Quart. J. Micros. Sci.* **94**, 445–460.

Lucas, Miriam S. (1932): The cytoplasmic phases of rejuvenescence and fission in *Cyathodiunium piriforme*. II. A type of fission heretofore undescribed for ciliates. *Arch. Protistenk.* **77**, 407–472.

Lund, E. E. (1935): The neuromotor system of *Oxytricha*. *J. Morph.* **58**, 257–277.

Lund, E. J. (1914): The relations of Bursaria to food. *J. Exptl. Zool.* **16**, 1–52; **17**, 1–39.

Lund, E. J. (1917–18): Reversibility of morphogenetic processes in Bursaria. *J. Exptl. Zool.* **24**, 1–33.

Lwoff, A. (1950): *Problems of Morphogenesis in Ciliates*. Wiley, New York.

McDougall, W. (1938): *The Riddle of Life*. Methuen, London.

Marsland, D. A. (1943): Quieting *Paramecium* for the elementary student. *Science* **98**, 414.

Mast, S. O. (1909): The reactions of *Didinium nasutum* (Stein) with special reference to the feeding habits and functions of the trichocysts. *Biol. Bull.* **16**, 91–118.

Mazia, D. (1952): Physiology of the cell nucleus. In *Modern Trends in Physiology and Biochemistry* (Edited by E. S. G. Barron), New York, pp. 77–122.

Monné, L. (1948): Functioning of the cytoplasm. *Advances in Enzymology* **8**, 1–65.

Moore, A. R. (1945): *The Individual in Simpler Forms*. University of Oregon Press.

Mugard, Hélène (1947): Division et morphogenèse chez les Ophryoglènes. *C.R. Acad. Sci., Paris* **225**, 70–72.

MUGARD, HÉLÈNE (1948): Régulation du nombre des cinéties au cours du cycle de croissance et de division chez un cilié: *Ichthyophthirsus multifilies* Fouguet. *Arch. d'Anat. micros.* **37**, 204–213.

MUGARD, HÉLÈNE (1957): L'infraciliature chez la larve d'Oursin *Paracentrotus lividus. Bull Soc. Zool. France* **82**, 81–88.

NADLER, J. E. (1929): Notes on the loss and regeneration of the pellicle in *Blepharisma undulans. Biol. Bull.* **56**, 327–330.

NEEDHAM, J. N. (1933): Dissociability of the fundamental processes in ontogenesis. *Biol. Rev.* **8**, 180–223.

NUSSBAUM, M. (1884): Über spontane und künstliche Zelltheilung. *Sitzber. niederrhein. Ges. Nat.-u. Heilk.*, Bonn **41**, 259–263.

ÖHLER, R. (1922): Die Zellverbindungen von *Paramecium bursaria* mit *Chlorella vulgaris* und anderen Algen. *Arb. Staatsinst. exper. Therapie Georg Speyer Haus* **15**. (Not seen.)

OKADA, Y. K. (1930): Transplantationsversuche an Protozoen. *Arch. Protistenk.* **69**, 39–94.

PÁRDUCZ, B. (1953): Zur Mechanik der Zilienbewegung. *Acta Biol., Acad. Sci. Hungari* **4**, 177–220.

PARKER, G. H. (1929): The neurofibril hypothesis. *Quart. Rev. Biol.* **4**, 155–178.

PRINGSHEIM, E. G. (1928): Physiologische Untersuchungen an *Paramecium bursaria*. Ein Beitrag zur Symbioseforschung. *Arch. Protistenk.* **64**, 289–418.

RAVEN, C. P. (1949): The influence of lithium on the development of the pond snail, *Limnæa stagnalis* L. *Exptl. Cell Research*, Suppl. **1**, 542–544.

REYNOLDS, MARY E. C. (1932): Regeneration in an amicronucleate infusorian. *J. Exptl. Zool.* **62**, 327–361.

ROBERTSON, T. B. (1925): The influence of certain dyes upon the multiplication of Infusoria (Enchelys) with special reference to the acridine dyes (Acriflavine and Proflavine). *Austral. J. Exptl. Biol. Med. Sci.* **2**, 21–44.

ROQUE, MARIE (1956): La ciliature buccale pendant l'autogamie et la conjugaison chez *Paramecium aurelia. C.R. Acad. Sci.*, Paris, **242**, 2592.

ROSE, S. M. (1957): Cellular interaction during differentiation. *Biol. Revs.* **32**, 351–382.

ROTH, L. E. (1956): Aspects of ciliary fine structure in *Euplotes patella. J. Biophys. Biochem. Cytol.* **2**, (Suppl.), 235–240.

SCHMÄHL, O. (1926): Die Neubildung des Peristoms bie der Teilung von *Bursaria truncatella. Arch. Protistenk.* **54**, 359–430.

SCHWARTZ, V. (1947): Über die Physiologie des Kerndimorphismus bei *Paramecium bursaria. Z. Naturforsch.* **26**, 369–381.

SOKOLOFF, B. (1913): Contribution au problème de la régénération des Protozoaires. *C.R. des Séances et Mémoires de la Soc. de Biol.* **75**, 297–301.

SOKOLOFF, B. (1934): *Vitality.* Dutton, New York.

SONNEBORN, T. M. (1932): Experimental production of chains and its genetic consequences in the ciliate protozoan, *Colpidium campylum* (Stokes). *Biol. Bull.* **63,** 187–211.

SONNEBORN, T. M. (1947): Recent advances in the genetics of Paramecium and Euplotes. *Advances in Genetics* **1,** 263–358.

SONNEBORN, T. M. (1951): The role of genes in cytoplasmic inheritance. In, *Genetics in the 20th Century* (Edited by L. C. Dunn). Macmillan, New York, pp. 291–314.

STERKI, V. (1878): Beiträge zur Morphologie der Oxytrichinen. *Z. wiss. Zool.* **31,** 28–58.

SUZUKI, S. (1957): Morphogenesis in the regeneration of *Blepharisma undulans japonicus* Suzuki. *Bull. Yamagata Univ., Nat. Sci.* **4,** 85–192.

SWANN, M. M. (1954): The control of cell division. In, *Recent Developments in Cell Physiology*. London.

TARTAR, V. (1940): Nuclear reactions in *Paramecium*. (Abstr.) *Anat. Rec.* **78,** (Suppl.), 109.

TARTAR, V. (1954): Anomalies in regeneration of *Paramecium*. *J. Protozool.* **1,** 11–17.

TAYLOR, C. V. (1928): Protoplasmic reorganization in *Uronychia uncinata* sp. nov. during binary fission and regeneration. *Physiol. Zool.* **1,** 1–25.

TAYLOR, C. V. and W. P. FARBER (1924): Fatal effects of the removal of the micronucleus in *Euplotes*. *Univ. Calif. Publ. Zool.* **26,** 131–144.

TURNER, J. P. (1940): Cytoplasmic inclusions in *Tillina canalifera* Turner. *Arch. Protistenk.* **93,** 255–272.

VISSCHER, J. P. (1923): Feeding reactions in the ciliate, *Dileptus gigas*, with special reference to the function of the trichocysts. *Biol. Bull.* **45,** 113–143.

WEISZ, P. B. (1949): The role of the macronucleus in the differentiation of *Blepharisma undulans*. *J. Morph.* **85,** 503–518.

WHITMAN, O. C. (1893): The inadequacy of the cell theory of development. *J. Morph.* **8,** 639–658.

WOODGER, J. H. (1929): *Biological Principles*. London.

WORLEY, L. G. (1933): The intracellular fibre systems of Paramecium. *Proc. Natl. Acad. Sci., U.S.,* **19,** 323–326.

YAGIU, R. (1951): Studies on *Condylostoma spatiosum* Ozaki and Yagiu. III. The relationship of the quantity of the macronucleus and the power of division. *J. Sci., Hiroshima Univ.,* Series B, Div. 1, **12,** 121–130.

YAGIU, R. (1952): Studies on *Condylostoma spatiosum* Ozaki and Yagiu. V. Abnormal phenomena caused by being kept in fresh water. *Ibid.* **13,** 92–109.

YOW, F. W. (1958): A study of the regeneration pattern of *Euplotes eurystomus*. *J. Protozool.* **5,** 84–88.

YUSA, A. (1957): The morphology and morphogenesis of the buccal organelles in *Paramecium* with particular reference to their systematic significance. *J. Protozool.* **4,** 128–142.

ZELENY, C. (1905): The relation of the degree of injury to the rate of regeneration. *J. Exptl. Zool.* **2,** 347–369.

AUTHOR INDEX

SUBJECT INDEX